Introduction to Statistics for the Social Sciences

Second Edition

Audrey J. Weiss, Ph. D.

Laura L. Leets, Ph. D.
Stanford University

The McGraw-Hill Companies, Inc.
Primis Custom Publishing

New York St. Louis San Francisco Auckland Bogotá
Caracas Lisbon London Madrid Mexico Milan Montreal
New Delhi Paris San Juan Singapore Sydney Tokyo Toronto

McGraw·Hill

A Division of The McGraw·Hill Companies

Introduction to Statistics
for the Social Sciences

McGraw-Hill's Primis Custom Series consists of products that are produced from camera-ready copy. Peer review, class testing, and accuracy are primarily the responsibility of the author(s).

Page 6: "Lies, Damned Lies and Statistics" by Robert Strauss, from *Los Angeles Times*, November 29, 1996. Copyright © 1996 by Robert Strauss. Reprinted with permission.

Page 13: "New Report Becomes a Weapon in the Debate Over TV Violence" by Bill Carter, from *New York Times*, February 7, 1996. Copyright © 1996 by *New York Times*. Reprinted with permission of the publisher.

Page 15: "Learning to Earn: A Survey Verifies Huge Boomer-to-Buster Shifts" by M. Hornblower, from *Time Magazine*, February 24, 1997.

Page: 17: "The Keys to Learning Math" by Thomas H. Maugh II, from *San Jose Mercury News*, February 28, 1997. Copyright © 1997 by Los Angeles Times Syndicate. Reprinted by permission of the publisher.

Page 18: Snapshot: "Genders Agree: Slobs Maker Worst Roommates" by A. Carey and M. Staimer, from *USA Today*, November 25, 1996. Copyright © 1996 by *USA Today*. Reprinted by permission of the publisher.

Page 19: "Most Gold Records" from *USA Today*, September 11, 1997. Copyright © 1997 by *USA Today*. Reprinted by permission of the publisher.

Page 19: Graphic: "The Facts About Global Warming" from *San Jose Mercury News*, October 23, 1997. Copyright © 1997 by Tribune Media Services. Reprinted by permission of the publisher.

Page 46: "Killer Tornado Distribution, 1950-1994" from *Tornado Project Online Web Site*. Copyright © 1997 by Tornado Project Online. Reprinted by permission of the publisher.

Page 46: Snapshot: "Fewer Cards, More E-Mail" by S. Boeck and K. Rechin, from *USA Today*, December 16, 1996. Copyright © 1996 by *USA Today*. Reprinted by permission of the publisher.

Page 46: Graphic: "After School is Crime Times" from article "Youth Crime in Afternoon" by the Justice Department; Fight Crime: National Center, from *San Jose Mercury News*, September 1997. Copyright © 1997 by Tribune Media Services. Reprinted by permission of the publisher.

Page 51: Snapshot: "Balancing Work and Play" by S. Boeck and G. Lynn, from *USA Today*, December 26, 1996. Copyright © 1996 by *USA Today*. Reprinted by permission of the publisher.

Page 51: "Lucrative Careers for Women" by A. Carey and G. Jerding, from *USA Today*, January 15, 1997. Copyright © 1997 by *USA Today*. Reprinted by permission of the publisher.

Page 52: "Beyond the Melting Pot: Growing Minority" by Patricia Mitchell, from *Los Angeles Times*, January 13, 1991. Copyright © 1991 by Los Angeles Times Syndicate. Reprinted by permission of the publisher.

Page 88: "Distress Calls: A New Study Links Car Phones with Accidents" by J. Kluger, from *Time Magazine*, February 24, 1997. Copyright © 1997 by *Time Magazine*. Reprinted by permission of the publisher.

Table III, r-table from *Statistical Tables for Biological, Agricultural and Medical Research* by Frank Yates. Copyright © 1974 by Longman Group, Ltd. Reprinted with permission.

F-test from *Statistical Methods, Eighth Edition*, by G.W. Snedecor & W.G. Cochran. Copyright © 1989 by Iowa State University Press. Reprinted with permission.

Table III from *Statistical Methods for Research Workers* by Ronald A. Fisher. Copyright © 1970 by Oliver & Boyd. Reprinted with permission

3 4 5 6 7 8 9 0 BKM BKM 9 0 9

ISBN: 0-07-290985-4
Set ISBN: 0-07-561820-6

Editor: Julie Kehrwald
Cover Designer: Caroline A. Berst
Printer/Binder: Bookmart Press

Contents

11. Multiple Regression ❖ 210

12. Chi-Square Analysis ❖ 236

Appendices ❖ 257

Forward

Knowledge of statistical methods is a fundamental skill required of most college students in a variety of disciplines. A solid foundation in statistics is achieved not only by understanding the conceptual logic behind statistics, but also by learning how to perform statistical analyses and interpret reported statistical results. Thus, the purpose of this book is to present a clear conceptual and analytical introduction to the most common statistical procedures used in the social sciences, with an emphasis on how statistics are contextualized within the larger scheme of research.

The primary audience for this text is introductory social science students who are taking a statistics course for the first time, reviewing statistical skills they already possess, or learning how to conduct analyses for their own research projects. Although no previous statistical knowledge is assumed, students with some prior background in statistics should find that this text both complements and extends their existing knowledge. We have written this book to be both basic enough for undergraduate students and comprehensive enough for graduate students to use.

Our primary goal in writing this text was to provide both a clear, conceptual description of statistics and a computational and computer component that focuses on how to actually perform and interpret each test. As such, the content and organization of the book are designed with three major objectives in mind. First, we describe the role of statistics in the research process and emphasize how to choose the appropriate statistical test to answer different types of research problems. The text includes numerous examples of statistics actu-

ally reported in popular media outlets as well as research findings from academic journals. We focus on teaching students how to be critical consumers of statistics and how to interpret the results of research studies.

Second, we provide a computational description of how each statistical test is actually performed, with a detailed explanation of both the conceptual reasoning and mathematical procedures involved in conducting each test. Each chapter features a step-by-step computational example, from the presentation of the problem through to the final conclusion. Additionally, each chapter includes a series of practice problems designed to assess students' conceptual understanding of the test as well as their ability to calculate and interpret the results of the analysis. Solutions to even-numbered exercises are provided in Appendix B.

Third, each chapter includes a computer section that teaches students how to use the computer to analyze data. We introduce a realistic study (with a dataset provided on the accompanying computer diskette) for students to use throughout the book to perform each statistical test on the computer. Students are instructed on basic data preparation procedures (e.g., creation of a codebook and data entry) and the general logic of how to perform each statistical test on the computer. Each chapter provides sample computer output for the statistical test and teaches students the process of interpreting the results obtained from statistical software programs. A series of homework exercises allows students to conduct computer analyses on the dataset for the hypothetical study described in the text. Instructors who are using this book in more advanced courses may wish to require students to write a complete results section for the study as an end of class assignment. Solutions to even-numbered exercises are provided in Appendix C.

We would like to acknowledge the efforts of several individuals who have been instrumental in our ability to produce this book. We extend our deepest appreciation to Julie Kehrwald, our editor at McGraw-Hill, for her continued support of our efforts to provide social science students with a basic and comprehensive introduction to statistics. We also are extremely grateful to Roberta Papazoglow for her skill in the design and layout of the text. Finally, we wish to thank Caroline Berst for her patience in working with us on the cover design, Elhám Mottahed for her help with the journal articles, and Emily Murase for her assistance with copy edits.

Chapter 1 ❖ Introduction to Statistics

Why Should I Care About Statistics?

If you begin this book questioning the worth of learning statistics, you are not alone. Many students wonder why they must take a statistics course, especially if they do not anticipate either attending graduate school or conducting research. Additionally, it is common to reason that if you wanted to learn statistics you would have majored in a discipline emphasizing math in the first place. We believe, however, that there are three important reasons why gaining an understanding of statistics is a worthwhile investment of your time and energy.

Academic Career as a Student. When you enroll in courses with a social science perspective you will read research reports and journal articles to satisfy course requirements, and you will write papers which require that you can read and conceptually understand statistics. The more you know about statistics the easier it will be for you to critique and interpret research findings, which in turn will increase the quality of your work at school.

Critical Thinking. Higher education is in large part concerned with training you to think critically and analytically, that is, to train you for citizenship and work: "The good life in a democratic society ... seems to rest fundamentally on one's ability to think critically about the problems with which one is confronted. The essence of the creed is that each person possesses potentialities for discovering their own problems and for developing personally satisfying and socially acceptable solutions to them ..." (American Council on Education).[1]

Statistics and research methods provide an avenue through which you can solve the abstract and practical problems of life. More specifically, mastering the logic of statistics can help you to become a better problem solver, to think more clearly, to weigh alternatives, and to recognize personal biases.

Consumer of Research. Perhaps the most important reason to learn statistics is the fact that all of us are consumers of research. Even as you enter the world of work you will most likely continue to read research articles to stay up to date or on the cutting edge in the career you choose. Additionally, understanding statistics and research methods will allow you to effectively utilize information and evaluate evidence in order to make intelligent, well-reasoned decisions in life. On a daily basis you are inundated with statistical results, such as the following: the latest election poll published in your voting precinct shows that the Republican candidate was favored with 53% of the vote while the Democratic candidate held 47% of the vote, with a margin of error of plus or minus (±) 4%. The American Medical Association introduces a new cure for travel sickness after a study using 50 volunteers showed that those who used the new medication were significantly less likely to experience motion sickness than were those who used other types of medication.

A Roper poll reports that one fourth of Americans believe the Nazi Holocaust never happened. Eight out of ten dentists surveyed recommend SMILE toothpaste for their patients who want a brighter, cleaner-looking smile. A national phone poll conducted by *People Magazine* asks for subscribers' opinions regarding the current state of the British monarchy. A local senator urges you to vote against the death penalty because statistical findings indicate that states implementing the death penalty have a higher number of murders than do states that do not have the death penalty.

As a consumer of research how do you know which statistical conclusions to believe and which are deceptive? Statistics can provide information that is both useful and misleading. For instance, do 80% of all dentists really recommend SMILE toothpaste, or do 8 of the 10 dentists the researcher chose to interview recommend SMILE? Do one fourth of Americans truly believe the Holocaust never happened or was the question on the survey poorly worded? Why do states with the death penalty have higher murder rates? Does implementing the death penalty result in more murders or do states with more murders implement the death penalty as a deterrent? Or, perhaps, the death penalty has no association with number of murders and is purely a function of the population size.

Lastly, consider the following example: a researcher claims a social intervention program reduced the number of inner-city high school drop-outs. On what basis can the researcher make this assertion? How does the researcher know that the numbers are not really due to chance? That is, how does the researcher know that the social intervention program really keeps youths in school? These are the types of questions intelligent consumers are able to answer and that you too will become properly equipped to answer as you read this book. Our goal is that you will approach statistical results with skepticism and a concern for alternative explanations.

Asking Questions

Keep in mind that at the most fundamental level research is about finding answers to questions. By nature we are all curious about the world around us. Granted, our levels of curiosity may vary (e.g., with topic and age), but at one time or another we all have been driven by the spirit of inquiry. Our curiosity is articulated through questions. The strategy we use to answer those questions will largely be governed by the questions we ask.

There are two general approaches to finding answers to questions. The first type of data gathering technique, the *qualitative method*, involves collecting information that cannot be subjected to numerical measurements. While qualitative research covers a wide range of approaches, it tends to focus on one or a small number of cases and entails intensive interviews with people or in-depth analysis of historical materials. The data analysis involves recording observations and interpreting patterns in these data. With the qualitative method, a researcher carefully examines a specific event (e.g., case studies) and attempts to provide a description of how or why the event occurred. Examples could include investigating the collapse of the former Soviet Union or the Chinese government violations of human rights after the Tiananmen Square demonstration. Qualitative research tends to be used for exploratory or descriptive analysis. A researcher often may choose this approach when looking for an in-depth understanding of a phenomenon, when attempting to become familiar with an area, when working in natural situations, or when seeking a new perspective.

On the other hand, the *quantitative method* focuses on gathering data that represents quantities of some phenomenon and involves measuring data on a numerical scale (e.g., weight, length, money). The numerical data, such as number of voters who indicate they will vote for a particular candidate or number of minutes to complete a puzzle task, can be subjected to various statistical analyses. These analyses, then, provide evidence for or against hypothesized relationships. Quantitative methodologies often move beyond description to explanation, looking for causes and reasons. A researcher employs quantitative research when s/he wants to determine the accuracy of a theory, to provide evidence to support or refute an explanation, to build and extend theories, or to investigate knowledge about an underlying process. Surveys and experiments are examples of quantitative research methods and we will talk briefly about these and other quantitative data collection techniques (research methods) in the next chapter.

Although some people may view qualitative and quantitative methodologies as competitive strategies, many scholars prefer to view them as complementary approaches. In line with the latter opinion, we believe that neither quantitative nor qualitative research is superior. Rather, the more appropriate research method is dependent upon the type of question the researcher asks. Both traditions advance knowledge about the social world; they simply differ in their style and techniques for discerning this knowledge. Frequently research combines features of each approach. In this book we will focus on analyzing data collected through quantitative methods. You will discover shortly that not only does the research question determine the general approach to doing research (qualitative or quantitative) but the research question also will influence which specific statistical analysis is conducted with quantitative data.

So, What Exactly Are Statistics?

Beginning with the grand picture, *statistics* is a branch of the field of mathematics which provides researchers with a set of tools to analyze and interpret numerical data, thereby allowing them to answer questions and test hypotheses from these data. In other words, statistics is a mathematical model for reasoning. In particular, there are two general types of statistics.

When one or two numbers are used to organize and summarize a set of data in a form that is easy to comprehend they are referred to as *descriptive statistics*. All research involves the goal of description at some level. For example, you probably use the mean of a group of test scores as a way to describe how everyone in your class performed on a particular exam. In Chapter 3 we will discuss in detail two types of descriptive statistics: measures of central tendency and measures of dispersion.

Inferential statistics go beyond simple description to make inferences about a population based on data gathered from a sample. Usually it is impossible or impractical for a researcher to collect data from an entire population. Instead, data is gathered from a subset or sample of the larger population. For example, when you are budgeting your finances for the academic school year, you may estimate your cost of living based on the prices you paid for housing, food, utilities, and fees over one month from the previous year. Based on this one set of observations (i.e., your financial costs for one month) you generalize to the following year. You examined a set of observations from a sample to find typical patterns and inferred what would be true for the entire year.

Along these lines, suppose a county waste management division wants to discover the recycling behavior of the residents in their community. Instead of surveying the thousands of people residing in their district, the researchers can produce estimates or generalize about their community based on survey results obtained from a sample of only several hundred residents. In later chapters we will discuss some of the most common quantitative analyses that fall in the domain of inferential statistics.

How Difficult Will This Be If I'm Not a Mathematical Genius?

Many statistics books concentrate on developing complex formulas, proofs, and computations. In contrast, the purpose of our book is to provide you with a conceptual foundation for many of the most common analyses used in research studies, with an emphasis on understanding how these statistical techniques work. Our goal is to provide you with knowledge of the nature and logic of statistics. We will do some essential mathematics but everything will be explained clearly to you.

If you feel a little intimidated about the mathematical aspects of statistics, relax. We will work through each of the statistical tests conceptually first, and then we will work through the problems mathematically. You only need to be equipped with a basic knowledge of arithmetic and have a calculator that computes simple addition, subtraction, multiplication, division, and square roots. Beyond that, we will instruct you in everything you need to know. We believe that once you understand conceptually what it is you are trying to do and why you are trying to do it, the math will be relatively easy.

Summary

Statistics is a branch of mathematics dealing with the analysis and interpretation of numerical data. Learning statistics will help you to read, write, and understand research, to think critically and develop problem-solving skills, and to be a savvy consumer of statistical results and research findings for your entire life.

Statistics are used to analyze data collected using quantitative research methods, which involve measuring phenomena numerically. In contrast, nonnumeric data which is not analyzed using statistical techniques is collected using qualitative research methods.

There are two general types of statistics: descriptive and inferential. Descriptive statistics involve describing and summarizing data whereas inferential statistics involve estimating and inferring what is true about a larger population based on a smaller sample of data.

Key Terms

- descriptive statistics
- inferential statistics
- qualitative method
- quantitative method
- statistics

Problems

1. Explain the difference between qualitative and quantitative research.
2. A researcher is interested in the impact of gender and type of romantic touch on perceptions of relational commitment. The researcher first constructs a questionnaire and has a total of 200 male and female students give their perceptions of relational commitment on the basis of a variety of intimate touches. Second, out of the 200 completed surveys the researcher selects ten students and conducts in-depth interviews with the students on the same topic.
   a. Describe how the researcher collects data in both parts of the study.
   b. What type of method (*quantitative* or *qualitative*) does the researcher use in the first part of this study? In the second part?
   c. What are some of the advantages of each method?
   d. Is one data collection method superior to the other or is it more advantageous to use both methods? Why?
3. Several research scenarios are provided below. Indicate which questions illustrate

a qualitative approach to data collection and which illustrate a quantitative approach.

a. A marketing firm conducts a series of experimental studies to determine how different types of music in television commercials influence audiences' attitudinal responses to the product being advertised.

b. A researcher wants to conduct in-depth interviews with several adolescents in a community to determine levels of HIV risk-taking and to develop ways to reduce such behaviors.

c. A researcher uses public opinion polls to survey a community as a means to assist a jury in determining community standards of obscenity.

d. A researcher examines the patterns of violence in abusive families by living with two different families over several weeks and keeping detailed notes on each.

4. _____ statistics use a small subset of observations to deduce characteristics about a much larger population, and _____ statistics describe overall characteristics of data.

5. For each of the following statements, indicate whether it is an example of descriptive or inferential statistics.

a. Based on last semester's text prices, you want to predict how much you will spend on textbooks for the following school year.

b. The student government wants to know the percentage of students who cast votes for each of two candidates in an election.

c. A baseball player wants to know his batting average over the last season.

d. A rape prevention center computes the probability of date rape in a community based on the number of reported assaults in the past ten years.

6. For each of the following, determine what might be misleading about the data that is presented. Use your critical abilities and try to generate alternative explanations for or limitations of the findings.

a. The latest issue of *Cosmopolitan* publishes the following statistical information based on the results of a write-in survey from a previous issue: 85% of women are unhappy in their relationships. Should you believe that 85% of all women in the U.S. are unhappy in their relationships? Why or why not?

b. In a court of law, defense lawyers believe that it is to their advantage if the jurors are of the same race as their client. This attitude was formed after the lawyers read an article reporting the results of an investigation conducted on university students who read short sample legal scenarios and made judgments of defendants' innocence or guilt. The evaluations differed according to race with more innocent judgments coming from student jurors who were of the same race as the alleged defendant. To what extent should lawyers rely on these findings?

c. CNN asks viewers to call in and indicate whether they favor universal health care coverage. Results reveal that 60% of the callers favored it and 40% did not. Do you think these data are representative of all citizens of the United States? Why or why not?

Notes

1 Dressel, P., & Mayhew, L. (1954). General education: Explorations in evaluation. Washington, D.C.: American Council on Education, p. 35.

Consuming Statistics

SOURCE: Robert Strauss, "Lies, Damned Lies and Statistics," *Los Angeles Times,* November 29, 1996, pp. E1, E4.

When the city of New York recently threw a ticker-tape parade for the world champion Yankees, the Mayor's office issued a release crowing that 3.5 million people had lined the mile-long route.

Even granting that the slimmest of folks showed up, they would still have had to line up 1,000 deep, an impossibility on Wilshire Boulevard let alone the cramped streets of lower Manhattan. Still, the 3.5 million statistic made front-page headlines and was repeated until it took on the aura of fact, just the way dubious Rose Parade crowd estimates have year in and year out.

While no one may have been harmed by this particular mathematical mismanagement, it is yet another case that demonstrates how we have become a statistically challenged society.

Statistics bludgeon us. They are out there everywhere, most often unencumbered by interpretation. Should I care about the Dow Jones 30, the S&P 500 or the Russell 2,000? Does anyone really understand the quarterback rating system, the hockey plus-minus or earned run average? Why does body temperature go up with the consumer price index and down with the wind-chill index?

The ubiquity of statistics is often laid at the feet of computers, but the real problem is not the preponderance of stats, but that they float in the data murk without understanding or clear interpretation.

"People are being overwhelmed by quantitative information," said Robert Stine, a professor of statistics at the University of Pennsylvania's Wharton School. "They don't always get to hear the origin of the information and they don't listen for good interpretations."

Said Prof. Donald Ylvisaker, consultant to the UCLA Statistics Counseling Center, "The real problem is this: We have to shift from an age of information to one of intelligence. Anyone can put data out there. The problem is really to filter it out and interpret what it all means."

But it can be a real mess when the stats aren't up to snuff. "The list of shortcomings in U.S. economic data is depressingly long," Alan Greenspan, the chairman of the Federal Reserve Board, testified recently before Congress.

In fact, a study by Michael Waldman of Cornell University and Seonghwan Oh of Seoul National University showed that a series of pessimistic economic data compiled by the government in the first half of 1989 was significant in persuading businesses and consumers to cut their spending. Later on, the statistics were revised upward — more than 10% of government statistics reported are later changed, Waldman said — but by that time, the country had lost an estimated $10 billion in production.

Another common complaint among economists is that the consumer price index, the statistic that newscasters are talking about when they tell you about inflation, is just plain wrong. The general feeling among these economists is that because the index doesn't try to quantify efficiencies in production and increased quality of products, it continually overstates inflation by about 1%.

This all wouldn't matter if the index were just another number, but many folks look upon it as their favorite number. More than three-quarters of all corporations use the index to help figure out employee raises. The index is the major factor in figuring out Social Security payout rates. Thus, an incorrect index is self-fulfilling. Revisions may be coming soon from a federal panel appointed by the Senate.

Stine once worked on a project to figure out how much gasoline was used in the United States. He discovered there were four sources of statistics, all seemingly accurate, that differed by 15% to 20%. "There were rational explanations for this: Some were by consumption, some were by production. But it gave you a way to interpret them," he said. "Unfortunately, the government now has only one number. There's no conflict now, but can you really believe the new number?"

Statistical sleight of hand figured in the recent election campaigns, when Democrats repeatedly accused Republicans of proposing to cut Medicare. Republicans complained bitterly that they merely proposed to cut the size of the increases the Democrats had proposed. Everybody understood the distinction, right?

But what about the weather? Surely, no stat could confuse that.

"The wind-chill index has confused people as to what the real temperature is," said Fred Godomski, the head of the Pennsylvania State University TV Meteorology program. "You have two temperatures floating around in the winter. Actually, it's an attempt to impart more drama to the weather.

"And the UV Index, ugh!" Godomski said. "Dermatologists say any type of sun is bad for your skin. It's just a proliferation of babble, just data for no reason because we can report it." Godomski said he has his students look at some old TV weather forecasts from 1957 to compare to statistically overloaded ones today. "The single biggest difference, beyond the magnetic blackboards, is the rate at which information is imparted. Today it is at breakneck speed," he said. "It's a wonder the average viewer can extract the necessary information from a mere weather cast."

It's even a greater wonder anyone without a doctorate in math can get through the sportscast or sports pages. "Occasionally I find there are overzealous uses of statistics," said Steve Hirdt, executive vice president of the Elias Sports Bureau in New York, the official statisticians of the National Football League, the National Basketball Assn. and Major League Baseball and, thus, the producer of most of this billowing flow of numbers.

Hirdt and his number-runners are the folks who compile all those arcane baseball statistics — like how many times left-handed batters walk against right-handed relievers during night games in May.

"There are times when the use of certain statistics makes me cringe because I know people think those uses emanate from us," Hirdt said. "But, hey, this is America, and if we can't keep guns out of the hands of the wrong people, how can we do that with sports stats?"

continued on page 8

Consuming Statistics (continued)

A particular misuse of sports statistics, Hirst said, is improper attribution of cause and effect. He noted that in the Dallas Cowboys glory years, it was constantly repeated that when Tony Dorsett rushed for 100 years, the Cowboys always won the game. "But if you step back from that, the reason he got so many yards is that the Cowboys were already ahead and were running the ball to run out the clock. It's like saying when people carry umbrellas, it starts to rain."

But rain statistics it does and we seem powerless to do anything about it.

There are the Nielsen ratings, for instance. Who won last year? Each network used the numbers differently. NBC said it won because it got the highest total prime-time Nielsen numbers. CBS claimed it won more nights than NBC. ABC claimed it was the winner because it got more young viewers, those who attract more advertisers. Meanwhile, the total of the three major networks was at an all-time low, so the cable networks claimed victory.

There is a general belief that standards for mathematical comprehension have declined. But, of course, it is hard to prove that through statistics. The Scholastic Aptitude Tests would have been a good year-by-year comparison, but last year, the Educational Testing Service, which administers the SATs, recalibrated the way it arrives at the English and math sores, so that the new scores are higher than in the past. The theory was that scores were going down, so something had to prop them up, even though there is evidence that since more students at the lower end of the curve are taking the SATs, it would be natural for scores to go down.

American students' deficiencies in math and science have been well-documented in a number of studies. Just last week, a new international study ranked American middle schoolers 28th of 45 countries studied in math performance. Based on an analysis of 1,0000 textbooks and teaching guides, another recent study by the National Science Foundation found that U.S. schools teach too many math and science concepts — and cover them too superficially.

Those who study statistics say there is crying need for improved math literacy.

"We have discussions around the university about having a requirement in quantitative reasoning — learning how to use numbers," UCLA's Ylvisaker said. "You have to sort these things out to go through life sensibly. The filter of the newspaper isn't enough because, frankly, newspapers tend to want us to see the sensational side of statistics."

Ylvisaker added that there is a general math phobia afoot. "People say, 'Oh, I was never good at math,' or, 'Numbers have always confused me,'" he said. Once people say that, Ylvisaker said, they release themselves from the responsibility of knowing what any set of numbers they see means.

By the same token, the poorly educated invest numbers with super significance they only sometimes merit. Words manipulate, these people imagine; numbers are trustworthy. And the more precise they seem, the more seriously we take them.

Remember the old ad for Ivory Snow? The product was "99 and 44/100% pure." Sounded pretty exact, but what did that mean? And would you drink water that was 99 and 44/100% pure and the rest strychnine?

"Somehow, when you put a numerical value on something, it takes on a new level of meaning," Stine said. "And once you quantify something, it sells your point of view better."

Take the Million Man March. Many agreed that it was a good thing: black men getting together for any number of spiritual and political reasons. Then the U.S. Park Service announced its estimate of how many people were actually on the Mall in Washington that afternoon. It was 400,000. An impressive number, to be sure, but short of the advertised number.

The leaders of the march threatened to sue, calling the number a "willful undercount." The hoo-ha over the number threatened to become more important than the spirit of the event. The Park Service decided the only prudent course was to get out of the crowd estimation business completely — but that one less statistic will hardly staunch the torrent.

The Numbers Game

As statistics proliferate, they unfortunately tend to confuse rather than enlighten. Experts point to a number of ways stats generally drive people batty.

- **Ecological Fallacy:** Statistics professor Robert Stine of the University of Pennsylvania said this is one way people use statistics as a smoke screen. He pointed to a study in the 1950s that showed that the percentage of crime was highest where the percentage of immigrants was greatest, thus "proving" that immigration caused crime. "In fact, when you looked at individuals, immigrants did almost none of the crimes." Ecological fallacies thus cause spurious correlations.
- **Butterfly Effect:** It's taken from the theory of chaos developed by Edward Lorenz, which tried to describe how a butterfly shaking its wings in Hawaii could cause changes in the weather around the world. In this way, statistics can be extrapolated far out of proportion. Sports is a great venue for this. A batter has a .500 average against right-handed pitchers. Yet maybe only two of his 350 at bats are against right-handers.
- **Strained Incidence Rate:** In the cell phone cancer scare a few years back, a study showed that six of every 100,000 cell phone users eventually suffered from brain cancer. That sounds very high, but it meant that 600 American cell phone users might get brain cancer in a year, which is a fairly insignificant number.
- **Halo Effect:** In "A Mathematician Reads the Newspaper" (Basic Books, 1995), John Allen Paulos noted that a statistic takes on a much greater effect if the user has a "halo," like an Ivy League professorship.

False Predictors: Stine (with the "halo" of an Ivy League professorship, by the way) says statistics are often used to predict things they can't. Computer models that claim to predict the weather or the Dow Jones industrial average six months in advance are great for newscasts, but hardly reliable. "I could tell you I have a statistical model where I can predict the gross national product in 2050 by cutting open chickens and counting grains in their stomachs," Stine said. "That's safe. No one will be around to check."

Computer Section

Introduction to Statistical Analysis Tools

In subsequent chapters, we will discuss the most common ways to analyze data, including the purpose of each statistical test, how each statistical test functions conceptually, and how to compute each type of analysis. Many of the homework problems involve calculating solutions using each statistical test.

For computationally short problems like in the homework exercises, performing tests such as analysis of variance and chi-square by hand is not very time consuming or difficult, particularly with a relatively small number of subjects and relatively little data. However, with a large number of subjects and a lot of data, performing many statistical tests by hand would consume a large chunk of time and be subject to human calculation errors. Yet for many years the only option available to researchers was to do all of their statistical analyses by hand. With the advent of mainframe and, more recently, personal computers, analyzing data has become substantially easier. Moreover, the ease with which statistical analyses can be performed on a computer has made such procedures available to many people who have statistical needs, from researchers and students in academic institutions to small and large businesses in the private sector.

Through the years, a number of different statistical software packages have emerged for users to analyze data. Many of these programs first appeared for mainframe computers. Users were required to submit a "job" to the mainframe that contained the commands the user wanted executed (naming of variables, analyses to be conducted, etc.). Data was submitted on individual cards that had holes punched out to indicate particular numeric values. More recently, statistical software packages have become available on personal computers allowing users to store data in a data file on the computer. Although some analyses still may be performed on mainframe computers, unless the job is particularly large and complex, most analyses researchers need to conduct can be run on smaller unix servers or on desktop personal computers.

Today, a variety of statistical packages are available to conduct analyses on computers. SPSS, SAS, BMDP, and SYSTAT are among the most common data analysis packages. Other less common and somewhat more specialized tools include MINITAB, PH-STAT, and STATDISK. In addition, spreadsheet programs such as EXCEL and LOTUS are now incorporating basic analysis tools in their software programs. The most common statistical package used by social scientists is SPSS: Statistical Package for the Social Sciences. Many of the conventions for structuring analyses in SPSS are consistent with those practices adopted by social scientists, making this package particularly well suited for their needs. Additionally, SPSS is among the more powerful of the statistical software packages available and among the easier to learn. Notably, once you have mastered analyzing data with one type of tool, you should easily be able to transfer these skills to other statistical software packages. With other programs, the logic behind the analyses remains the same; the syntax for submitting commands differs.

SPSS has a number of different versions that have emerged over the years. For instance, SPSS-X was designed for running analyses on a mainframe computer, whereas SPSS/PC was designed for performing statistics on a personal computer. The basic syntax and structure of commands, however, is fundamentally the same.

In the remaining chapters we will introduce you to running statistical analyses on the computer. We will present a hypothetical data set from an instructional technology study and continue to refer to this example in each chapter. We will discuss how to transform a completed questionnaire into analyzable data and how to perform the statistical technique from each chapter on the computer. We also will provide sample computer output for each chapter and describe how to interpret the analyses. Finally, homework exercises are provided for conducting each analysis on the computer using data from the instructional technology study.

Chapter 2 ❖ Collecting and Measuring Data

Collecting Data

Prior to conducting any type of statistical analysis data must be collected. Researchers have a variety of data collection techniques, referred to as research methods, at their disposal. The particular methodology chosen for data collection is determined by the questions and topics the researcher is addressing. No single research method can be used to answer all questions raised in any particular area. In the following section we will provide a brief overview of four main research methods. In particular, we emphasize three important quantitative data collection techniques since the purpose of this book is to introduce you to the logic and application of statistical analysis of quantitative data.

Research Methods

We will begin by describing one of the most common qualitative methodologies, *field research*. Field research involves the study of people in natural settings; essentially it is a sophisticated form of people watching. The researcher enters into the daily routine of some group (e.g., homeless people, gangs, cults, detectives) and attempts to describe behavior as it naturally occurs in a real-life setting. While taking detailed notes on a regular basis, the researcher may directly talk with and observe people. The goal is to acquire an insider's perspective while simultaneously maintaining the distance or objectivity of an outsider. When a researcher wants to learn something that can only be studied through direct involvement and close, detailed obser-

vation, field research should be used to gather data. Field research generally is valuable for exploratory and descriptive studies. For example, one researcher desired to investigate the impact of conservatism and antifeminism on nine organizations of NOW (National Organization of Women). The researcher obtained access to NOW and their documents, and interviewed past and current members.[1] In another example of field research, researchers conducted interviews with the management and staff at Disneyland to examine the impact of changing the root-metaphor of the organization from that of "drama" to "family."[2]

The remaining three research methods we will describe, content analysis, surveys, and experiments, are all quantitative methodologies. *Content analysis* is an approach for analyzing the content of written, visual, or spoken material. The researcher identifies the material to be analyzed (e.g., violent acts on television) and then creates a coding system for recording it (e.g., verbal violence, physical violence). The coding process is used to turn content into numbers that can be subjected to statistical analysis. Content analysis tends to be used in both descriptive and explanatory research. For example, in one investigation researchers interested in the sexual content of music videos conducted a content analysis of a sample of television music videos taped over several weeks.[3] The videos were coded into five categories of physical intimacy: flirtation, nonintimate touch, intimate touch, hug, and kiss. Statistical results revealed that sex in music videos tended to be more implied (nonintimate touch, flirtation) than direct (kiss, hug, intimate touch).

Content Analysis of Television Violence

Adapted from Bill Carter, "New Report Becomes a Weapon in the Debate Over TV Violence," *The New York Times*, February 7, 1996, p.C11.

A new report [content analysis] suggesting that violence pervades television entertainment shows is shaping as a central point of confrontation in a political battle between advocates of the V-chip – a device that can block transmission of violent programs into homes – and the broadcast network, which adamantly oppose enforced censorship of their programs....

The report, which labels itself "the most comprehensive scientific assessment of television violence ever conducted," was due to be released officially today by a group called the National Television Violence Study. A broad coalition of researchers, media executives and mental health experts from several universities, including the University of Texas, the University of North Carolina and the University of California at Santa Barbara, took part in the study, which was assembled by Mediascope, a nonprofit organization hired by the National Cable Television Association last year....

Overall, the study finds that premium cable channels like HBO and Showtime are the most violent, with 85 percent of their programming including some violence, followed by basic cable channels with 59 percent, and independent television shows with 55 percent. Broadcast television has the lowest violence level – 44 percent – according to the study....

The study offers no specific examples of what constitutes violence in a specific show. Instead it lists a grid of the shows that were monitored: 2,693 separate programs, as seen on 23 different channels in the course of a composite week of viewing. The shows were broadcast between 6 A.M. and 11 P.M.

Groups of coders, selected from the volunteer undergraduates at two of the participating universities, were asked to watch the shows and decide what was a violent act based on the following definition: "Any overt depiction of the use of physical force or the credible threat of such force intended to physically harm an animate being or group of beings."

Barbara Wilson, a professor of communication at the University of California at Santa Barbara, said the study was intended to answer complaints about previous academic examinations of violence on television where all incidents, whether comedic violence or acts of nature, were considered equally.

"We made an effort to identify the contextual features of every act," Ms. Wilson said. "Each act had to fit into the definition, so a doctor performing a life-saving operation would not count. And I doubt a food fight in a comedy would count because there would be no intent to harm."

If Wile E. Coyote is injured falling thousands of feet from a cliff in a Roadrunner cartoon, it probably would count, she said, because there was intent to harm.

Ms. Wilson said the report accepted previous research concluding that children imitate the violence they see on television, a point that broadcasters have rejected as unproven....

The report is expected to drive a further wedge between the broadcast and cable sectors of the television industry. Mr. Hundt praised the cable industry for financing a study "that is critical of their own industry," adding, "It's clear now that broadcasters should do the same thing."

Surveys are the most frequently conducted of all quantitative research methods. More than likely you have filled out several surveys during your lifetime (in the mail, on the phone, maybe even you have been personally interviewed by someone). A *survey* is constructed by translating research problems into items on questionnaires. The answers provided by respondents to the various questions can be statistically analyzed. The objective of survey research may be either explanatory or descriptive.

Often surveys are used because researchers want to describe some characteristic about a particular group of people. The large group of people (or objects, such as TV shows) in which a researcher is ultimately interested is referred to as a *population*. For example, political researchers might be concerned with all American voters, child psychologists might be interested in the population of children, sociologists might care about the population of urban youths, and communication scholars might focus on all violent programs on television. Most of the time populations are too large to reasonably survey every single member or item of that population. Imagine, for example, if the Nielsen Company attempted to solicit the viewing habits of every single individual in America, or if the Gallup polling service tried to ask every American who he or she was going to vote for in the presidential election! Even though obtaining data from all members of a population is usually an insurmountable task, researchers still may wish to make statements or inferences about a larger population. The best way to accomplish this goal without having to contact every member of a population is to survey a subset or *sample* of the population of interest.

Typically, samples selected for survey research are random or representative samples. A *random sample* is chosen in such a way that data collected from those members of the sample are representative of all members of the population. A random sample commonly involves giving every single member of the population an equal chance of being included in the final sample. Determining which members of the population are included in the sample can be accomplished through a variety of random methods including a coin toss, table of random numbers, or selection of names from a hat. With random sampling, the statistical results obtained from the sample members can be generalized to the larger population of all members from which the sample was drawn. For instance, political researchers inevitably sample only 1,000 or 2,000 people regarding their voting behavior. Yet the statistical results obtained from these few people are generalized to the entire population of voters, such that at any point during an election the percentage of the voting population that is going to vote for each candidate is known (within some margin of error due to sampling).

A third important quantitative methodology is the *experiment*. As a college student, it is possible that you have been asked to participate in a research experiment as part of a course you are taking. The experimental procedure is primarily aimed at discovering cause-and-effect relationships. Thus, experiments are restricted to questions in which the researcher can control all variables and manipulate only specific aspects of the situation. Usually experiments involve dividing subjects into two or more groups where one group receives a treatment or stimulus (the experimental group) and the other group receives no treatment (the control group). Assignment to groups in an experiment is done randomly to insure that all groups are equal at the start of the study. *Random assignment* means that the study participants, who may or may not be a random sample from the population, are assigned to groups or conditions in such a

Survey of College Freshman Attitudes

SOURCE: Margot Hornblower, "Learning to Earn: A Survey Verifies Huge Boomer-to-Buster Shifts," *Time*, February 24, 1997, p.34.

Once upon a time boys and girls went to college to learn the meaning of life. They ruminated over Kierkegaard and Kant, dealt with existential dilemmas (sic), argued over war, the Bomb and whether to protest or not to protest. "Thirty years ago," recalls Alexander Astin, a professor of education at the University of California, Los Angeles, "students were preoccupied with questions such as 'What is life all about?' and 'Who is God?'"

Once upon a time is over. A study released last week by UCLA and the American Council on Education compares the attitudes of 9 million freshmen who have answered questionnaires on 1,500 campuses over the past three decades. In 1967, 82% of entering students said it was "essential" or "very important" to "develop a meaningful philosophy of life" – making that the top goal of college freshmen. Today that objective ranks sixth, endorsed by only 42% of students. Conversely, in 1967 less than half of freshmen said that to be "very well off financially" was "essential" or "very important." Today it is their top goal, endorsed by 74%. Idealism and materialism, says Astin, who has directed the surveys since their creation, "have basically traded places."

Today there is a convergence in the goals of men and women. Three decades ago, less than half of female freshmen planned to get a graduate degree. Now nearly 68% of women plan to get higher degrees, vs. 65% of males. Thirty years ago, men were nine times more likely to want to be lawyers. Today there is less than half a percent difference. Among freshmen who want to be doctors and dentists, females outnumber males.

Feminist values are now entrenched. "It is hard to believe that in 1967 fully two-thirds of men agreed with the statement 'The activities of married women are best confined to the home and family,'" Astin remarks. Today that has dropped to 31%. But a gender gap persists: only 19% of female freshman agree. University of South Carolina professor John Gardner, head of the National Resource Center for the Freshman Year Experience, laments that the survey also confirms how "women have taken on some of our worst habits. They smoke and drink more – binge drinking has become their problem too. "Thirty years ago, male freshmen were nearly 50% more likely to be frequent smokers. Today more females than males smoke frequently – about 16%, vs. 13%. A point of divergence: only 31.9% of women, vs. 53.8% of men, agree that "if two people really like each other, it's all right for them to have sex, even if they've only known each other a very short time."

Freshmen who reported feeling "overwhelmed" nearly doubled, from 16% in 1985 to nearly 30% in 1996. As a result of such anxieties, says Gardner, "students today are practical and grade grubbing." Many scholars blame economic insecurity for the change. Says James Spring, associate admissions director at the State University of New York at Binghamton: "As a student in the '60s, I could think about my philosophy of life because I didn't worry about getting a job." Indeed, those who report a "major concern" that they will lack funds to complete college jumped from less than 9% three decades ago to 19% now. Still, there are positives. Today's freshmen, says Gardner, "hold down jobs after school and volunteer in community service as much as ever. We don't recognize their fine qualities enough."

way that each participant has an equal chance of being in any group. For example, a researcher is interested in whether a new drug can cure attention deficit disorder. With a sample of sixty volunteers (which is not a random sample), each participant is randomly assigned to one of the two conditions (drug or placebo). Using a coin toss procedure, if the coin is heads the subject is assigned to receive the new drug (experimental condition) and if the coin is tails the participant is assigned to receive the placebo (control condition). Random assignment is a characteristic of true experiments because it ensures that any observed differences between groups (e.g., between the experimental group and the control) can be explained only by the researcher's manipulation (e.g., type of drug – real vs. placebo). Note that random sampling and random assignment are independent concepts. Random sampling is a method for obtaining a sample that yields representativeness and generalizable results. Random assignment is a process for assigning subjects, who may or may not be a random sample, into groups in an experiment.

In another example of an experiment, a psychologist is interested in the extent to which positive reinforcement affects performance at a task. The psychologist randomly assigns one group of participants in the study to receive positive words of encouragement while completing a difficult puzzle task, whereas another group of participants does not receive any encouragement at all while completing the task. The researcher then measures how long it takes for each subject to complete the puzzle task. This experimental design allows the researcher to determine whether those who received reinforcement were able to accomplish the task more quickly than those who did not receive reinforcement. In this study presence of positive reinforcement is the *independent variable* that the re-

searcher manipulated. In general, a *variable* is anything that has more than one level or can assume multiple values. In this case, the independent variable has two values or levels: presence of positive reinforcement, absence of positive reinforcement. The result or outcome of the study is measured by the *dependent variable*, which in this study is the number of minutes required to complete the puzzle task. This dependent measure is free to take on any value between zero and infinity. Statistical tests are performed on the data collected with the dependent variable.

Levels of Measurement

A researcher cannot gather data and test hypotheses without measures. *Measurement* is the process of assigning numbers to objects in such a way that properties of the objects are reflected in the numbers themselves. When these numbers are examined statistically the researcher can obtain new information about the phenomenon under investigation. Notably,

TABLE 2.1: Levels of Measurement

Scale	Characteristic of Scale
NOMINAL	Numbers represent categories; a classification scale.
ORDINAL	Numbers indicate rank order of observations; the order of the numbers but not the interval between them is given.
INTERVAL	Numbers represent equal intervals with an *arbitrary* zero point.
RATIO	Numbers represent equal intervals with an *absolute* zero point.

Experiment on Piano Lessons and Math Skills

SOURCE: Thomas H. Maugh II, "Research Indicates Preschool Pianists Develop ... The Keys To Learning Math," *San Jose Mercury News*, p.1A.

Giving piano lessons to preschoolers significantly increases their ability to perform the types of reasoning required for excellence in science and math, researchers at the University of California-Irvine and the University of Wisconsin have found.

Lessons on using a computer keyboard provided no similar benefit, the team reported today in the journal Neurological Research.

The study involved 78 California children in preschools in Santa Ana, Long Beach and West Covina, and the team found that the beneficial effect was independent of socioeconomic class and parental interest.

An earlier study by the same team found that listening to Mozart improved performance on an IQ test taken immediately afterward, but the effect fades within an hour. In this case, the researchers believe the improvements in mental ability will persist, perhaps for a lifetime, although they do not have data to prove that.

The researchers also believe the effect they discovered is related to playing any musical instrument, not just a keyboard instrument.

"These children have plastic (malleable) brains that are just forming connections," said psychologist Frances Rauscher of the University of Wisconsin. "We're influencing pattern development in the cortex through neural training."

The great improvement shown by the children from the musical training "should be of great interest to scientists and educators," said physicist Gordon Shaw of UC-Irvine, who is also on the staff of the university's Center for the Neurobiology of Learning and Memory.

The team recruited 111 3- and 4-year-olds at three preschools. One was an inner-city school for single mothers who had gone back to community college, while the two others served more-conventional middle-class families. Thirty-three of the children withdrew from the schools during the study and were not included in the analysis.

The children were randomly divided into four groups. One group received daily singing lessons and two 15-minute private piano lessons per week at school. A piano also was made available if the children wished to practice on their own. A second group received only the group singing lessons. Members of the third group received two 15-minute private computer lessons each week, while those in the fourth group received no lessons at all.

At the beginning of the study all the students scored at the national norm on a battery of tests.

At the end of six months, those who received piano lessons scored an average of 34 percent higher on the tests of spatial temporal ability, while those in the three other groups showed no improvement on any of the tests. Because the children subsequently enrolled in public schools, the team was unable to follow up to determine how long the effect persisted.

The research was sponsored by grants from, among others, the National Piano Foundation and the National Association of Music Merchants. But the results were reviewed by other scientists before publication.

Rauscher, who studied piano and cello as a child, thinks the lessons were beneficial because "music is one of the few art forms that occur over time. It requires mental imagery, transforming mental images and being able to reason in sequence. It seems as if music and science share some things in common."

there is some controversy regarding the nature of the empirical "facts" that are actually represented by this approach to measurement.[4] Although there are many ways to categorize and assign measurement, we will introduce you to the four scales of measurement that have the widest acceptance among social scientists (see Table 2.1). Not only do these levels of measurement provide different amounts of information about data but they also serve as one important criterion in determining which statistical test should be used for analyzing the data. The nominal, ordinal, interval, and ratio scales are distinguished by their precision. The nominal scale provides the least amount of information and the ratio scale offers the most information. Notice that in moving sequentially from nominal- to ratio-level data, the measurement scale contains the same information as the previous scale(s) while simultaneously adding a new piece of information.

With a *nominal scale,* numbers are used simply to classify or categorize objects, people, or characteristics. No ranking is possible; numbers simply are assigned to distinguish categories from one another. Examples of nominal-level measurement are a blood bank classifying a person's blood type (O, A, B, AB) or the Census Bureau gathering demographic information such as gender (male, female) and religion (Protestant, Catholic, Buddhist, etc.).

With an *ordinal scale*, the data are ordered or ranked. However, the intervals between these observations are undefined and likely unequal. For example, consider houses ordered on a street. When someone gives directions to a house on this street, s/he may indicate that it is the third house on the left. From this information, only the order or rank of this house on the street is known, not how far away the house is from the first, second, or fourth houses on the street. The actual interval between the first and second houses may be 100 feet, whereas the difference between the

second and third houses may be 1,000 feet (an unequal interval and somewhat longer drive).

As another example, consider finishing places in a race: Bob, Cindy, Heidi, Greg. Cindy finished after Bob, but did she finish one second, one minute, five minutes, 20 minutes, or one hour behind Bob? And, there is nothing to indicate that this interval is the same between all runners. Whereas Cindy may have finished five seconds after Bob, Heidi may have finished 45 minutes behind Cindy. There is no information in an ordinal-level scale regarding the interval between ranked data points.

When the intervals between ranks are meaningful and equal the data are measured on an *interval scale*. With this scale the distance between values is known – how much greater than and how much less than one value is from another. An example of an interval scale is the Fahrenheit temperature scale. The difference between 22°F and 23°F is the same as the difference between 86°F and 87°F – one degree, a known and equal interval. Interval scales

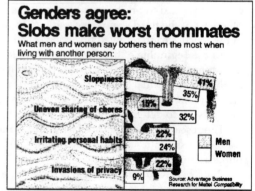

USA SNAPSHOTS®

A look at statistics that shape our lives

Genders agree:
Slobs make worst roommates

What men and women say bothers them the most when living with another person:

Sloppiness — 41% / 35%

Uneven sharing of chores — 15% / 32%

Irritating personal habits — 22% / 24%

Invasions of privacy — 22% / 9%

Men / Women

Source: Advantage Business Research for Mattel Compatibility

11/25/96   By Anne R. Carey and Marcia Staimer, USA TODAY

Nominal-level data: Individuals were classified into categories according to what bothered them the most about roommates

USA SNAPSHOTS®

A look at statistics that shape our lives

Most gold albums
(sales of 500,000-plus)

61   38   36   36

Elvis   The   Rolling   Barbara
       Beatles Stones Streisand

3/31/97   **USA TODAY**

Ordinal-/ratio-level data: If recording artists with the most gold albums were only ranked from highest to lowest (e.g., Elvis, Beatles, Rolling Stones, etc.), this would be ordinal-level data; if we looked solely at the specific number of gold albums (e.g., 61, 38, 36, etc.), this would be ratio-level data

also are characterized by an *arbitrary zero point*. An arbitrary zero point is not a substantively meaningful zero; that is, zero does not imply the absence of what is being measured. For example, the Gregorian calendar date 0 A.D. does not represent the absence of time. Rather, it is a point of reference (to the birth of Christ) in a system developed for ordering the construct of time. With an arbitrary zero point, interval scales preclude the use of relative comparisons. For instance, if the temperature during October was a pleasant 80°F in Los Angeles and a chilly 40°F in San Francisco, we know how much warmer Los Angeles was than San Francisco (40 degrees) but we cannot say that Los Angeles was twice as warm as San Francisco. Other common examples of interval scales are IQ scores and Celsius temperature.

On a *ratio scale*, the most information is obtained: the measurements are ranked, intervals between the ranks are known and equal, and

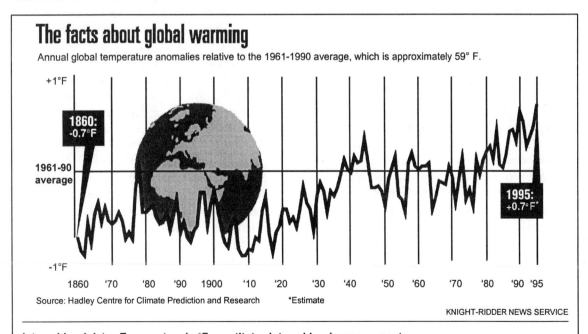

The facts about global warming

Annual global temperature anomalies relative to the 1961-1990 average, which is approximately 59° F.

1860: -0.7°F

1961-90 average

1995: +0.7°F*

Source: Hadley Centre for Climate Prediction and Research   *Estimate

KNIGHT-RIDDER NEWS SERVICE

Interval-level data: Temperature in °F constitutes interval-level measurement

there is an *absolute zero point* (i.e., a substantively meaningful zero). With a ratio scale the relative difference between two numbers can be determined. For example, if Tom's savings account has $2,000 and Bob's savings account has $500, Tom has four times more money than Bob does. Notice that a zero on the ratio scale implies the absence of what is being measured. Thus, a zero on Tom's banking statement implies that he is out of money. Zero degrees on a Kelvin temperature scale corresponds to the absence of temperature (and life). Other common examples of ratio scales include mass or weight, volume, height, and distance.

In the beginning of this section we acknowledged that there are multiple theories to data measurement, some accepting and others rejecting the four levels of measurement. Even within this typology of scaling there is debate among researchers regarding which level of measurement is applicable to certain types of data. For example, suppose you won two promotional tickets to director Steven Spielberg's newest film release on its opening night. As you leave the theater with your date a newspaper reporter asks you to rate the movie on the following Likert-type scale:

very poor 1 2 3 4 5 6 7 8 9 10 superior

How would you classify data collected on this scale? Is it ordinal or interval? The numbers are certainly in a rank order but are the intervals between these data points equal? That is, is the difference between ratings of 3 and 4 the same as the difference between ratings of 8 and 9? The more conservative approach is to treat this as an ordinal-level scale, which limits the types of statistical tests that can be conducted. The more common and perhaps more practical approach is to consider Likert-type scales as interval-level data, which allows for more powerful statistical analyses.

We should make one final point regarding the numbers resulting from data collection. Data at one level of measurement can sometimes be converted to data at another level of measurement. For example, suppose the owner of a popular nightclub wants to know the income of the patrons frequenting the facility. One evening she asks all guests to complete a survey indicating their exact monetary income. The owner has collected data at the ratio-level (dollars have an absolute zero point and equal intervals). However, if she later chose, the owner could turn this ratio-level data into ordinal-level data by ranking people according to their income level, from lowest to highest.

Summary

Data collection can occur with either qualitative or quantitative research methods. One of the most common qualitative methodologies is field research, where the researcher collects data by case studies or in-depth observation in a naturalistic setting. Three quantitative methods for data collection are content analysis, surveys, and experiments. Content analysis involves a systematic coding of content from artifacts such as television programs, books, or legal documents. A survey involves asking questions via a questionnaire or interview protocol and is the most common of the quantitative research methods. In order to obtain results generalizable to a larger population of people, a random sample of respondents is often used. Finally, experimental research involves careful manipulation of independent (causal) variables and measurement of the outcome or effect via dependent variables. In order to draw valid cause-effect conclusions, true experiments include random assignment of subjects to conditions in the study.

Data can be collected at one of four major levels of measurement: nominal, ordinal, interval, and ratio. Nominal scales involve categories and classification of data. Ordinal scales rank data but have unknown and unequal differences between data points. In contrast, interval and ratio scales both feature known and equal intervals between data points. These latter scales differ in that interval scales have an arbitrary zero point whereas ratio scales have an absolute zero point.

Key Terms

- content analysis
- dependent variable
- experiment
- field research
- independent variable
- interval scale
- measurement
- nominal scale
- ordinal scale
- population
- random assignment
- random sample
- ratio scale
- sample
- survey
- variable

Problems

1. Which research method:
   a. is aimed at discovering cause-and-effect relationships?
   b. uses questionnaires to find answers to research problems?
   c. examines people in natural settings?
   d. analyzes the composition of written, visual, or spoken material?
2. All American voters can be termed a _____ (*population* or *sample*), whereas 1,000 randomly selected American voters can be called a _____ (*population* or *sample*).
3. An educational researcher is interested in discovering whether using computers in the classroom facilitates elementary school children's ability to read. Thirty elementary classrooms that required children to work on computers were identified and these children's scores on national reading exams were found to be higher than those of the average child in elementary school. What is the population and sample of interest?

4. With a _____ sample every member of the population has an equal chance of being selected.
5. Which of the following are random samples (indicate all that apply):
   a. A researcher wants to know how college students at a particular university feel about a writing requirement. All students in an English course are given a questionnaire to assess their opinion about this requirement.
   b. The researcher also wants to know how university professors feel about this same writing requirement. A list of all currently employed professors are obtained from the administrative building. All of the professors' names are written on a piece of paper and thrown into a hat. Twenty professors are selected from the hat to receive a questionnaire assessing their opinion of the writing requirement.
   c. You want to analyze the gender of celebrities' pictures on the cover of *TV Guide* over the past ten years. You take a coin and flip it for every week's *TV Guide* and analyze only those that were present on a "tail" flip.
6. What is the difference between random sampling and random assignment?
7. Sixty students volunteered to receive public speech training and were randomly assigned to two groups. The experimental group completed a set of exercises that

were designed to increase public speaking ability. The control group spent the same amount of time discussing why they had volunteered for the training. Both groups of students then gave short speeches in front of a class and were evaluated. Identify the independent and dependent variable(s).

8. A fashion designer wanted to know if overall sales of his line of clothing would be different between a major department store vs. a specialty store. The percentage of sales were gathered from both outlets every month for a year. The fashion designer then compared profits to see where the most money was grossed. Identify the independent and dependent variable(s).

9. In one class 15 students are randomly assigned to receive extra help (experimental group) whereas the other 15 students are randomly assigned to take the course as in previous years with no extra help (control group). Six weeks later all of the students take the midterm exam and the researcher compares the two groups' test scores to see who performed better. Identify the independent and dependent variable(s).

10. Which scale of measurement (ratio, nominal, ordinal, internal):
    a. has an arbitrary zero point and equal intervals between data points?
    b. classifies people into categories?
    c. rank orders people?
    d. has an absolute zero point and equal intervals between data points?

11. Order the four levels of measurement (*ratio, nominal, ordinal,* and *interval*) from the least to the most informative. What

makes each scale more precise than the one preceding it?

12. A researcher wants to measure your knowledge of the material in this course. How might the researcher measure this phenomenon? What scale of measurement is this?

13. For each of the following variables, identify the appropriate scale of measurement.
    a. nationality
    b. age
       i.   in years (0 to 100+)
       ii. ranked from youngest to oldest
    c. outcomes of a high school track race
       i.   finishing time in minutes and seconds
       ii. finishing places (1st, 2nd, 3rd)
       iii. team names of competing schools
    d. heart rate (beats per minute)
    e. SAT scores
    f. distance in meters

Notes

1 Hyde, C. (1994). Reflections on a journey: A research story. In C.K. Riessman (Ed.) Qualitative studies in social work research (pp. 169-189). Thousand Oaks, CA: Sage.

2 Smith, R., & Eisenberg, E. (1987). Conflict at Disneyland: A root-metaphor analysis. *Communication Monographs, 54,* 367-380.

3 Sherman, B., & Dominick, J. (1986). Violence and sex in music videos: TV and rock 'n' roll. *Journal of Communication, 36,* 79-93.

4 For a good summary of various theoretical approaches to measurement, we recommend: Mitchell, J. (1986). Measurement scales and statistics: A clash of paradigms. *Psychological Bulletin, 100,* 398-407.

🖳 Computer Section

Introduction to a Hypothetical Data Set

Overview

Throughout the remainder of the computer section of this book, we will focus on using a computer to perform statistical analyses on a hypothetical data set derived from student evaluations of a course. The evaluation form may look familiar to many evaluations you have completed for your own classes. Questions on this student evaluation form will serve as the dependent measures for this study. The study examines differences in the evaluation of an instructor and course as a function of a number of independent variables: gender of the instructor (male vs. female), learning location (live vs. mediated), and structure of the class (cooperative, competitive, or individualistic). The rationale (literature review) and methodology for this study is the focus of the remainder of this chapter.

Instructional Technology Study

Characteristic of the modern era, the explosion of new technologies has drastically expanded the horizons of classroom instruction (Saba, 1992). While there is little disagreement that communicative relationships between teachers and students are a central component of the teaching-learning process (Devito, 1986; Gorham, 1988; Greenfield, 1984), there are many new delivery devices that arguably can facilitate learning outcomes (Seamons, 1989). Over the past century, with the advent of each new instructional medium, research followed that compared the learning impact of the newer media (e.g., motion pictures, television,

computers) with the more traditional media (live classroom instruction). A typical study would entail comparing the achievement of two groups receiving the same subject matter from two different media. However, this research tradition has been criticized for not accurately describing the relationship between instructional media and learning outcomes (e.g., Clark, 1983).

One major weakness of many instructional studies has been that effects due to the medium have been confounded with the instructional method used. For instance, consider a study that compares learning outcomes from a traditional live instruction class with outcomes from a course that utilizes computer technology as the primary medium for instruction. The traditional live instruction class might involve heavy classroom discussion whereas the computer class might involve primarily individualized instruction. Thus, learning outcomes from such a study might be due to the instructional method (discussion vs. individual learning) and not the nature of the medium (live vs. computer). Cognizant of these kinds of limitations with the comparison methodology, researchers have turned to more meaningful avenues of research.

Recent approaches to studying the impact of instructional technologies on learning-related outcomes have focused on how technology can be used to facilitate teaching and learning. That is, many researchers now believe that media do not affect learning in and of themselves. Rather, the media are delivery vehicles for instruction which influence the way information is processed (Clark & Sugrue, 1988). Thus, factors such as instructional method (e.g., classroom structure), instructor gender, and method of evaluation (e.g., exams, oral presentations, papers) may influence the way in which instructional technologies impact learning outcomes. The purpose of the present study is to examine the relationship between new technologies and instructional factors such as instructor gender and classroom structure in terms of their effect on students' perceptions of learning and learning-related outcomes.

Method

Two professors (male and female) offered the exact same course to a total of 120 undergraduates at a large university. These two instructors were selected from a pilot study based on their similar presentation style. In addition, the instructors were matched in terms of their status, experience, and age. Each professor had three sections of the course and allowed an enrollment of twenty students per class (a total of 60 students per instructor). In each class, half of the students (N=10) were randomly assigned to the same room as the instructor and the other half (N=10) were randomly assigned to an adjacent room that simultaneously telecast the instructor's lectures. The professors also structured each section differently. One class was structured competitively, another individualistically, and the third cooperatively. The design of the study can be conceptualized as shown in Figure 2.1. The factorial design with the total number of subjects per condition is also depicted in Table 2.2.

The rationale for examining the three independent variables used in this study is discussed in the following section.

Gender of Instructor

Many studies over the last twenty years have shown differential evaluations of males and females with identical performances on different tasks. Research focused on college teaching, however, has not generally documented this gender bias (Dukes & Victoria, 1989). We wanted to investigate whether a gender bias existed in students' evaluation of college professors.

Learning Location

Teachers and students who are physically separated can be connected – via satellite television and computer networks – in programs known as distance learning (Zimmerer, 1988). Students who had previously been prevented from continuing their education because of geographic location, family responsibilities, job requirements, and physical handicaps now have access to learning. We are interested in examining differences in perceptions of the course and instructor between lectures presented in person versus mediated through a television (i.e., telecourses).

TABLE 2.2: 2 x 2 x 3 Factorial Design

Gender of Instructor	Learning Location	Class Structure		
		Competitive	Individual	Cooperative
Male	Live	N = 10	N = 10	N = 10
	Mediated	N = 10	N = 10	N = 10
Female	Live	N = 10	N = 10	N = 10
	Mediated	N = 10	N = 10	N = 10

2 x 2 x 3 Factorial Design

Male

Female

Lecture 1 — Cooperative

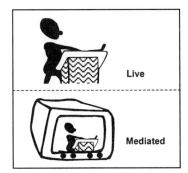

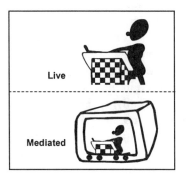

Live

Mediated

Live

Mediated

Lecture 2 — Competitive

Live

Mediated

Live

Mediated

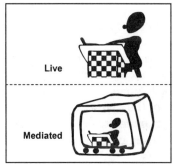

Lecture 3 — Individualistic

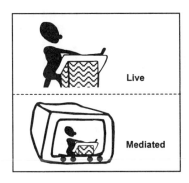

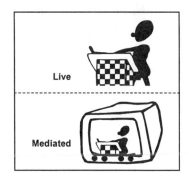

Live

Mediated

Live

Mediated

FIGURE 2.1: 2 x 2 x 3 Factorial Design

Class Structure

The social atmosphere of the classroom is largely created by the instructor and can have a tremendous impact on students' motivation (Staton, 1990). In particular, the structure of the class specifies the ways in which students will interact with each other and the instructor during the course. University classes may be structured in three ways: competitively, individualistically, and cooperatively (Johnson, Johnson, & Smith, 1991). In the present study, we systematically distinguish among these levels in terms of the grading, homework assignments, and in-class reflection.

Competitive Learning Classroom

Students are required to compete with each other for their final grade which is determined by a *curve* ranked from best to worst. All homework assignments are completed *alone* and also graded on a curve. During various parts of the lecture, the instructor provides three minute breaks to allow each student to cognitively process the material being taught. Students write down the three most important points they just heard during this time. These lists are later corrected and students are provided with feedback concerning how well they performed in comparison to other students.

Individualistic Learning Classroom

Students' final grades are determined by how well they perform against a *preset criteria*. Their unique performance has no influence on other students and vice versa. All homework assignments are representative of the *individual* and similarly graded against a preset criteria. During various parts of the lecture, the instructor provides three minute *silent breaks* to allow each student to cognitively process the material being taught.

Cooperative Learning Classroom

Students' final grades are determined by how well they have improved throughout the course. All homework assignments are accomplished in groups. Students work *together* to maximize their own and their classmates' understanding and their output is graded as a function of their level of improvement during the course. During various parts of the lecture, the instructor provides three minute *discussion breaks* to allow students to cognitively process the material being taught in cooperative pairs.

In addition to examining the role of telecommunication in the classroom, we also were interested in studying the influence of electronic mail (e-mail). At the beginning of the course all students were given training sessions and access to e-mail accounts. An exploratory analysis investigating the pattern of and underlying motives for students' use of e-mail was undertaken.

E-mail

Computers and electronic mail are frequently being used to accompany classroom instruction, not only to reinforce and expand learning but also to increase teacher-student interaction (Williams & Brown, 1991). In the present study, e-mail was available to all students for four functions: (1) class communication of official notices such as day and time of exams (i.e., bulletin boards), (2) anonymous complaints and suggestions on course activities and content, (3) contact with the professor regarding questions and help, and (4) contact between students.

At the end of the course all students completed an evaluation form. These questions comprise the dependent measures for the study. The student evaluation survey completed by all students in this study is shown in Figure 2.2.

Codebook

In order to prepare students' responses for statistical analyses, the answers from the questionnaire were coded into a numerical format. To assist this coding process, a *codebook* is constructed from a blank questionnaire and each item is labeled with: (1) a variable name, (2) a number corresponding with the variable's column location in a data file, and (3) for open-ended items, the possible categories of responses and their numerical codes.

If the question is forced-choice or "closed-ended" it already incorporates a range of numeric values and the respondent's answer is reported. If the question is "open-ended" the range of answers is not identified. The researcher must develop a coding frame and rules for assigning responses to categories. Once the answers are arranged in mutually exclusive categories, they can be assigned numeric codes.

When all the answers have been translated into numeric codes, these codes from the questionnaire are input into a data file. The data file consists of a string of numbers with each column representing an item from the questionnaire. All student evaluation forms (N=120) are input into the data file. The closed-ended codes are taken directly from the questionnaires and the codebook is consulted for open-ended questions and assigned the appropriate code.

Students' open-ended responses for the two questions dealing with the primary strength and weakness of the course were classified into one of four categories. For the major strength of the course, responses were coded into one of the following four categories: 1 – course structure, 2 – pace of lectures, 3 – subject matter, and 4 – textbook/readings.

Responses for the main weakness of the course were coded into one of the following four categories: 1 – work load, 2 – grading/exams, 3 – textbook/readings, and 4 – assignments.

With regard to students' reasons for using electronic mail, five categories emerged for the coding framework for each of the four open-ended questions: 1 – diversion (escape from routine), 2 – social function (relationship development), 3 – surveillance (seek and provide information), 4 – convenience (could not make office hours), and 5 – expression (give opinion).

The final codebook includes variable names in the left-hand shaded column, column locator number for each variable in the right-hand shaded column, and open-ended categories with numerical codes for each open-ended item. The complete codebook for this study is provided in Figure 2.3.

Data File

Data collected from a study are entered and stored in a *data file* on the computer. One format for such a data file is a *flatfile*, which is simply a basic text file containing numeric data. For instance, following are the contents of a flatfile with five subjects' data for ten variables:

$$0\,0\,1\,2\,2\,1\,3\,7\,5\,6\,4\,5\,4$$
$$0\,0\,2\,3\,1\,2\,5\,6\,7\,4\,5\,4\,3$$
$$0\,0\,3\,2\,8\,2\,6\,5\,7\,5\,4\,6\,4$$
$$0\,0\,4\,4\,5\,1\,5\,3\,1\,5\,4\,6\,5$$
$$0\,0\,5\,3\,7\,1\,5\,4\,3\,5\,6\,7\,5$$

Notice that only numeric data is listed with no formatting (e.g., tabs, bold, italics). Each row contains a new subjects' set of data. For instance, the first row contains all of the data for the first subject (Subject 001), the second row contains all of the data for the second subject

(Subject 002), and so forth. Multiple rows also can be used per subject if there is a substantial amount of data collected from each participant in the study. Each column contains exactly the same data for each subject. In the sample data above columns 1-3 contain the subject's identification number (from Subject 001 to Subject 005), columns 4-5 contain each subject's age (e.g., Subject 001 is 22 years old, Subject 004 is 45 years old), column 6 contains a numeric code corresponding to subjects' gender (e.g., 1=male, 2=female; in these data Subject 002 is female, Subject 005 is male), and columns 7-13 contain subjects' ratings of a person on Likert-scales (ranging from 1 to 7) for such characteristics as intelligence, attractiveness, and dynamism.

Data also can be stored in a *spreadsheet* or table from statistical, spreadsheet, or database software. Again, each row represents one subject's data and each column represents a variable. Specific data values are entered into the cells of the spreadsheet. Variable names are usually limited to eight or ten characters. An example of the spreadsheet file for the above data set follows (Table 2.3).

Data for the Instructional Technology Study are located in a flatfile called TECHFLAT.DAT and in a spreadsheet file called TECHSPRD.DAT on the computer diskette accompanying this book. The codebook provides a name for each variable as well as the column number(s) in which each variable's data is located in the flatfile.

Program Commands: Batch File vs. Interactive Mode

All statistical programs (e.g., SPSS, SAS) require the user to submit commands indicating the function to be performed. These *program commands* tell the computer to do a variety of things, such as locate data, label variables, merge data files, and run statistical analyses. Program commands can be submitted to statistical programs in one of two ways: via a batch file or interactively.

One way to submit program commands to a statistical program is through a batch file which the researcher writes. A *batch file* is a file that contains a series of program commands to be executed by the statistical program. The term "batch file" comes from the fact that multiple commands are submitted simultaneously (i.e., in a batch) to the statistical program for execution. For instance, a batch file might contain a command that reads in data from a flatfile, a command that labels each variable, a command that labels the values for each variable, a command that produces basic descriptive statistics (such as the average) for each variable, and a command that produces a cor-

TABLE 2.3									
	subject	age	gender	intellig	attract	extrov	honest	dynam	moral	assert
1	001	22	1	3	7	5	6	4	5	4
2	002	31	2	5	6	7	4	5	4	3
3	003	28	2	6	5	7	5	4	6	4
4	004	45	1	5	3	1	5	4	6	5
5	005	37	1	5	4	3	5	6	7	5

relation analysis for two variables to see if they are related. Batch files are very useful for analyzing data if a researcher believes s/he may need to add, change, or delete program commands or replicate an analysis.

Program commands also can be submitted to the computer interactively. When running commands in *interactive mode* the user submits a single command for analysis and the computer immediately executes the command. Many statistical software packages feature pull-down menus that allow users to easily submit commands interactively to the computer. However, because program commands are not stored in a file when using interactive mode, the researcher must rerun every command if s/he wishes to replicate a particular analysis. Interactive mode is useful for analyzing data if the researcher is conducting a one-time analysis.

Reading Data and Producing Variable and Value Labels

The first major program command submitted to a statistical program (either via a batch file or interactively) is a command to inform the program where to find the data that will be analyzed. This command includes information about the variable name to give to each variable and the column(s) in which the data for each variable is located. For instance, for the Instructional Technology Study, the program command to read data from the flatfile would contain the following command information: (1) the location of the data file (on the floppy disk in a data file called TECHFLAT.DAT); (2) the columns in which data for separate variables are located (e.g., columns 1-3 contain data for one variable, column 4 contains data for another variable, column 5 contains data for another variable); and (3) the names for each variable (e.g., the variable whose data is in columns 1-3 should be labeled SUBID, the

variable whose data is in column 4 should be labeled GENDER, the variable whose data is in column 5 should be labeled CONDIT).

After submitting a program command to read the desired data into the statistical program, it is common to run a program command that produces labels for each variable and another program command that produces labels for the values of certain variables. Because variable names usually are restricted to eight characters by statistical programs, it is helpful to provide descriptive labels to each variable for ease of reference. For example, it may be hard to remember that the variable MORELIKE corresponds with the 7-point Likert question "Did your interest in the subject matter increase as a result of taking this class?" Thus, variable labels allow a researcher to produce longer, more descriptive labels for each variable which appear in statistical printouts.

Similarly, labels often are provided for the numeric values of certain variables, particularly categorical or nominal-level variables where the meaning of the value is not obvious. For instance, what does a 1 mean for the variable WEAK? By providing a label "work load" for this value, interpretation of statistical output is greatly facilitated.

Computer Problems

1. On the following pages you will find respondent #120's questionnaire (Figure 2.4). Input this student's data into the data file located on the computer disk accompanying this book (either TECHFLAT.DAT or TECHSPRD.DAT). Be sure to save your changes. The data file should now consist of 120 cases and will be the basis for analyses in all subsequent chapters.

2. Add descriptive labels for each of the *variables* to more clearly identify what question each variable represents.

3. Add descriptive labels to each *value* (e.g., 1 = Female, 2 = Male) of each categorical or nominal-level variable on the survey to more clearly identify what each numeric code represents.

References

Clark, R. (1983). Reconsidering research on learning from media. *Review of Educational Research, 53,* 445-460.

Clark, R., & Sugrue, B. (1988). Research on instructional media. In D. Ely, B. Broadbent, & R. Wood (Eds.), *Educational media and technology yearbook* (pp. 19-36). Littleton, CO: Libraries Unlimited.

Devito, J. (1986). Teaching as relational development. In J. M. Civikly (Ed.), *Communicating in college classrooms.* San Francisco: Jossey-Bass.

Dukes, R., & Victoria, G. (1989). The effects of gender, status, and effective teaching on the evaluation of college instruction. *Teaching Sociology, 17,* 447-457.

Gorham, J. (1988). The relationship between verbal teacher immediacy behaviors and student learning. *Communication Education, 37,* 198-207.

Greenfield, P. (1984). *Mind and media: The effects of television, video games and computers.* Cambridge, MA: Harvard University Press.

Johnson, D., Johnson, R., & Smith, K. (1991). *Active learning: Cooperation in the college classroom.* Edina, MN: Interaction Book Company.

Saba, F. (1992). Digital media: A platform for converging educational technology 'preparadigms.' In D. Ely & B. Minor (Eds.), *Educational media and technology yearbook* (pp. 127-139). Littleton, Co: Libraries Unlimited.

Seamons, R. (1989). Electronic distance education: New methods for the future. In B. Branyan-Broadbent & R. Wood (Eds.), *Educational media and technology yearbook* (pp. 52-58). Littleton, Co: Libraries Unlimited.

Staton, A. (1990). An ecological perspective on college/university teaching. In J. Daly, G. Friedrich, & A. Vangelisti (Eds.), *Teaching communication: Theory, research, and methods* (pp. 39-52). New Jersey: Lawrence Erlbaum Associates.

Williams, C., & Brown, S. (1991). A review of the research issues in the use of computer-related technologies for instruction: An agenda for research. In B. Branyan-Broadbent & R. Wood (Eds.), *Educational media and technology yearbook* (pp. 26-46). Littleton, Co: Libraries Unlimited.

Zimmerer, J. (1988). Computer conferencing: A medium for facilitating interaction in distance education. In D. Ely, B. Broadbent, & R. Wood (Eds.), *Educational media and technology yearbook* (pp. 19-36). Littleton, Co: Libraries Unlimited.

┌─────────────────┐
│ **S**tudent   │   Instructor:_____   Department:_____
│   │
│   **E**valuation│
│   │   Course:_____   Time:_____
│   **S**urvey│
└─────────────────┘

Please anonymously express your views by completing all the items below. There are no right or wrong answers; it is your opinion that is important.

Student Demographics

Indicate your:
   Age_____

Gender: 1—female
        2—male

Class Level: 1—freshman   3—junior
              2—sophomore   4—senior

Estimated Grade: 1—A   3—C
                   2—B   4—D
                          5—F

Instructor Evaluation

The instructor:	very strongly disagree (1)	strongly disagree (2)	disagree (3)	neutral (4)	agree (5)	strongly agree (6)	very strongly agree (7)
1. presented material in an interesting way.	(1)	(2)	(3)	(4)	(5)	(6)	(7)
2. demonstrated enthusiasm for the subject.	(1)	(2)	(3)	(4)	(5)	(6)	(7)
3. had a thorough knowledge of the subject matter.	(1)	(2)	(3)	(4)	(5)	(6)	(7)
4. summarized or emphasized major points in lectures.	(1)	(2)	(3)	(4)	(5)	(6)	(7)
5. was clear and audible.	(1)	(2)	(3)	(4)	(5)	(6)	(7)
6. knew when students did not understand the material.	(1)	(2)	(3)	(4)	(5)	(6)	(7)
7. made objectives for the course clear.	(1)	(2)	(3)	(4)	(5)	(6)	(7)
8. made helpful comments on papers and/or exams.	(1)	(2)	(3)	(4)	(5)	(6)	(7)
9. showed a genuine interest in me as an individual.	(1)	(2)	(3)	(4)	(5)	(6)	(7)
10. had a good rapport with students.	(1)	(2)	(3)	(4)	(5)	(6)	(7)

FIGURE 2.2: Blank Student Evaluation Survey

In general, how would you *describe* your instructor:

11.	expert	____:____:____:____:____:____:____	nonexpert
12.	unfriendly	____:____:____:____:____:____:____	friendly
13.	dynamic	____:____:____:____:____:____:____	boring
14.	calm	____:____:____:____:____:____:____	anxious
15.	unintelligent	____:____:____:____:____:____:____	intelligent
16.	good natured	____:____:____:____:____:____:____	irritable
17.	outgoing	____:____:____:____:____:____:____	shy
18.	composed	____:____:____:____:____:____:____	excitable
19.	nice	____:____:____:____:____:____:____	mean
20.	tired	____:____:____:____:____:____:____	energetic
21.	poised	____:____:____:____:____:____:____	nervous
22.	inexperienced	____:____:____:____:____:____:____	experienced
23.	approachable	____:____:____:____:____:____:____	distant
24.	active	____:____:____:____:____:____:____	passive
25.	confident	____:____:____:____:____:____:____	lacks confidence
26.	unqualified	____:____:____:____:____:____:____	qualified

Overall ratings:

27. Overall, how do you rate this instructor?

    very poor   (1)   (2)   (3)   (4)   (5)   (6)   (7)   very good

28. Overall, how do you rate the course?

    very poor   (1)   (2)   (3)   (4)   (5)   (6)   (7)   very good

Students' Perception of Learning/Academic Value

29. To what extent did you find the class intellectually challenging?

    not at all   (1)   (2)   (3)   (4)   (5)   (6)   (7)   definitely

30. To what extent did you learn something from this course that you consider valuable?

    not at all   (1)   (2)   (3)   (4)   (5)   (6)   (7)   definitely

FIGURE 2.2: Blank Student Evaluation Survey

31. How much of an understanding do you feel you have of the material from this class?

    none   (1)   (2)   (3)   (4)   (5)   (6)   (7)   a great deal

32. How well do you think you are able to apply the subject matter from this course in other contexts?

    very poor   (1)   (2)   (3)   (4)   (5)   (6)   (7)   very well

33. How interested were you in the subject matter of this course?

    not at all   (1)   (2)   (3)   (4)   (5)   (6)   (7)   definitely
    interested   interested

34. Did your interest in the subject matter increase as a result of taking this class?

    not at all   (1)   (2)   (3)   (4)   (5)   (6)   (7)   definitely

35. How much effort did you put into this course?

    none   (1)   (2)   (3)   (4)   (5)   (6)   (7)   a great deal

36. How comfortable did you feel seeking help/advice from your professor in or outside of class?

    not at all   (1)   (2)   (3)   (4)   (5)   (6)   (7)   very
    comfortable   comfortable

37. Do you consider yourself a person who likes to learn?

    not at all   (1)   (2)   (3)   (4)   (5)   (6)   (7)   definitely

38. How well do you think you did in this course?

    very poor   (1)   (2)   (3)   (4)   (5)   (6)   (7)   very well

(**Course Evaluation**)

39. In your opinion, what is the major strength of this course?

40. In your opinion, what is the primary weakness of this course?

FIGURE 2.2: Blank Student Evaluation Survey

> **Electronic Mail Use**

In general, indicate your attitudes about using the electronic mail system in this course:

41.	stimulating	____:____:____:____:____:____:____	dull
42.	dreary	____:____:____:____:____:____:____	fun
43.	easy	____:____:____:____:____:____:____	difficult
44.	impersonal	____:____:____:____:____:____:____	personal
45.	helpful	____:____:____:____:____:____:____	hindering
46.	threatening	____:____:____:____:____:____:____	comfortable
47.	efficient	____:____:____:____:____:____:____	inefficient
48.	unfavorable	____:____:____:____:____:____:____	favorable

Announcement Board

49. How often did you use electronic mail to read or post class announcements?

    never (1)   (2)   (3)   (4)   (5)   (6)   (7)   daily

50. What was the main reason you checked the announcement board?

Feedback Board

51. How often did you use electronic mail to provide anonymous feedback to your instructor?

    never (1)   (2)   (3)   (4)   (5)   (6)   (7)   daily

52. What was the major reason you provided feedback to your instructor?

Instructor

53. How often did you use electronic mail to contact your professor for any reason?

    never (1)   (2)   (3)   (4)   (5)   (6)   (7)   daily

54. What was the main reason you contacted your instructor through electronic mail?

Students

55. How often did you use electronic mail to contact your classmates?

    never (1)   (2)   (3)   (4)   (5)   (6)   (7)   daily

56. What was the major reason you contacted your classmates through electronic mail?

FIGURE 2.2: Blank Student Evaluation Survey

Variable		Codebook	Column

Codebook

Variable			Column
	Student **E**valuation **S**urvey	Subject ID #	1-3
subid		Instructor: 1—female 2—male	4
gender		Condition: 1—live 2—mediated	5
condit		Class: 1—cooperative 2—competitive	6
class		3—individualistic	

Student Demographics

Indicate your:

age	Age_____	Class Level: 1—freshman	3—junior	7-8
clslvl		2—sophomore	4—senior	9
stdtsex	Gender: 1—female	Estimated Grade: 1—A	3—C	10
grade	2—male	2—B	4—D	11
			5—F	

Instructor Evaluation

Variable	The instructor:	very strongly disagree (1)	strongly disagree (2)	disagree (3)	neutral (4)	agree (5)	strongly agree (6)	very strongly agree (7)	Column
interest	1. presented material in an interesting way.	(1)	(2)	(3)	(4)	(5)	(6)	(7)	12
enthus	2. demonstrated enthusiasm for the subject.	(1)	(2)	(3)	(4)	(5)	(6)	(7)	13
know	3. had a thorough knowledge of the subject matter.	(1)	(2)	(3)	(4)	(5)	(6)	(7)	14
sum	4. summarized major points in lectures.	(1)	(2)	(3)	(4)	(5)	(6)	(7)	15
clear	5. was clear and audible.	(1)	(2)	(3)	(4)	(5)	(6)	(7)	16
aware	6. knew when students didn't understand material.	(1)	(2)	(3)	(4)	(5)	(6)	(7)	17
obj	7. made objectives for the course clear.	(1)	(2)	(3)	(4)	(5)	(6)	(7)	18
critiq	8. made helpful comments on papers and/or exams.	(1)	(2)	(3)	(4)	(5)	(6)	(7)	19
care	9. showed a genuine interest in me as an individual.	(1)	(2)	(3)	(4)	(5)	(6)	(7)	20
rapport	10. had a good rapport with students.	(1)	(2)	(3)	(4)	(5)	(6)	(7)	21

FIGURE 2.3: Student Evaluation Survey Codebook

Variable	In general, how would you *describe* your instructor:		Column
expert	11. expert __7_ : _6_ : _5_ : _4_ : _3_ : _2_ : _1_	nonexpert	22
friend	12. unfriendly _1_ : _2_ : _3_ : _4_ : _5_ : _6_ : _7_	friendly	23
dyn	13. dynamic __7_ : _6_ : _5_ : _4_ : _3_ : _2_ : _1_	boring	24
calm	14. calm __7_ : _6_ : _5_ : _4_ : _3_ : _2_ : _1_	anxious	25
smart	15. unintellige _1_ : _2_ : _3_ : _4_ : _5_ : _6_ : _7_	intelligent	26
good	16. good natur _7_ : _6_ : _5_ : _4_ : _3_ : _2_ : _1_	irritable	27
outgoing	17. outgoing __7_ : _6_ : _5_ : _4_ : _3_ : _2_ : _1_	shy	28
compose	18. composed _7_ : _6_ : _5_ : _4_ : _3_ : _2_ : _1_	excitable	29
nice	19. nice __7_ : _6_ : _5_ : _4_ : _3_ : _2_ : _1_	mean	30
energy	20. tired __1_ : _2_ : _3_ : _4_ : _5_ : _6_ : _7_	energetic	31
poised	21. poised __7_ : _6_ : _5_ : _4_ : _3_ : _2_ : _1_	nervous	32
exper	22. inexperien _1_ : _2_ : _3_ : _4_ : _5_ : _6_ : _7_	experience	33
distant	23. approachab _7_ : _6_ : _5_ : _4_ : _3_ : _2_ : _1_	distant	34
active	24. active __7_ : _6_ : _5_ : _4_ : _3_ : _2_ : _1_	passive	35
confid	25. confident _7_ : _6_ : _5_ : _4_ : _3_ : _2_ : _1_	lacks confide	36
qual	26. unqualifie _1_ : _2_ : _3_ : _4_ : _5_ : _6_ : _7_	qualified	37

Overall ratings:

instruct 27. Overall, how do you rate this instructor?

very poor   (1)   (2)   (3)   (4)   (5)   (6)   (7)   very good   38

course 28. Overall, how do you rate the course?

very poor   (1)   (2)   (3)   (4)   (5)   (6)   (7)   very good   39

Students' Perception of Learning/Academic Value

chall 29. To what extent did you find the class intellectually challenging?

not at all   (1)   (2)   (3)   (4)   (5)   (6)   (7)   definitely   40

value 30. To what extent did you learn something from this course that you consider   41
valuable?

not at all   (1)   (2)   (3)   (4)   (5)   (6)   (7)   definitely

FIGURE 2.3: Student Evaluation Survey Codebook

Variable

Column

underst | 31. How much of an understanding do you feel you have of the material from this class?

none　　(1)　(2)　(3)　(4)　(5)　(6)　(7)　a great deal | 42

apply | 32. How well do you think you are able to apply the subject matter from this course in other contexts?

very poor　(1)　(2)　(3)　(4)　(5)　(6)　(7)　very well | 43

likeclas | 33. How interested were you in the subject matter of this course?

not at all　(1)　(2)　(3)　(4)　(5)　(6)　(7)　definitely
interested　　　　　　　　　　　　　　　　interested | 44

morelike | 34. Did your interest in the subject matter increase as a result of taking this class?

not at all　(1)　(2)　(3)　(4)　(5)　(6)　(7)　definitely | 45

effort | 35. How much effort did you put into this course?

none　　(1)　(2)　(3)　(4)　(5)　(6)　(7)　a great deal | 46

seek | 36. How comfortable did you feel seeking help/advice from your professor in or outside of class?

not at all　(1)　(2)　(3)　(4)　(5)　(6)　(7)　very
comfortable　　　　　　　　　　　　　　comfortable | 47

learn | 37. Do you consider yourself a person who likes to learn?

not at all　(1)　(2)　(3)　(4)　(5)　(6)　(7)　definitely | 48

outcome | 38. How well do you think you did in this course?

very poor　(1)　(2)　(3)　(4)　(5)　(6)　(7)　very well | 49

Course Evaluation

strength | 39. In your opinion, what is the major strength of this course? | 50

　　1—course structure　　　　3—subject matter
　　2—pace of lectures　　　　4—textbook/readings

weak | 40. In your opinion, what is the primary weakness of this course? | 51

　　1—work load　　　　　　3—textbook/readings
　　2—grading/exams　　　　4—assignments

FIGURE 2.3: Student Evaluation Survey Codebook

Variable   Column

Electronic Mail Use

In general, indicate your attitudes about using the electronic mail system:

Variable					
dull	41. stimulating	7 : 6 : 5 : 4 : 3 : 2 : 1	dull	52
fun	42. dreary	1 : 2 : 3 : 4 : 5 : 6 : 7	fun	53
easy	43. easy	7 : 6 : 5 : 4 : 3 : 2 : 1	difficult	54
personal	44. impersonal	1 : 2 : 3 : 4 : 5 : 6 : 7	personal	55
hinder	45. helpful	7 : 6 : 5 : 4 : 3 : 2 : 1	hindering	56
threat	46. threatening	1 : 2 : 3 : 4 : 5 : 6 : 7	comfortable	57
effic	47. efficient	7 : 6 : 5 : 4 : 3 : 2 : 1	inefficient	58
favor	48. unfavorable	1 : 2 : 3 : 4 : 5 : 6 : 7	favorable	59

Announcement Board

board1 49. How often did you use electronic mail to read or post class announcements?

      never (1)   (2)   (3)   (4)   (5)   (6)   (7)   daily   60

board2 50. What was the main reason you checked the announcement board?

    1—diversion (escape)   3—surveillance   5—expression   61
    2—social function   4—convenience   6—never checked

Feedback Board

fdback1 51. How often did you use electronic mail to provide feedback to your instructor?

      never (1)   (2)   (3)   (4)   (5)   (6)   (7)   daily   62

fdback2 52. What was the major reason you provided feedback to your instructor?

    1—diversion (escape)   3—surveillance   5—expression   63
    2—social function   4—convenience   6—never gave feedback

Instructor

teach1 53. How often did you use electronic mail to contact your professor for any reason?

      never (1)   (2)   (3)   (4)   (5)   (6)   (7)   daily   64

teach2 54. What was the main reason you contacted your instructor through electronic mail? 65

    1—diversion (escape)   3—surveillance   5—expression
    2—social function   4—convenience   6—never contacted

Students

student1 55. How often did you use electronic mail to contact your classmates? 66

      never (1)   (2)   (3)   (4)   (5)   (6)   (7)   daily

student2 56. What was the major reason you contacted your classmates through electronic mail? 67

    1—diversion (escape)   3—surveillance   5—expression
    2—social function   4—convenienee   6—never contacted

FIGURE 2.3: Student Evaluation Survey Codebook

#120

┌─────────────────┐
│ **S**tudent   │   Instructor:__male_____   Department:_____
│ **E**valuation │
│   **S**urvey │   Course:___mediated_____   Time:__cooperative_____
└─────────────────┘

Please anonymously express your views by completing all the items below. There are no right or wrong answers; it is your opinion that is important.

Student Demographics

Indicate your:

Age___20_____

Gender: 1—female
(2)—male

Class Level: 1—freshman   (3)—junior
               2—sophomore   4—senior

Estimated Grade: (1)—A   3—C
                   2—B   4—D
                              5—F

Instructor Evaluation

The instructor:	very strongly disagree (1)	strongly disagree (2)	disagree (3)	neutral (4)	agree (5)	strongly agree (6)	very strongly agree (7)
1. presented material in an interesting way.	(1)	(2)	(3)	(4)	(5)	(6)	(7)
2. demonstrated enthusiasm for the subject.	(1)	(2)	(3)	(4)	(5)	(6)	(7)
3. had a thorough knowledge of the subject matter.	(1)	(2)	(3)	(4)	(5)	(6)	(7)
4. summarized or emphasized major points in lectures.	(1)	(2)	(3)	(4)	(5)	(6)	(7)
5. was clear and audible.	(1)	(2)	(3)	(4)	(5)	(6)	(7)
6. knew when students did not understand the material.	(1)	(2)	(3)	(4)	(5)	(6)	(7)
7. made objectives for the course clear.	(1)	(2)	(3)	(4)	(5)	(6)	(7)
8. made helpful comments on papers and/or exams.	(1)	(2)	(3)	(4)	(5)	(6)	(7)
9. showed a genuine interest in me as an individual.	(1)	(2)	(3)	(4)	(5)	(6)	(7)
10. had a good rapport with students.	(1)	(2)	(3)	(4)	(5)	(6)	(7)

FIGURE 2.4: Student Evaluation Survey Subject #120 Data

In general, how would you *describe* your instructor:

11.	expert	____ : ____ : ____ : X : ____ : ____ : ____	nonexpert
12.	unfriendly	____ : ____ : ____ : ____ : ____ : X : ____	friendly
13.	dynamic	____ : ____ : X : ____ : ____ : ____ : ____	boring
14.	calm	X : ____ : ____ : ____ : ____ : ____ : ____	anxious
15.	unintelligent	____ : ____ : ____ : X : ____ : ____ : ____	intelligent
16.	good natured	____ : X : ____ : ____ : ____ : ____ : ____	irritable
17.	outgoing	____ : ____ : X : ____ : ____ : ____ : ____	shy
18.	composed	X : ____ : ____ : ____ : ____ : ____ : ____	excitable
19.	nice	____ : X : ____ : ____ : ____ : ____ : ____	mean
20.	tired	____ : ____ : ____ : ____ : X : ____ : ____	energetic
21.	poised	X : ____ : ____ : ____ : ____ : ____ : ____	nervous
22.	inexperienced	____ : ____ : ____ : X : ____ : ____ : ____	experienced
23.	approachable	____ : X : ____ : ____ : ____ : ____ : ____	distant
24.	active	____ : ____ : X : ____ : ____ : ____ : ____	passive
25.	confident	X : ____ : ____ : ____ : ____ : ____ : ____	lacks confidence
26.	unqualified	____ : ____ : ____ : X : ____ : ____ : ____	qualified

Overall ratings:

27. Overall, how do you rate this instructor?

very poor   (1)   (2)   (3)   (4)   (5)   ⑥   (7)   very good

28. Overall, how do you rate the course?

very poor   (1)   (2)   (3)   ④   (5)   (6)   (7)   very good

Students' Perception of Learning/Academic Value

29. To what extent did you find the class intellectually challenging?

not at all   (1)   (2)   ③   (4)   (5)   (6)   (7)   definitely

30. To what extent did you learn something from this course that you consider valuable?

not at all   (1)   (2)   (3)   (4)   (5)   ⑥   (7)   definitely

---

FIGURE 2.4: Student Evaluation Survey Subject #120 Data

31. How much of an understanding do you feel you have of the material from this class?

    none   (1)   (2)   (3)   (4)   ((5))   (6)   (7)   a great deal

32. How well do you think you are able to apply the subject matter from this course in other contexts?

    very poor   (1)   (2)   (3)   (4)   (5)   (6)   ((7))   very well

33. How interested were you in the subject matter of this course?

    not at all   (1)   (2)   (3)   (4)   ((5))   (6)   (7)   definitely
    interested   interested

34. Did your interest in the subject matter increase as a result of taking this class?

    not at all   (1)   (2)   (3)   (4)   (5)   ((6))   (7)   definitely

35. How much effort did you put into this course?

    none   (1)   (2)   (3)   (4)   (5)   (6)   ((7))   a great deal

36. How comfortable did you feel seeking help/advice from your professor in or outside of class?

    not at all   (1)   (2)   (3)   (4)   (5)   (6)   ((7))   very
    comfortable   comfortable

37. Do you consider yourself a person who likes to learn?

    not at all   (1)   (2)   (3)   (4)   (5)   ((6))   (7)   definitely

38. How well do you think you did in this course?

    very poor   (1)   (2)   (3)   (4)   (5)   (6)   ((7))   very well

Course Evaluation

39. In your opinion, what is the major strength of this course?

    I liked the way the course was organized.

40. In your opinion, what is the primary weakness of this course?

    I thought the exams were too demanding

FIGURE 2.4: Student Evaluation Survey Subject #120 Data

Electronic Mail Use

In general, indicate your attitudes about using the electronic mail system in this course:

41. stimulating	_____: _X_ : _____: _____: _____: _____: _____	dull
42. dreary	_____: _____: _____: _____: _____: _X_ : _____	fun
43. easy	_X_ : _____: _____: _____: _____: _____: _____	difficult
44. impersonal	_____: _____: _____: _____: _____: _X_ : _____	personal
45. helpful	_X_ : _____: _____: _____: _____: _____: _____	hindering
46. threatening	_____: _____: _____: _____: _____: _X_ : _____	comfortable
47. efficient	_X_ : _____: _____: _____: _____: _____: _____	inefficient
48. unfavorable	_____: _____: _____: _____: _____: _X_ : _____	favorable

---

Announcement Board

49. How often did you use electronic mail to read or post class announcements?

    never (1)   (2)   (3)   ④   (5)   (6)   (7)   daily

50. What was the main reason you checked the announcement board?
    before assignments were due to see if there were any changes I
      should know about

Feedback Board

51. How often did you use electronic mail to provide anonymous feedback to your instructor?

    never (1)   (2)   (3)   (4)   ⑤   (6)   (7)   daily

52. What was the major reason you provided feedback to your instructor?
    give my input regarding the fairness of the exams

Instructor

53. How often did you use electronic mail to contact your professor for any reason?

    never (1)   (2)   (3)   ④   (5)   (6)   (7)   daily

54. What was the main reason you contacted your instructor through electronic mail?
    for clarification on points in the lecture I didn't understand

Students

55. How often did you use electronic mail to contact your classmates?

    never (1)   (2)   (3)   (4)   ⑤   (6)   (7)   daily

56. What was the major reason you contacted your classmates through electronic mail?
    to find out what they were doing or what was going on

FIGURE 2.4: Student Evaluation Survey Subject #120 Data

Chapter 3 ❖ Describing Data

Describing Data

As introduced in Chapter 1, there are two general types of statistics: descriptive statistics, which involve describing data, and inferential statistics, which involve making general statements about a population based on data collected from a sample. In this chapter we will introduce the major kinds of descriptive statistics that allow a researcher to describe quantitative data.

Consider a class of 20 students who take a midterm exam that is graded on a scale from 0 to 100, which is a ratio-level scale. During the class period following the exam, the professor informs the class that the 20 students obtained the following test scores: 87, 81, 79, 85, 85, 98, 79, 86, 91, 69, 81, 85, 86, 86, 78, 85, 91, 78, 87, 81. Although this listing of data points is somewhat informative, it is difficult to get a good sense of how students scored in general. Imagine how difficult it would be to understand the nature of these exam data if there were 100 or 1,000 scores here. By simply looking at these data it is fairly difficult to get a good idea of how well the class performed overall on this exam. Did students do well on the exam on average? How spread out were their scores? In this chapter we will present several methods for answering these questions which involve describing data in simple ways using a single number. In fact, most students already are familiar with one of these descriptive statistics because they routinely ask their professors this question whenever a test is returned — "what was the average (mean) score on the test?"

Distributions of Data

Because of the difficulty in eyeballing data to get an overall sense for what is happening, it is convenient to begin by putting a jumble of data into some type of order. Consider the 20 example test scores above, which are not in any particular numeric order. If the data were ordered from low to high (or high to low) we could get a better sense of what the scores are like in general: 69, 78, 78, 79, 79, 81, 81, 81, 85, 85, 85, 85, 86, 86, 86, 87, 87, 91, 91, 98.

These data now look a bit more informative — there seem to be more scores in the 80s and 90s and fewer scores in the 60s and 70s. When data are ordered numerically as above, from the lowest number to the highest number or from the highest number to the lowest number, this is called a *distribution*. The same test score data would look as follows if ordered from high to low: 98, 91, 91, 87, 87, 86, 86, 86, 85, 85, 85, 85, 81, 81, 81, 79, 79, 78, 78, 69. Because all of the data points are given in numeric order (albeit from high to low this time), this is also a distribution of numbers.

Certainly the test scores are more useful when they are in the form of a distribution rather than a random ordering of data. However, data can be presented in an even more informative form if each data point is given along with its corresponding frequency of occurrence (e.g., how many students received each exam score). For the example test score data, the score 69 occurred one time (only one of the 20 students scored a 69). The score 78 occurred twice. The score 79 also occurred twice. In this way a distribution of data can be created in which the data points are ordered numerically and each value occurs only once in the distribution along with its corresponding frequency of occurrence. For the example test score data, this type of distribution would look as follows:

Score	Frequency
69	1
78	2
79	2
81	3
85	4
86	3
87	2
91	2
98	1

Perhaps not surprisingly this type of distribution is called a *frequency distribution* because it is a distribution of numbers with a corresponding frequency of occurrence for each data point. Looking at this frequency distribution, it is easy to see that more students scored an 85 than any other score (a measure of central tendency called the "mode").

Graphing Distributions

Often one of the best ways to get a feel for a set of data is to take a look at the numbers visually or graphically. Once the data are in the form of a frequency distribution (where each observed data point occurs once along with an associated frequency of how many individuals had that value), the data can be graphed and inspected visually. To graph a frequency distribution, the scores or data points are plotted on the horizontal x-axis in order from lowest to highest, and the corresponding frequencies are placed on the vertical y-axis. An example of

how the x- and y-axes would be labeled for the example test score data is as follows:

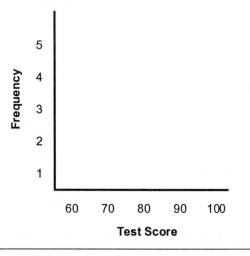

FIGURE 3.1: General format for plotting a frequency distribution

The frequency distribution of the example test score data can now be graphed, with one point representing each score along with its corresponding frequency. The graph of these data follows:

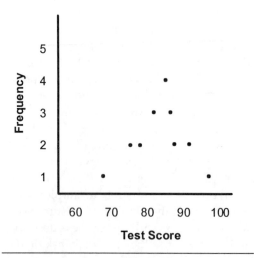

FIGURE 3.2: Plot of frequency distribution of test score data (exam score plotted with corresponding frequency of occurrence)

By connecting the plotted points with a line, the following graphical depiction of the frequency distribution of the 20 example test scores is obtained:

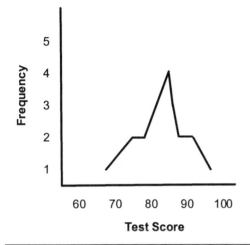

FIGURE 3.3: Line graph (frequency polygon) of frequency distribution of test score data

This type of graph (Figure 3.3) is known as a *line graph*. A somewhat more technical term for this graph is *frequency polygon*. "Frequency" refers to the number of times a data point occurs and "polygon" refers to a shape bounded by lines. The most frequently occurring score (the mode) is represented by the highest point on the line graph. With the example test score data a score of 85 occurred with a frequency of four; that is, four people scored an 85 on the midterm exam, which was the score that occurred more frequently than any other score. The frequency polygon is a particularly important graph because the frequency distributions we will be working with in the next few chapters will be represented by frequency polygons.

Instead of connecting the plotted data points representing each score and its frequency of occurrence as in Figure 3.3, another way to depict a frequency distribution is by

drawing a bar centered beneath each data point. The following graph is obtained for the example exam score data using this graphical method:

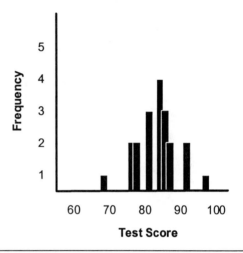

FIGURE 3.4: Bar graph (histogram) of frequency distribution of test score data

This type of graph is known as a *bar graph*. The name bar graph comes from the bars the fall underneath each data point. A more technical term frequently used to refer to this type of graph is a *histogram*.

Bar graphs are particularly useful for depicting nominal-level data visually. Although such data cannot be ordered in the form of a frequency distribution, the concept of visually depicting nominal-level data is similar to how interval- and ratio-level data is displayed in a histogram. For nominal-level data, each category is represented along with the corresponding frequency of occurrence or percentage of responses falling into each category. Nominal data is also commonly depicted in the form of a *pie chart*, where the percentage of responses falling into each category are graphed as wedges of a pie; the larger the wedge, the greater the percentage of responses that fall into a particular category.

Killer Tornado Distribution, 1950–1994 by Month

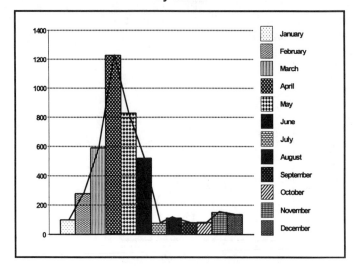

http://www.tornadoproject.com/safety/klrtmnth.htm, 4/12/97

A bar graph example

After school is crime time

A new study documents what time of day children under 18 commit violent crime on school days. Some highlights:

When kids commit crime
Percent of violent juvenile crimes by time period:

11 p.m. - 7 a.m.   7 a.m. - 2 p.m.
15%   22%
18%
45%
8 p.m. - 11 p.m.
2 p.m. - 8 p.m.

By the hour
Percent of violent juvenile crimes by hour:

3 p.m.
11.4%

7 8 9 10 11 12 1 2 3 4 5 6 7 8 9 10 11 12 1 2 3 4 5 6
a.m.   p.m.   a.m.

SOURCES: Justice Dept., Fight Crime: Invest in Kids, National Center for Juvenile Justice

A line graph example

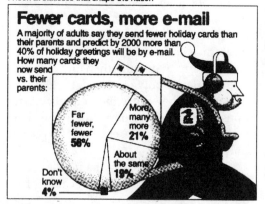

USA SNAPSHOTS®

A look at statistics that shape the nation

Fewer cards, more e-mail

A majority of adults say they send fewer holiday cards than their parents and predict by 2000 more than 40% of holiday greetings will be by e-mail. How many cards they now send vs. their parents:

Far fewer, fewer 56%

More, many more 21%

About the same 19%

Don't know 4%

12/16/96   By Scott Boeck and Kevin Rechin, USA TODAY

A pie chart example

Shapes of Distributions

Frequency polygons and histograms of interval- and ratio-level data (frequency distributions) can assume many different shapes. One of the most common shapes for a frequency polygon is a bell-shaped curve, so called because when a line is drawn connecting the data points the resulting frequency polygon looks like a bell:

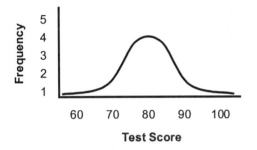

FIGURE 3.5: Normal Curve

The bell-shaped curve is one of the most important shapes for a frequency polygon because many types of data in the world, such as test scores, follow this bell shape. Such a bell-shaped curve is commonly referred to as a *normal curve*; thus, data that follow the shape of a normal curve are referred to as normally distributed. A frequency distribution that has a bell-shaped frequency polygon is termed a *normal distribution*.

The normal curve has a number of features that distinguish it from distributions of other shapes, as shown in Table 3.1. One of the most important characteristics of the normal curve is that all of the scores cluster around the middle or center of the distribution. Notice that the most frequently occurring score, which has the highest frequency on the y-axis, is in the middle of the graph (see Figure 3.5). Another important characteristic is that the normal curve is perfectly balanced or symmetrical. If a line is drawn exactly down the center of the distribu-

tion (through the most frequently occurring score), the left half will be exactly the same as the right half (see Figure 3.5). Thus, exactly half of the scores fall to the left and half of the scores fall to the right of the center. As will be discussed in the next chapter, this property of symmetry is a particularly important feature of normal distributions. A third characteristic of the normal curve is that the tails of the curve never actually touch the x-axis; they are asymptotic to it (see Figure 3.5). This is true when dealing with the normal curve as a theoretical distribution, which is commonly done for statistical analysis purposes. Finally, there are two other important characteristics of normal curves that are related to measures of central tendency and dispersion, which will be discussed shortly.

TABLE 3.1: Characteristics of a Normal Curve

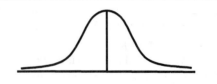

Mean = Mode = Median

- Most of the scores cluster in the middle of the distribution.
- The normal curve is perfectly balanced or symmetrical.
- The tails will never touch the x-axis (abscissca).
- All three measures of central tendency fall at the same point – the center.
- The normal curve has a constant relationship with the standard deviation.

Although many types of data do follow a normal curve, other types of data yield frequency polygons of different shapes. Two of the most common shapes for nonnormal distributions are when the "tail" of one side of the distribution is spread out substantially more than the other side. When the tail on the left side of the distribution (toward the y-axis) is the longest and most spread out, the resulting distribution looks like the following:

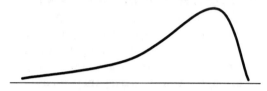

FIGURE 3.6: Negatively (left) skewed distribution

This type of distribution is referred to as *negatively* or *left skewed* because the longest tail is to the left or more negative end of the graph. An example of data that might produce a negatively skewed distribution is age at which people become president of a company. Relatively few children are expected to be company presidents, slightly more young adults (early twenties) presumably will be presidents, and those in their middle or senior years of life are likely to constitute the bulk of company presidents (the mode).

When the tail on the right side of the distribution is the longest, the resulting distribution looks like the following:

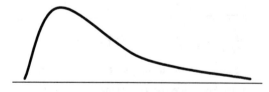

FIGURE 3.7: Positively (right) skewed distribution

This type of distribution is referred to as *positively* or *right skewed* because the longest tail is to the right or more positive end of the graph. An example of data that might produce a positively skewed distribution is income. Most people earn $20,000-$30,000 per year while very few people earn $100,000 or more per year.

Measures of Central Tendency

In addition to ordering data as a distribution and graphing it, an important way to get a good overall sense of a set of data is through a few summary numbers that characterize the data. Consider again the example of 20 test scores. A student in the class probably would not find it particularly useful to have a list of 20 scores even if they were in order (a distribution). What is likely to be more useful is to know the average of those 20 scores. That is, a single number that describes or represents all 20 data points is substantially more helpful in understanding the data in general than are each of the individual data points. As we have suggested already this type of summary number (the average, in this case) is an example of a *descriptive statistic* because it describes data. There are two important classes or types of descriptive statistics: measures of central tendency and measures of dispersion.

Measures of central tendency are descriptive statistics that measure the central tendency of a distribution of data, that is, how the data cluster around the center or middle of a distribution. There are three measures of central tendency: the mean, median, and mode (see Table 3.2).

Most of us already are familiar with the concept of a mean. The *mean* of a distribution of data is simply the arithmetic average of all of the individual scores. When the mean is computed for a *sample* of data, or a subset of a larger population, the symbol "$\overline{X}$" is used. In contrast, when the mean refers to an entire population, the Greek symbol "μ" (mu) is used. Descriptive statistics for a sample, such as the mean $\overline{X}$, are referred to as *statistics* whereas descriptive measures for a population, such as the mean μ, are referred to as *parameters*.[1] To illustrate the calculation for each descriptive measure we will refer to the sample statistic, but these formulas can be applied to the corresponding population parameter as well. The mean ($\overline{X}$) is computed as the sum (Σ) of each of the individual scores (X) divided by the total number of scores (N):

$$\overline{X} = \frac{\Sigma X}{N}$$

For example, the mean for the 20 example test scores is computed as follows:

$$\overline{X} = \frac{\Sigma X}{N} = \frac{\begin{pmatrix} 87+81+79+85+85+98+79+86+91+69+ \\ 81+85+86+86+78+85+91+78+87+81 \end{pmatrix}}{20} = \frac{1678}{20} = 83.9$$

On average, then, the 20 students scored almost 84 points on this exam.

Although the mean is the most common measure of central tendency, and probably the one with which people are most familiar, it is not the only way to describe the central tendency of data (nor is it necessarily the best measure for all types of data). Suppose, for example, that the mean income for a particular area is computed as $125,000. People in this area must be quite wealthy!! Unfortunately, this conclusion is not necessarily accurate (remember the discussion in Chapter 1 about how statistics can be misleading). In fact, it may be the case that most households are only earning around $25,000 a year, but that a few households are making $500,000, $1 million, and $5 million a year, which might be true in a place such as Hollywood. A frequency polygon of these data might look like the one in Figure 3.8.

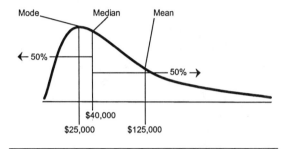

FIGURE 3.8: Positively (right) skewed distribution of income data

As mentioned earlier, income is an example of a positively (right) skewed distribution. The bulk of the income data in this example is clustered around $25,000 and only a few data points are at extremely high income amounts. Because of the very extreme incomes in this particular city, the mean is very high, yielding a somewhat misleading measure of central tendency. A more informative way to look at the central tendency of these income data is to

TABLE 3.2: Measures of Central Tendency

Statistic	Use
MODE (MO)	Identifies the most frequently occurring score in a distribution. Most often used with nominal data and bimodal distributions.
MEDIAN (MDN)	Identifies the middle score of a distribution. Most often used with ordinal data and skewed distributions. It cannot be used with nominal data.
MEAN ($\overline{X}$)	Identifies the average score in a distribution. Only used with interval or ratio data and often used with normal distributions. It cannot be used with nominal or ordinal data.

find the middlemost income, that is, the income level which 50% of the households exceed and 50% of the households fall below. In the positively skewed income distribution (Figure 3.8) note that the middlemost score or median is $40,000: 50% of all incomes fall above $40,000 and 50% of all incomes fall below $40,000.

The measure of central tendency which is the middlemost score in a distribution of data is known as the *median,* symbolized as "Mdn." Again, referring to the example test score data, the median of this distribution can be found as follows:

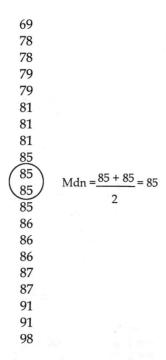

69
78
78
79
79
81
81
81
85
85
85
85
86
86
86
87
87
91
91
98

$$Mdn = \frac{85 + 85}{2} = 85$$

In this example there are actually two numbers which fall in the middle of the distribution. The median is computed by simply averaging these two middle numbers (85 and 85): Mdn = 85. Notice that in order to compute the median the data must first be in the form of a distribution; that is, all of the data must be ordered

from low to high or high to low. The median cannot be obtained as the middlemost score from a set of randomly ordered data. For instance, consider the original nonordered 20 example test scores: 87, 81, 79, 85, 85, 98, 79, 86, 91, 69, 81, 85, 86, 86, 78, 85, 91, 78, 87, 81. The two scores in the middle are 69 and 81. However, these scores indicate nothing about the central tendency of these data; they just happen to be the two scores that fall in the middle of a random ordering of data. Be certain to order data numerically (i.e., create a distribution) prior to computing the median.

Just as there are times when the median serves as a better measure of central tendency than the mean (e.g., with skewed distributions), sometimes neither the mean nor the median provides the best measure of the central tendency of a set of data. For instance, consider the following data on divorce: out of 100 married couples who eventually got divorced, 45 couples divorced after 5 years, 4 couples divorced after 10 years, 2 couples divorced after 15 years, 4 couples divorced after 20 years, and 45 couples divorced after 25 years. A frequency polygon that might represent these data is as follows:

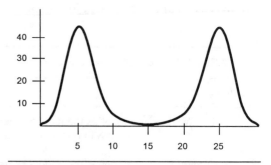

FIGURE 3.9: Bimodal distribution of years married prior to divorce

The mean for these data can be computed by summing all 100 numbers (5 appears 45 times, 10 appears 4 times, etc.) and dividing by 100.

Alternatively, a shorthand way to compute the mean is to take each value multiplied by its frequency of occurrence and divide by 100:

$$\overline{X} = \frac{[(45 \times 5) + (4 \times 10) + (2 \times 15) + (4 \times 20) + (45 \times 25)]}{100} = 15$$

The median for these data is identical to the mean in this example: Mdn = 15. Notice that 49 couples divorced in under 15 years and 49 couples divorced after more than 15 years of marriage, with 15 years falling in the middle of the distribution of these data. Using either the mean or the median to describe the central tendency of these data gives the misleading impression that most couples divorced after 15 years of marriage. However, the data in Figure 3.9 clearly reveal that this is not true. In fact, most couples divorced after either a brief period of marriage (5 years) or after being married a long period of time (25 years). The most frequently occurring score in a distribution of data is known as the *mode,* symbolized as "Mo." In this example of divorced couples, there actually are two modes: 5 years and 25 years. Such a distribution with two modes is

referred to as a *bimodal distribution*. Most distributions, such as the normal distribution and positively and negatively skewed distributions, have only one mode (there is only one peak). The mode for the 20 example test scores is 85; that is, four students scored an 85, which was the most frequently occurring score (note that the peak is at 85 in Figure 3.3).

Clearly, one measure of central tendency may be more appropriate than another depending on how a set of data is distributed. The median is the most appropriate measure of central tendency for skewed data. The mode is the most appropriate measure of central tendency for bimodally distributed data. And the mean is the most common measure of central tendency for normally distributed data. This brings us to the fourth important characteristic of normal distributions. First, recall the other three characteristics of the normal curve: (1) scores cluster around the middle, (2) the distribution is symmetrical, and (3) the tails are asymptotic to the x-axis (see Table 3.1). The fourth important characteristic of a normal distribution is that all three measures of central tendency fall at exactly the same point – the

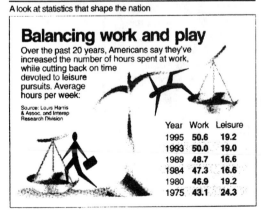

USA SNAPSHOTS®
A look at statistics that shape the nation

Balancing work and play
Over the past 20 years, Americans say they've increased the number of hours spent at work, while cutting back on time devoted to leisure pursuits. Average hours per week:

Source: Louis Harris & Assoc. and Interep Research Division

Year	Work	Leisure
1995	50.6	19.2
1993	50.0	19.0
1989	48.7	16.6
1984	47.3	16.6
1980	46.9	19.2
1975	43.1	24.3

12/26/96　　　By Scott Boeck and Genevieve Lynn, USA TODAY

The mean is used to describe the increased amount of time spent at work

USA SNAPSHOTS®
A look at statistics that shape the nation

Bachelor's degree pay for men
The U.S. median income for men age 30 or older with bachelor's degrees and earning wages or salaries was $43,856[1]. Fields of study with highest median pay:

Major	Median income
Engineering	$52,998
Mathematics	$52,316
Physics	$51,819
Pharmacy	$50,805
Economics	$50,360

1 – Excludes self-employed, through 1993 ('atest year available)
Source: Bureau of Labor Statistics Occupational Outlook Quarterly, Summer 1996

1/15/97　　　By Anne R. Carey and Grant Jerding, USA TODA

The median is used to describe incomes related to particular bachelor's degrees

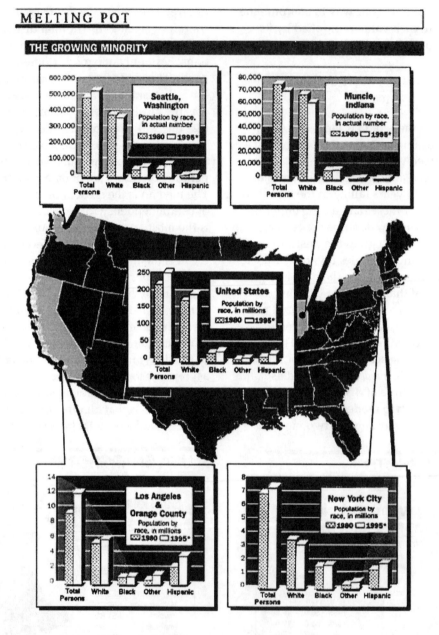

MELTING POT

THE GROWING MINORITY

U.S. Census & National Planning Data Co., 1/13/91, *Los Angeles Times*, p.E8

The mode can be used to describe the ethnic distribution found within the United States

middle of the distribution. The mode is in the middle because it clearly falls at the peak. The median is in the middle because half of the scores fall above it and half fall below it, as guaranteed by the symmetrical nature of the normal curve. The mean also will fall at the middle when computed statistically. With normal distributions, the commonly used measure of central tendency is the mean; however, it is important to remember that the median and the mode also fall at exactly this same point.

Unlike the normal distribution, skewed distributions do not have the three measures of central tendency fall at exactly the same point. Recall the earlier example with household income (see Figure 3.8). A few very high incomes pulled the mean to a high value of $125,000, yielding a positively (right) skewed distribution. In contrast, the median was much lower, around $40,000. Notice that the mean is the highest measure of central tendency ($125,000), the mode is the lowest measure of central tendency ($25,000), and the median is between these two values ($40,000).

In contrast, what would happen with the three measures of central tendency with a negatively skewed distribution? Consider the earlier example of a distribution of data that represents the age at which someone becomes president of a company. Not surprisingly, the majority of people will probably be in their 50s or 60s. However, occasionally, a child genius might establish and become president of his or her own company. Thus, a few very low ages would skew this distribution negatively. Figure 3.10 shows a possible graphical representation of these data. In this case, a few low ages will pull the mean down. The mean, then, is the smallest value on a negatively skewed distribution (e.g., 35 years of age). The mode is the highest value (the most frequently occurring age of a company president, 55 years) and the median falls in between these two values

(e.g., 47 years).

So far, each of the examples discussed with respect to the measures of central tendency have involved interval- or ratio-level data (e.g., test scores, number of years of marriage, age). We have until now excluded a discussion of nominal- and ordinal-level data because certain measures of central tendency are not relevant concepts with these types of data. Consider, for example, the Nielsen rankings of the top 20 television programs, which is ordinal-level data. What is the mean of these 20 shows? How about if we ask Joan to list her ten favorite classes in order. What is the mean of her ten favorite classes? Clearly, with ordinal-level data the concept of a mean does not make sense. Only the median and the mode are relevant concepts with data measured at an ordinal level. For example, Joan might have 5 classes tied for her number 1 favorite class (Mo = 1), and the class that falls in the middle on her list might be ranked as her third favorite class, Experimental Psychology (Mdn = 3).

The mean also is not a meaningful concept for nominal-level data. Suppose there are 50 men and 46 women in this class. What would the mean or average of these data be? Now consider what the median for these data would be. What is the middle score of men and women? With data measured with a nominal scale, a median also makes no conceptual sense. Only the mode is a relevant

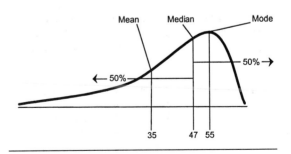

FIGURE 3.10: **Negatively skewed distribution of age of company presidents**

concept for nominal-level data. In this example, the mode is "men"; since more men are in the class than women, "men" is the most frequently occurring observation or data point. Neither a mean nor a median are conceptually valid ideas with nominal-level data.

Measures of Dispersion

Although the three measures of central tendency are useful statistics for describing the central tendency of data, they do not provide a complete sense of the nature of the data. In particular, the mean, median, and mode provide no information about how the scores differ or vary from one another. For example, suppose the mean number of years a murderer spends in prison is 20 years. Does this mean that most murderers spend 20 years in prison or that some murders spend only three or four years in prison while other murderers spend 40 or 50 years in prison? The answer to this question is important for obtaining a more complete understanding of the nature of the data.

TABLE 3.3: **Measures of Dispersion**

Statistic	Use
RANGE (R)	Identifies how far apart the lowest and highest scores are in a distribution.
STANDARD DEVIATION (SD)	Identifies how spread out the scores are in a distribution and indicates how the scores vary.
VARIANCE (V)	Identifies how scores are dispersed in a distribution. Conceptually similar to the standard deviation, variance is the square of the standard deviation.

Measures of dispersion are descriptive statistics that measure how far apart scores are from one another, or how spread out the data is in a distribution. There are three measures of dispersion commonly applied to describe the variability of interval- and ratio-level data: the range, standard deviation, and variance (see Table 3.3).

The *range* is simply the difference between the highest and lowest numbers in a distribution and is represented by the symbol "R." For the set of 20 example exam scores, the lowest score was 69 and the highest score was 98; thus, the range is computed as: R = 98-69 = 29. These scores appear to be fairly spread out according to this measure. However, are most scores clustered around 69 and 98, 29 points apart, or is there only one person who had a 69 and everyone else clustered around a 98 with little spread in the data? This type of question can be answered by another measure of dispersion, the standard deviation.

Standard deviation and variance are closely related measures of the variability in scores. In fact, one measure (the standard deviation) is the square root of the other measure (the variance). The *standard deviation* measures how far away, on average, scores are from the mean of a set of data. In other words, standard deviation measures the standard or average variability in scores. The statistic which represents the standard deviation for a sample is "SD" and the parameter which represents the standard deviation for a population is the Greek

Student	Score
Alf	86
Kahanu	91
Sue	75
Aldo	80
Ben	93
	$\overline{X} = 85$

symbol "σ" (sigma). To calculate the standard or average deviation in a set of scores, consider the example of five student exam scores shown above.

Obviously not every student scored exactly the mean of 85. In fact, none of these students scored the mean of the group; every student varied to some extent around this mean: Sue scored 10 points below the mean, Kahanu scored 6 points above the mean, and so forth. By computing a difference (d) between each individual score (X) and the mean ($\overline{X}$) for the entire group, d = $X - \overline{X}$, we can get a sense for how much these individual scores vary around the group mean:

Student	Score	Difference ($X - \overline{X}$)
Alf	86	86 - 85 = +1
Kahanu	91	91 - 85 = +6
Sue	75	75 - 85 = -10
Aldo	80	80 - 85 = -5
Ben	93	93 - 85 = +8
	$\overline{X}$ = 85	

We now want to express the total variability in scores as a single number. One possibility involves simply summing all of the calculated differences: (+1) + (+6) + (-10) + (-5) + (+8) = 0. Unfortunately, this approach suggests that the total variability in scores is zero, which obviously is not true. The problem with summing the differences is that positive and negative differences cancel each other out, and the total sum will always equal zero. To prevent this problem and provide a measure of the total variability in scores, the differences are squared, or multiplied by themselves, which removes negative values. These differences can then be summed to produce a measure of the total variability in scores:

Student	Score	Difference ($X - \overline{X}$)	Squared Difference ($X - \overline{X}$)²
Alf	86	86 - 85 = +1	(+1)² = 1
Kahanu	91	91 - 85 = +6	(+6)² = 36
Sue	75	75 - 85 = -10	(-10)² = 100
Aldo	80	80 - 85 = -5	(-5)² = 25
Ben	93	93 - 85 = +8	(+8)² = 64
	$\overline{X}$ = 85		Sum (Σ) = 226

This sum of squared differences is a very important calculation in statistics and is termed the *sum of squares* (SS). Indeed, in later chapters we will see how sum of squares forms the basis for one of the most common statistical tests, the F-test. As computed above, the sum of squares is:

$$SS = \sum (X - \overline{X})^2$$

Sum of squares represents the overall or total variability in scores. To translate this to a standard or average measure of variability, the sum of squares is divided by the total number of scores (N) and then unsquared ($\sqrt{}$):

$$SD = \sqrt{\frac{SS}{N}} = \sqrt{\frac{\sum (X - \overline{X})^2}{N}}$$

Because the deviation scores were squared $(X - \overline{X})^2$ in order to remove negative signs, the final result must be unsquared to produce an average variability measure.[2] For the sample of five student exam scores, the standard deviation is calculated as:

$$SD = \sqrt{\frac{SS}{N}} = \sqrt{\frac{226}{5}} = \sqrt{45.2} = 6.72$$

There is one slight modification to the standard deviation formula given above if this sample standard deviation is being used to estimate the standard deviation for the larger population. As we will see, much of the time data from an entire population is unavailable. Consequently, the results from a subset of this population, a sample, must be used to estimate what is likely true about the larger population. This is the field of inferential statistics. If the standard deviation from a sample is being used to estimate the standard deviation in a larger population, the computation of the standard deviation given above (SD) produces a slight underestimation or bias in the true population standard deviation (σ). Thus, statisticians use a slightly smaller denominator "N-1" instead of "N" in the standard deviation formula to produce an unbiased estimator of the population standard deviation. This unbiased standard deviation is symbolized as "s" to distinguish it from the true sample standard deviation "SD" and is computed as follows:

$$s = \sqrt{\frac{SS}{N-1}}$$

The *variance* is equal to the square of the standard deviation (SD²) and is denoted symbolically as "V" for a sample or "σ^2" for a population. Computationally, the variance is calculated identically to the standard deviation except that the final result is not unsquared:

$$V = \frac{SS}{N} \text{ or } V = \frac{\sum(X - \bar{X})^2}{N}$$

For the example with five student exam scores, the variance is:

$$V = \frac{SS}{N} = \frac{226}{5} = 45.2$$

Conceptually, variance is very similar to

standard deviation in that it represents the average variability about the mean of a set of scores. Variance proves to be a very useful computational measure in inferential statistics and is common with many statistical tests. As with the standard deviation, the variance (V) computed for a sample of data using the above formula is a somewhat biased estimator of the variance for a population (σ^2). Thus, an unbiased estimator (s^2) is used when attempting to estimate the population variance from sample data:

$$s^2 = \frac{SS}{N-1}$$

Because of the importance of standard deviation and variance in inferential statistics, we will explore this concept conceptually a bit further. Consider the two sets of data for 12 people's weights shown in Table 3.4. The mean for both sets of data is 150 pounds. However, the weights in Set 1 appear to be very similar to each other or homogeneous whereas the weights in Set 2 are quite dissimilar from one another or heterogeneous. The range is a full 120 pounds (R = 210-90) in Set 2 compared with only 10 pounds (R = 155-145) in Set 1. In order to get a sense of the homogeneity and heterogeneity of these two sets of data, the standard deviation (or variance) is computed.

TABLE 3.4

Set 1		Set 2	
Joe	145	Mia	90
Meg	145	Guy	110
Bob	150	Jan	130
Ann	150	Ali	170
Sue	155	Sam	190
Tim	155	Art	210
$\bar{X}_1 =$	150	$\bar{X}_2 =$	150

In Set 1, each person's weight is very close to the overall group mean:

- Joe's weight of 145 is 5 pounds away from the mean of 150.
- Meg's weight of 145 is 5 pounds away from the mean of 150.
- Bob's weight of 150 is 0 pounds away from the mean of 150.
- Ann's weight of 150 is 0 pounds away from the mean of 150.
- Sue's weight of 155 is 5 pounds away from the mean of 150.
- Tim's weight of 155 is 5 pounds away from the mean of 150.

The six people in Set 1 are less than 5 pounds away from the mean on average. Thus, the standard deviation for these data is relatively small (the actual standard deviation of these data is SD = 4.08).

In Set 2, however, each person's weight is quite far away from the overall group mean:

- Mia's weight of 90 is 60 pounds away from the mean of 150.
- Guy's weight of 110 is 40 pounds away from the mean of 150.
- Jan's weight of 130 is 20 pounds away from the mean of 150.
- Ali's weight of 170 is 20 pounds away from the mean of 150.
- Sam's weight of 190 is 40 pounds away from the mean of 150.
- Art's weight of 210 is 60 pounds away from the mean of 150.

The six people in Set 2 are about 40 pounds away from the mean on average. Thus, the standard deviation for this second set of weights is quite large (the actual standard deviation of these data is SD = 43.20). On average, then, the weights in Set 1 are much more homogeneous with a small standard deviation than are the weights in Set 2 which are more heterogeneous and have a large standard deviation.

Frequency polygons for homogeneous and

heterogeneous data sets look like the following:

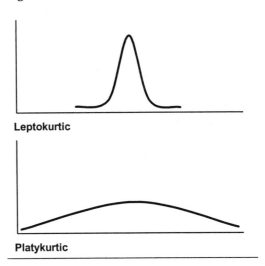

Leptokurtic

Platykurtic

FIGURE 3.11: Homogeneous and heterogeneous distributions: leptokurtic distribution (top) with a small standard deviation and homogeneous scores; platykurtic distribution (bottom) with a large standard deviation and heterogeneous scores

The graph on the top represents a very homogeneous set of data in which the standard deviation is very small. This type of narrowed distribution with a distinct peak indicating that most scores cluster around the mean is called a *leptokurtic distribution*. The scores are very similar to each other and no score deviates too far from the mean. In contrast, the graph on the bottom represents a very heterogeneous set of data in which the standard deviation is very large. The scores are very dissimilar from each other and scores are spread out quite far from the mean. A distribution having this flattened type of shape is called a *platykurtic distribution*.

The concept of standard deviation brings up the fifth and final characteristic of a normal curve (see Table 3.1). When a set of data is distributed normally the normal curve has a constant, fixed relationship with the standard deviation. Specifically, there are roughly six standard deviations under the normal curve. That is, the range is approximately six standard deviations: R ≈ 6SD (the symbol ≈ means "approximately equals"). This is an approximation because there are a few additional scores beyond six standard deviations under the tails where the theoretical normal curve never actually touches the x-axis (the asymptotic property of the normal curve). This idea of six standard deviations under the normal curve will be discussed further in the next chapter as it is an important basis for inferential statistics.

Summary

Describing data involves visualizing and summarizing the values in a data set to obtain an overall sense of the nature of the data. A distribution of data is a set of data points which are ordered from low to high or high to low. A frequency distribution orders the data with each value appearing only once along with its corresponding frequency of occurrence. A common visual depiction of a frequency distribution is a line graph or frequency polygon. Frequency distributions also can be displayed via a bar graph or histogram. Bar charts and pie charts are common graphical depictions for categorical data. A very common shape for a frequency distribution is the normal or bell-shaped curve. Other shapes for distributions are left or negatively skewed (tail pulled out to left), right or positively skewed (tail pulled out to right), and bimodal (two peaks).

Measures of central tendency and measures of dispersion are both used to summarize or describe data. Descriptive measures for a sample, such as the mean "$\overline{X}$," standard deviation "SD," and variance "V," are called statistics. Descriptive measures for a population, such as the mean "μ," standard deviation "σ," and

variance "σ^2," are called parameters. The mean (average), median (middlemost score), and mode (most frequently occurring score) are used to summarize the central tendency of a set of data. Only the mode is applied to nominal-level data; both the mode and median are applicable to ordinal-level data; all three measures of central tendency can be used to describe interval- and ratio-level data. The mean is the most common measure of central tendency for normal distributions, the median is the best measure of central tendency for skewed distributions, and the mode is the preferred measure of central tendency for bimodal distributions. The range (difference between high and low scores in a distribution), standard deviation (average of how far away each score is from the mean), and the variance (square of the standard deviation) are used to describe how interval- and ratio-level data is dispersed or varies. Homogeneous data with a very small standard deviation typically has a peaked or leptokurtic-shaped distribution while heterogeneous data with a large standard deviation typically has a flat or platykurtic-shaped distribution.

Key Terms

- bimodal distribution
- descriptive statistic
- distribution
- frequency distribution
- frequency polygon (line graph)
- leptokurtic distribution
- histogram (bar graph)
- mean ($\overline{X}$ or μ)
- median (Mdn)
- measures of central tendency
- measures of dispersion
- mode (Mo)
- negatively (left) skewed distribution
- normal curve/distribution
- parameter

- pie chart
- platykurtic distribution
- positively (right) skewed distribution
- range (R)
- standard deviation (SD, s, or σ)
- statistic
- sum of squares (SS)
- variance (V, s², or σ²)

Problems

1. What is a distribution?
2. When graphing a frequency distribution of scores, _____ go/goes on the x-axis and _____ go/goes on the y-axis.
3. What are more common names for a frequency polygon and a histogram? What is the difference between a frequency polygon and a histogram?
4. How does a skewed distribution differ from a normal distribution?
5. Match the verbal description with the graphical depiction for each of the following distributions:
   a. positively skewed distribution
   b. negatively skewed distribution
   c. bimodal distribution
   d. normal distribution

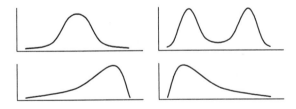

6. Consider the following four sets of data, each of which is graphed using a frequency polygon with a range of values from 0 to 100 on the x-axis. Which of these four sets of data would be likely to yield a negatively skewed distribution such as the one in the following diagram:

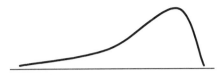

   a. number of children per American family?
   b. age at graduation from high school?
   c. scores on a very easy test?
   d. number of weekly winners of lottery tickets of more than $1 million?

7. If the mean salary for ten assistant professors in a university's department is $35,000, the mean for 15 associate professors is $45,000, and the mean for 20 full professors is $60,000, what is the mean salary for all 45 faculty members?

8. The following questions refer to the relationship between measures of central tendency and types of distributions:
   a. Which measure of central tendency is most appropriate with skewed distributions?
   b. Which measure of central tendency will have the largest value with a positively skewed distribution?
   c. Which measure of central tendency will have the smallest value with a positively skewed distribution?
   d. Which measure of central tendency will have the largest value with a negatively skewed distribution?
   e. Which measure of central tendency will have the smallest value with a negatively skewed distribution?
   f. In a positively skewed distribution, will the value of the mode be higher or lower than the value of the median?
   g. In a negatively skewed distribution, will the value of the median be higher or lower than the value of the mean?
   h. Which measure of central tendency is most appropriate and most frequently used with normal distributions?

i. Which measure of central tendency will have the largest value with a normal distribution?

j. Which measure of central tendency is most appropriate with a bimodal distribution?

9. The following questions refer to the relationship between measures of central tendency and levels of measurement.

a. Which measures of central tendency can be computed when data are in ordinal-level form?

b. Which measures of central tendency can be computed when data are in interval- or ratio-level form?

c. Which measures of central tendency can be computed when data are in nominal-level form?

10. The following questions refer to the two distributions below:

a. Which distribution has the largest standard deviation?

b. Which distribution has the smallest standard deviation?

c. Which distribution's scores are the most homogeneous?

d. Which distribution's scores are the most heterogeneous?

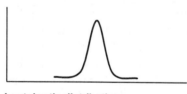

Leptokurtic distribution

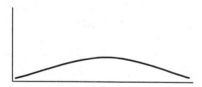

Platykurtic distribution

11. The following questions refer to two different sets of IQ scores:

a. If the variance of the first set of IQ scores is found to be 225, what is the value of the standard deviation?

b. If the standard deviation of a second set of IQ scores is 11, what is the value of the variance?

c. Which set of IQ score above (a or b) is the most homogeneous?

12. The following questions refer to measures of central tendency and measures of dispersion:

a. Which measure is the square of the standard deviation?

b. Which measure is the middlemost score of a distribution?

c. Which measure is the difference between the highest and lowest scores in a distribution?

d. Which measure is approximately the average distance of any given score in a distribution from the mean of the distribution?

e. Which measure provides the arithmetic average of a distribution of numbers?

f. Which measure is the most frequently occurring score in a distribution?

13. Which of the following is a distribution of numbers (choose all that apply)?

a. 78	b. 63	c. 70	d. 99	e. 73	f. 67	g. 2
69	71	94	82	81	67	6
92	79	94	73	81	82	3
83	82	82	65	81	67	3
55	88	84	65	86	77	4
76		82		87		1

14. For each of the following two sets of data representing six people's heights and weights, calculate the mean ($\overline{X}$), median (Mdn), mode (Mo), range (R), standard deviation (SD), and variance (V):

Height (inches)	Weight (pounds)
69	150
67	135
64	108
66	138
62	113
65	125

15. What is the difference between the biased sample standard deviation (SD) and the unbiased sample standard deviation (s)? When do you want to use one vs. the other?

Notes

1 Be careful not to confuse the two uses of the term "statistics": (1) summary descriptive measures such as the mean and standard deviation of data in a sample, vs. (2) a branch of applied mathematics which is the topic of this book.

2 A somewhat easier computational version of the standard deviation formula is:

$$SD = \sqrt{\frac{\sum X^2}{N} - \overline{X}^2}$$

Computer Section

Frequency/Descriptive Information

One of the first sets of analyses researchers typically conduct is basic frequencies and descriptive statistics for all variables. Frequencies of responses for nominal-level data and means and standard deviations for interval- and ratio-level data are commonly obtained as a first step in any data analysis approach. All statistical analysis packages feature frequency and descriptive commands to obtain this type of output.

Example Output for Frequencies

Many research reports include information on a variety of characteristics of the study's subjects, such as how many participants were male vs. female. This type of information can be obtained by running a *frequency* command in the statistical program. Conducting frequencies on the computer involves specifying the variable for which frequency output is desired. Following is an example of output for a frequency analysis of respondent's gender for a study:

Interpretation of Frequency Output

This example analysis provides frequencies of the values (1 and 2) for the nominal-level variable GENDER, which is the respondent's gender or sex. The label "Respondent's Gender" is referred to as a *variable label* because it is a more descriptive label than the variable name itself. In addition, for each of the possible values the variable GENDER can assume, *value labels* or descriptive labels of the values of the variable are provided to help with interpreting the output. In this example, the variable GENDER can assume one of two possible values: 1 or 2. The label "Male" corresponds with the value "1" for the variable GENDER, and the label "Female" corresponds with the value "2" for the variable GENDER. Variable and value labels are extremely useful for helping a researcher to recall what question each variable represents and what each possible value of a variable means. With well-chosen variable and value labels a researcher should not have to refer back to the codebook very frequently to help understand statistical output.

The example frequency output indicates that a total of 500 subjects participated in this study: 227 males and 273 females. Of the total

GENDER Respondent's Gender

Value Label	Value	Frequency	Percent	Valid Percent	Cumulative Percent
Male	1	227	45.4	45.4	45.4
Female	2	273	54.6	54.6	100.0
Total		500	100.0	100.0	

Valid cases   500
Missing cases   0

participants, 45.4% (227/500) were male and 54.6% (273/500) were female. The *cumulative percentage* also is provided and can be useful for understanding how data are clustered (e.g., the cumulative percent having the lowest three scores on a variable).

Example Output for Descriptive Statistics

Suppose a researcher is interested in knowing how frequently university students use their on-campus health center each year. The researcher asks 350 students an open-ended question regarding how many times they visited their campus health center in the past year. The following descriptive statistics are obtained:

Number of valid observations (listwise) = 336.00						
Variable	**Mean**	**Std Dev**	**Min**	**Max**	**N**	**Label**
HTHVISIT	3.06	2.19	0	16	336	Visits per year

Interpretation of Descriptive Output

A total of N = 336 students responded to the questionnaire, indicating that 14 students either did not answer the question or had invalid/unusable data. The ratio-level data was given the variable name HTHVISIT and the variable was labeled "Visits per year." On average, students visited their campus health center $\overline{X}$ = 3.06 times per year with a standard deviation of SD = 2.19 times per year. The range in the number of times any of the 336 respondents used the health center last year was from a minimum of never (0 times) to a maximum of 16 times (R = 16).

Sometimes a researcher is interested only in describing characteristics of a subgroup of the subjects under study. For instance, although the overall mean number of visits to the student health center for the 336 respondents may be of interest, the researcher also may care about the mean number of visits of male students and the mean number of visits of female students separately. Statistical packages include a program command that allows the researcher to select or process only a subset of all of the data and to run additional program commands (e.g., frequencies, descriptives) on only the selected subset of data.

Computer Problems

1. Compute a frequency distribution for students' age (**AGE**).
   a. What is the most frequent age?
   b. What is the lowest age?
   c. What is the highest age?
   d. How many students were 19 or younger?
   e. How many students were 23 or older?
2. Compute the frequency distribution for students' gender (**STDTSEX**).
   a. How many women were enrolled in the classes?
   b. How many men were enrolled in the classes?
3. Compute the frequency distribution for students' class level (**CLSLVL**).
   a. How many freshmen were enrolled in the classes?
   b. How many sophomores were enrolled in the classes?
   c. How many juniors were enrolled in the classes?
   d. How many seniors were enrolled in the classes?
4. Compute the frequency distribution for students' self-reported grades in the class (**GRADE**).
   a. How many students believed they earned A's?

b. How many students believed they earned B's?

c. How many students believed they earned C's?

d. How many students believed they did not pass the class (D's or F's)?

5. Compute descriptive statistics for students' overall rating of the course (COURSE).

   a. What is the mean ($\overline{X}$)?

   b. What is the standard deviation (SD)?

   c. Describe in words how students felt about the class generally.

6. Compute descriptive statistics for students' overall rating of the course for students in the *live* course condition. Hint: remember that the course was conducted under two conditions (live and mediated). You well also need to see the instructions for selecting cases from your computer program.

   a. What is the mean?

   b. What is the standard deviation?

   c. Describe in words how students felt about the class generally.

7. Compute descriptive statistics for students' overall rating of the *mediated* course (COURSE).

   a. What is the mean?

   b. What is the standard deviation?

   c. Describe in words how students felt about the class generally.

8. Compute descriptive statistics for students' overall rating of the instructor (INSTRUCT).

   a. What is the mean?

   b. What is the standard deviation?

   c. Describe in words how students felt about the instructor generally.

9. Compute descriptive statistics for students' overall rating of the *female* instructor (INSTRUCT).

   a. What is the mean?

   b. What is the standard deviation?

   c. Describe in words how students felt about the female instructor generally.

10. Compute descriptive statistics for students' overall rating of the *male* instructor (INSTRUCT).

    a. What is the mean?

    b. What is the standard deviation?

    c. Describe in words how students felt about the male instructor generally.

11. Compute descriptive statistics for students' attitudes toward the female instructor. In other words, examine both the means and standard deviations for the 16 descriptive items (EXPERT-QUAL) used to describe the instructor and summarize how students characterized her.

12. Compute descriptive statistics for students' attitudes toward the male instructor. Examine both the means and standard deviations for the 16 descriptive items (EXPERT-QUAL) used to describe the instructor and summarize how students characterized him.

13. Compute descriptive statistics for students' attitudes toward e-mail. Taking into account both the means and standard deviations for the eight descriptive items (DULL-FAVOR), summarize how students felt generally about electronic mail in the course.

14. Compute descriptive statistics for how often students used electronic mail to: (1) examine the announcement board (BOARD1), (2) provide feedback to the instructor (FDBACK1), (3) contact the instructor (TEACH1), and (4) contact other students (STUDENT1). Taking into account both the means and standard deviations:

    a. Which of the four functions of e-mail did students use most frequently?

    b. Which of the four functions of e-mail did students use least frequently?

    c. Which function(s) would you suggest e-mail be used for in future classes?

Chapter 4 ❖ Working with Distributions

Types of Normal Distributions

In Chapter 3 we introduced the normal distribution, which is an extremely important distribution because a substantial amount of data in the real world resembles a normal curve when graphed as a frequency polygon (line graph). In this chapter we will present four normal distributions: the sample distribution, population distribution, sampling distribution, and distribution of differences. These four distributions share many common characteristics because they are all normally distributed. The major difference among these distributions is the type of data in the distribution: individual scores from a sample, individual scores from a population, sample means, or differences between sample means.

Sample Distribution

The first two normal distributions, the sample distribution and population distribution, are distributions of individual data points from a sample or a population, respectively. Recall from Chapter 2 that a population is the entire group of people or observations in which a researcher is interested (e.g., all students, voters, criminals, men, newspapers). A sample is a subset of the population. In most research studies the population of interest is far too large to have everyone participate, so a subset or sample of this population is selected. It is these subjects' responses which are then used as a basis for inferring what is likely true of the larger population of interest, an idea we have referred to as *inferential statistics*.

Imagine, for example, that a university is

offering ten sections of an introductory statistics class and that each section enrolls 150 students. A researcher might be interested in studying how well the population of all 1,500 students perform in this statistics class. One approach to solving this problem is for the researcher to gather data from the entire population of 1,500 students enrolled in the class. Although potentially a feasible solution in this case, an alternative approach to answering the question of how well students perform in the class is to randomly sample a subset of the 1,500 students (e.g., N = 25 or some other sample size) and determine how well this smaller subset of students scores in the class. Based on the data gathered from the sample, the researcher can then infer, within some margin of error, how well all students in the class performed. Suppose the researcher adopts this latter approach and obtains midterm exam scores from 25 randomly sampled students in the course. The frequency distribution of these 25 scores looks like the following:

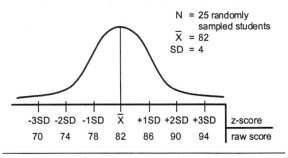

FIGURE 4.1: Sample distribution of individual exam scores with mean $\overline{X}$ = 82 and standard deviation SD = 4

This resulting distribution is known as a *sample distribution* because it is a distribution of the data from a sample. The mean of the sample data is $\overline{X} = 82$ and the standard deviation is SD = 4. The original data points (exam scores in this example) are called *raw scores* (X). For instance, a student who scored an 86 on the exam has a raw score of $X = 86$.

Raw scores, which are unstandardized, can be distinguished from transformed or standardized data points called z-scores. The derivation of a standardized (z) score is based on the *standard deviation unit*, which is simply the value of the standard deviation in raw score terms. With the above exam score data the standard deviation unit is four since the standard deviation of the distribution of raw scores is SD = 4.

Understanding the concept of a standard deviation unit provides a variety of information about a distribution of data. Recall from Chapter 3 that one property of a normal distribution is that the standard deviation has a constant relationship with the normal curve such that approximately six standard deviations (or six standard deviation units) fit under the normal curve. That is, the range of normally distributed data is approximately equal to six standard deviation units: $R \approx 6SD$. For the example exam score data, the range is $R \approx 6 \times 4 = 24$ raw score points. Because of the symmetrical or balanced nature of a normal distribution (another important characteristic of the normal curve discussed in Chapter 3), three standard deviation units fall above the middle point of the distribution and three standard deviation units fall below the middle point. Therefore, the high point of the example exam score distribution is three standard deviation units above the mean ($3 \times 4 = 12$). Since the mean of these data is 82, the highest score in this distribution is approximately 94 (see Figure 4.1). Similarly, the low point of the distribution is three standard deviation units below the mean ($3 \times 4 = 12$) corresponding to a raw score of 70. Thus, almost all of the raw scores in this exam

score distribution fall between 70 and 94. Note that a very small number of scores (less than one percent, in fact) fall beyond either +3SD to the right of the distribution or -3SD to the left of the distribution. These few extreme scores are reflective of the asymptotic property of the normal curve discussed in Chapter 3. In general, though, 99% of the scores of any normal distribution fall within ±3SD of the mean of the distribution.

The translation of raw scores into standard deviation units creates what is in essence a standardized expression of the raw scores. These standardized raw scores are called *z-scores*. Any raw score can be expressed as a z-score and any z-score can be transformed into its corresponding raw score. Consider the example exam scores where the standard deviation unit is 4, corresponding to a standard deviation of SD = 4 in the raw scores. If a student had a raw score of 94 on the exam, s/he scored three standard deviation units above the mean (+3SD), which translates to a z-score of z = +3.00. Similarly, if a student scored a 78 on the exam, s/he scored one standard deviation unit below the mean (-1SD) with a z-score of z = -1.00. What would the z-score be for a student who had a raw score of 88 on the exam? Since a raw score of 88 falls halfway between 86 and 90, the corresponding z-score for a raw score of 88 also falls halfway between the z-scores for 86 and 90 (z = +1.00 and z = +2.00 respectively): z = +1.50.

With the mean and standard deviation of a distribution of raw scores, any z-score can be transformed to its corresponding raw score. For instance, consider the example exam scores with $\overline{X} = 82$ and SD = 4. If a student scored two standard deviation units above the mean (z = +2.00), s/he scored a 90. What did a student score if s/he fell at a z-score of z = -2.50? Since z = -2.50 is halfway between the z-scores of z = -2.00 and z = -3.00, the raw score corresponding to z = -2.50 must be halfway between the raw scores for z = -2.00 and z = -3.00 (74 and 70 respectively): 72.

The transition between raw scores and z-scores was calculated quite easily for the example exam score data. In fact, any raw score in this exam score distribution can easily be expressed as a z-score. For instance, since a raw score of 83 is one fourth of a standard deviation unit above the mean, the corresponding z-score is z = +0.25. Although the transition between raw scores and z-scores was straightforward with these data, not all raw scores can be transformed to z-scores as easily. Thus, there is a simple formula available for the computation of z-scores when the data are too complex to easily translate raw scores into z-scores and vice versa. All of the z-scores we calculated for the exam score example also can be computed using the z-score formula.

Recall that a z-score is simply an expression of a raw score that is standardized in terms of standard deviation units. That is, the z-score is computed as how far a raw score deviates from the mean of the distribution as expressed in standard deviation units. The z-score is calculated as the difference between whatever type of data is in the distribution and the mean of the distribution divided by the standard deviation of the distribution:

$$z = \frac{(\text{type of data in distribution}) - (\text{mean of distribution})}{\text{standard deviation of distribution}}$$

The z-scores for all four of the distributions discussed in this chapter follow this same general formula. For the sample distribution, which involves a frequency distribution of raw scores from a sample, the type of data in the distribution is individual raw scores, X; the mean of the distribution is $\overline{X}$; and, the standard deviation of the distribution is SD. Thus, the specific z-score formula for a sample distribution is:

$$z = \frac{X - \overline{X}}{SD}$$

With the example exam score data, what would the z-score be for a student who earned a 92 on the exam? This is an easy problem to solve without the z-score formula: since the student scored halfway between 2 standard deviation units above the mean (z = +2.00, raw score = 90) and 3 standard deviation units above the mean (z = +3.00, raw score = 94), a raw score of 92 must have a corresponding z-score of z = +2.50. This z-score value can be verified by using the z-score formula:

$$z = \frac{X - \overline{X}}{SD} = \frac{92 - 82}{4} = \frac{10}{4} = 2.50$$

Expressing data in terms of z-scores is very useful because no matter what type of raw scores are being considered (e.g., age, test scores, income, IQ) the meaning of the z-scores is the same. For instance, a z-score of z = +1.00 always refers to a score that is one standard deviation unit above the mean, regardless of the mean and standard deviation of the original set of raw scores. Using z-scores to refer to a distribution of data permits meaningful comparisons of different distributions, even if the distributions do not have the same mean and standard deviation in the raw scores. Consider again the sample of 25 students' exam scores where $\overline{X}$ = 82 and SD = 4 (see Figure 4.1). Suppose the researcher samples another group of 25 students from a statistics course the following semester and examines their scores on the same midterm exam. The mean for these students is $\overline{X}$ = 80 and the standard deviation is SD = 5. The frequency polygon of these data is shown in Figure 4.2.

By expressing both sets of exam scores in standard deviation units (i.e., as z-scores), the two sets of data can be directly compared. For example, suppose the researcher is actually the professor for both statistics courses and he wants to assign grades in the same way in each course. He decides that students who score more than two standard deviations above the mean should receive an A in the course, students scoring between one and two standard deviations above the mean should receive a B, those scoring between -1SD and +1SD should receive a C, those scoring between -1SD and -2SD should receive a D, and students who score more than two standard deviations below the mean should receive an F. Figure 4.3 depicts how the professor wishes to assign grades in both classes based on standard deviation units (z-scores). Even though the raw scores corresponding to each z-score are different for the two sets of data, grades can still be assigned in a consistent way for both classes by using z-scores to determine grades. Using the students' z-scores rather than their raw scores as the basis for their grades allows the professor to insure that he is giving the same percentage of students in each of the two classes an A, B, C, D, and F. The fact that the normal curve has a constant relationship with the standard deviation guarantees a fixed percentage of scores under the normal curve between various z-scores.

Recall earlier that we indicated that a fixed percentage of scores (approximately 99%) falls between ±3SD in a normal distribution. That is, between z-scores of z = -3.00 and z = +3.00

fall 99% of all scores in a distribution. With the two sets of exam scores, this means that 99% of all students from the first semester scored between a 70 and 94 (see Figure 4.1) and 99% of all students from the second semester scored between a 65 and 95 (see Figure 4.2). Similarly, a fixed percentage of scores (approximately 95%) falls between ±2SD under a normal curve (between z = -2.00 and z = +2.00). For the first semester students, 95% scored between 74 and 90 and for the second semester students, 95% scored between 70 and 90. Finally, there is a fixed percentage of scores (approximately 68%) that fall between ±1SD in a normal distribution (between z = -1.00 and z = +1.00). For the exam score data, 68% of first semester students scored between 78 and 86 and 68% of second semester students scored between 75 and 85. These fixed percentages, corresponding to ±1SD, ±2SD, and ±3SD around the mean, are summarized by what we term the *68-95-99 rule*.

Based on the 68-95-99 rule, the professor assigned a C grade to 68% of the students in each of his two classes. Students who scored between a 78 and 86 the first semester received a C and students who scored between 75 and 85 the second semester received a C. Using the 68-95-99 rule along with the symmetry property of the normal curve, the professor assigned grades for all of the other students in his two courses. Recall that the symmetry

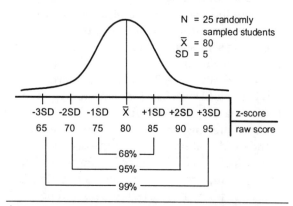

FIGURE 4.2: Sample distribution of individual exam scores with mean X̄ = 80 and standard deviation SD = 5

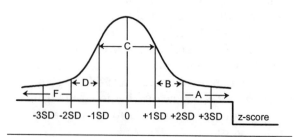

FIGURE 4.3: Assigning grades based on z-scores

property of the normal curve means that the right half and left half of the curve are identical. For example, 50% of the scores fall above the middle point (the mean, median, and mode on a normal curve) and 50% of the scores fall below this middle point.

The professor decided to assign an A grade to all students who scored beyond +2SD above the mean in both classes. That is, students who achieved above a 90 the first semester or above a 90 the second semester received A's. What percentage of students in each class received an A? Using the first semester students as an example, the percentage of students scoring beyond +2SD above the mean can be computed as illustrated in Figure 4.4. Based on the 68-95-99 rule, 95% of students scored between ±2SD around the mean (between raw scores of 74 and 90). Using this information along with the symmetry property of the normal curve, 47.5% of students scored between the mean and +2SD (between $z = 0.00$ and $z = +2.00$). Using this same symmetry property, 50% of students scored above the mean ($z = 0.00$). By simple subtraction, then, 50% - 47.5% = 2.5% of students scored above +2SD (above $z = +2.00$ or above a raw score of 90) and received an A in the course. Exactly the same percentage of students (2.5%) received an A in the second semester statistics class as well, since approximately 2.5% of all scores fall above $z = +2.00$ on any normal distribution. By this same

reasoning, it can be determined that 2.5% of students in both classes also received an F. In the first semester group, students who scored below a 74 received an F and in the second semester group students who scored below a 70 received an F.

Finally, the percentage of students who received a B and a D in each of the two classes can be determined. This time the second semester students will be used to illustrate the computation of the percentage of students who received a D in the course, as shown in Figure 4.5. Based on the 68-95-99 rule, 68% of students scored between ±1SD (between raw scores of 75 and 85). Using this fact in conjunction with the symmetry property of the normal curve, 34% of students scored between the mean and -1SD below the mean (between 75 and 80). Similarly, 95% of students scored between ± 2SD (between 70 and 90) and 47.5% of students scored between $z = 0.00$ and $z = -2.00$ (between 70 and 80). Using simple subtraction 47.5% - 34% = 13.5% of students scored between -1SD and -2SD below the mean (between raw scores of 70 and 75) and earned a D in the course. By this same logic, 13.5% of students earned a B, and these percentages are identical for the first semester students.

The concepts developed so far (z-scores, 68-95-99 rule) are applicable not only to the sample distribution discussed in this section but to all four types of normal distributions in this

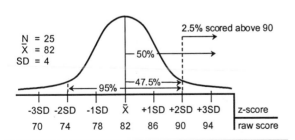

FIGURE 4.4: Deriving the percentage of students who scored above a 90

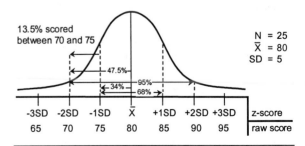

FIGURE 4.5: Deriving the percentage of students who scored between 70 and 75

chapter. In fact, the only major difference among the four distributions is the type of data in the distribution. Because z-scores can be computed for any set of normally distributed data, such a normal distribution, demarcated in terms of z-scores, is frequently called a *z-distribution*. We now turn to the other three important normal distributions.

Population Distribution

Consider the population of 1,500 students enrolled in the statistics class described at the beginning of this chapter. If data from the entire population (e.g., N = 1,500) rather than a sample (e.g., N = 25) is examined, the resulting distribution is called a *population distribution*. As with the sample distribution, the population distribution is a distribution of individual raw scores, X. Assuming that these data are normally distributed, the population distribution for the 1,500 students in this example is the following:

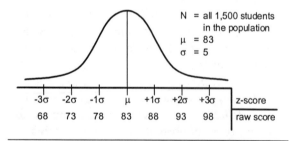

N = all 1,500 students in the population
μ = 83
σ = 5

| z-score | -3σ | -2σ | -1σ | μ | +1σ | +2σ | +3σ |
| raw score | 68 | 73 | 78 | 83 | 88 | 93 | 98 |

FIGURE 4.6: Population distribution of individual exam scores with mean μ = 83 and standard deviation σ = 5

As with the sample distribution, the population distribution has a mean and standard deviation. Recall that the symbols $\overline{X}$ and SD are used to refer to the mean and standard deviation for a sample, whereas the symbols " μ " (mu) and " σ " (sigma) are used to refer to the mean and standard deviation for a population. In this example, the population mean is μ = 83 and the standard deviation is σ = 5.

The same principles of z-scores and percentages discussed with the sample distribution also can be applied to the population distribution. Because it is a normal curve, the population distribution comprises approximately six standard deviation units. With a mean of 83 and a standard deviation of 5 (the standard deviation unit), the range of this population distribution is 68 to 98 (see Figure 4.6).

Computation of z-scores is done in exactly the same way as with the sample distribution. Recall the general formula for computing a z-score:

$$z = \frac{(\text{type of data in distribution}) - (\text{mean of distribution})}{\text{standard deviation of distribution}}$$

Applying this general formula to the population distribution, the type of data in this distribution is individual raw scores, X (just as with the sample distribution); the mean of this distribution is μ; and, the standard deviation of the population distribution is σ. Thus, the specific formula for computing a z-score for the population distribution is the following:

$$z = \frac{X - \mu}{\sigma}$$

What would the z-score be for a student who scored an 80? Using the z-score formula the z-score can be computed as follows:

$$z = \frac{X - \mu}{\sigma} = \frac{80 - 83}{5} = -\frac{3}{5} = -0.60$$

Determination of the percentage of scores falling between various z-scores also is accomplished identically to the procedure used with the sample distribution. For instance, what percentage of students scored between a 78 and 93? The answer to this problem is illustrated in Figure 4.7. Using the 68-95-99 rule and the property of symmetry of the normal curve, 34% of students scored between 83 and 88 (between z = 0.00 and z = +1.00) and 47.5% of students scored between 83 and 93 (between z = 0.00 and z = +2.00). Thus, 47.5% - 34% = 13.5% of students scored between 88 and 93 (between z = +1.00 and z = +2.00). Since 68% of students scored between 78 and 88 and 13.5% of students scored between 88 and 93, then by simple addition 68% + 13.5% = 81.5% of students scored between 78 and 93 (between z = -1.00 and z = +2.00).

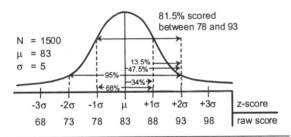

FIGURE 4.7: Deriving the percentage of students who scored between 78 and 93

Sampling Distribution

The third important type of normal distribution differs from the sample and population distributions in terms of the type of data in the distribution. Both the sample and population distributions consisted of individual raw scores, X. Unlike these distributions, the sampling distribution involves sample means, $\overline{X}$, rather than individual raw scores. The sampling distribution is a theoretical distribution that is a fundamental basis for inferential statistics so it is important to understand how it is derived.

Consider the random sample of 25 students from the statistics class of 1,500 students that was used to create the sample distribution earlier in this chapter:

Student	Exam Score
1. Joseph	86
2. Bob	79
and so forth...	
25. Mary	82

Recall the mean for this distribution was $\overline{X}$ = 82 (see Figure 4.1), calculated as follows:

$$\overline{X} = \frac{86 + 79 + ... + 82}{25} = 82$$

If these 25 students (Joseph, Bob, etc.) are returned to the population of 1,500 students, it will be possible to select them again if another random sample is drawn. This type of sampling procedure is called *sampling with replacement* because the sampled units are replaced or returned to the population and possibly can be selected again as part of another random sample. Sampling with replacement allows one to continue to draw random samples of size N (e.g., N = 25) from a population indefinitely. A second random sample of size 25 that might be drawn from the population of 1,500 students is the following:

Student	Exam Score
1. Marcia	81
2. Peter	75
and so forth...	
25. Charlie	90

Again, a mean for this sample is computed as follows:

$$\overline{X} = \frac{81 + 75 + ... + 90}{25} = 86$$

There are now two sample means, 82 and 86, obtained from random samples of the same population of 1,500 students. In theory, random samples (using sampling with replacement) continue to be drawn and sample means calculated an indefinite number of times. For illustration, we will stop after 1,000 samples have been drawn and 1,000 sample means computed. These 1,000 sample means are now graphed as a frequency polygon in the following figure:

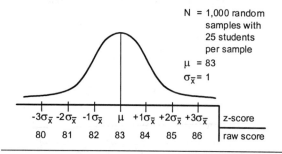

FIGURE 4.8: Sampling distribution of exam score sample means with mean $\mu = 83$ and standard deviation $\sigma_{\bar{x}} = 1$

The resulting distribution is called a *distribution of sample means* or the *sampling distribution* because it is sample means not individual raw scores which are the data points for this distribution.

As with all distributions, the sampling distribution has a mean symbolized "μ" and a standard deviation symbolized "$\sigma_{\bar{x}}$." The standard deviation of the sampling distribution is often called the *standard error of the mean* because it is a representation of the average or standard variation (error) in sample means about the population mean. Notice that Greek symbols are used for the descriptive measures of the sampling distribution, indicating that data from the entire population is represented in this distribution (in the form of sample means rather than individual raw scores).

One important feature of the parameters of the sampling distribution is that the mean of this distribution is exactly the same as the

mean of the population distribution: $\mu = 83$ in this example (see Figures 4.6 and 4.8). Because both the population and sampling distributions include all 1,500 students, the mean of these same 1,500 students must be identical. The population distribution includes all 1,500 students in terms of their individual raw scores whereas the sampling distribution includes all 1,500 students in terms of sample means from samples of size N = 25. Regardless of the form of the 1,500 scores (individual raw scores, X, or sample means, $\bar{X}$), all 1,500 students are included in both distributions, so the mean of this population of 1,500 students' exam scores must be identical, $\mu = 83$.

Although the mean for the population and sampling distributions is the same, the standard deviations are different. The standard error of the mean is calculated based on the standard deviation of the population of raw scores and the size of the sample.[1] In the present example the standard deviation for the population distribution is $\sigma = 5$ and the standard deviation for the sampling distribution is $\sigma_{\bar{x}} = 1$. Clearly, there is less variability with the sampling distribution than with the population distribution. Extreme individual scores have a much larger impact on the standard deviation of the population than on the standard deviation of the sample means.

To understand this idea, consider an individual who scored a 68, which is one of the lowest possible scores in the population (see Figure 4.6). This 68 is counted as one data point in computing the standard deviation of the population distribution. However, this same score of 68 is averaged in with 24 other scores when creating a sample mean that is the data point used in computing the standard deviation of the sampling distribution. When the extreme low score of 68 is averaged in with 24 other scores (e.g., 85, 89, 78, 92, 86, 87, 93, 92, 86, 83, 90, 84, 92, 84, 85, 89, 78, 84, 89, 92, 86, 80, 93, 85), the resulting data point, a sample mean, is much less extreme: $\overline{X} = 86$. This data point of $\overline{X} = 86$ used in computing the standard deviation of the sampling distribution is much closer to the mean of the distribution ($\mu = 83$) than is the data point of $\overline{X} = 68$ used in computing the standard deviation of the population distribution. The impact of the extreme score of 68 is lessened through the process of computing a mean, so the variation in sample means is much smaller than the variation in individual scores. That is, the standard deviation is smaller with the sampling distribution than with the population distribution: $\sigma_{\overline{X}} < \sigma$.

As with the sample and population distributions, z-scores and percentages can be computed for the sampling distribution. Again, recall the general form for the z-score formula:

$$z = \frac{(\text{type of data in distribution}) - (\text{mean of distribution})}{\text{standard deviation of distribution}}$$

Applied to the sampling distribution, the type of data in the distribution is sample means, $\overline{X}$; the mean of the distribution is μ; and, the standard deviation of the distribution is $\sigma_{\overline{X}}$. Thus, the specific formula for computing a z-score for the sampling distribution is as follows:

$$z = \frac{\overline{X} - \mu}{\sigma_{\overline{X}}}$$

What is the z-score of a sample whose mean is 85? The sample mean of 85 lies $+2\sigma_{\overline{X}}$ above the mean of the distribution, so z = +2.00. Using the z-score formula:

$$z = \frac{\overline{X} - \mu}{\sigma_{\overline{X}}} = \frac{85 - 83}{1} = \frac{2}{1} = 2.00$$

Once again, percentages are computed in the same way as with the sample and population distributions. What percent of samples had a mean less than 84? The following figure

depicts the solution to this problem:

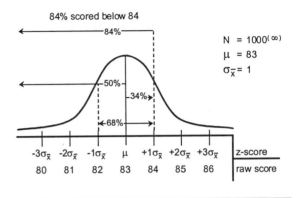

FIGURE 4.9: Deriving the percentage of samples whose mean is below 84

Using the 68-95-99 rule, 68% of sample means were between 82 and 84, so by the symmetry property 34% of sample means were between 83 and 84. Again, by the symmetry property, 50% of sample means were below 83. Thus, by simple addition 50% + 34% = 84% of sample means were below 84.

Distribution of Differences

The distribution of differences is the fourth important normal distribution and, like the sampling distribution, is a fundamental distribution for inferential statistics. As with the sampling distribution, the distribution of differences does not consist of individual raw scores but instead involves sample means. Unlike the sampling distribution, however, the distribution of differences consists of *differences* between pairs of sample means not individual sample means. Again, because of its importance in inferential statistics, we will discuss the derivation of this important theoretical distribution.

A random sample of size N = 25 is drawn from the population of 1,500 students and a mean is computed. Then, a second sample of size N = 25 is drawn from the same population and a mean is computed for this sample. Instead of plotting each of these two sample means as separate values, as with the sampling distribution, a difference between the two sample means is calculated. For instance, consider the following two random samples which were drawn when creating the sampling distribution:

Sample One		Sample Two	
Student	Test Score	Student	Test Score
1. Joseph	86	1. Marcia	81
2. Bob	79	2. Peter	75
and so forth...		and so forth...	
25. Mary	82	25. Charlie	90
$\overline{X}_1 = 82$		$\overline{X}_2 = 86$	

The difference between these two sample means is d = $\overline{X}_1 - \overline{X}_2$ = 82 - 86 = -4. This process of computing difference scores (d) between two sample means continues indefinitely using sampling with replacement to draw two random samples from the same population. Again, for the purposes of illustration, we will stop at a reasonable point, after computing 500 difference scores involving 1,000 random samples. These difference scores are graphed as shown in the following frequency polygon:

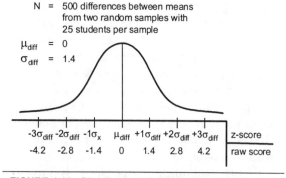

N = 500 differences between means from two random samples with 25 students per sample

μ_{diff} = 0
σ_{diff} = 1.4

$-3\sigma_{diff}$	$-2\sigma_{diff}$	$-1\sigma_x$	μ_{diff}	$+1\sigma_{diff}$	$+2\sigma_{diff}$	$+3\sigma_{diff}$	z-score
-4.2	-2.8	-1.4	0	1.4	2.8	4.2	raw score

FIGURE 4.10: Distribution of differences of exam score sample means with mean μ_{diff} = 0 and standard deviation σ_{diff} = 1.4

The resulting distribution is known as the *distribution of differences* because it involves differences between sample means.

The distribution of differences, as with all distributions, has a mean symbolized " $\mu_{\overline{X}_1-\overline{X}_2}$ " or " μ_{diff} ", and a standard deviation symbolized " $\sigma_{\overline{X}_1-\overline{X}_2}$ " or " σ_{diff} ." The standard deviation for the distribution of differences has a special name, the *standard error of the difference*, because it is a representation of the average or standard variation (error) in difference scores on the distribution of differences. Again, notice that Greek symbols are used for the mean and standard deviation of the distribution of differences, indicating that this distribution includes the data from all members of the population (in the form of differences between sample means).

An important feature of the parameters for this distribution is that the mean of the distribution of differences is *always* equal to zero, regardless of the nature of the raw scores and sample means underlying the distribution. The reason for this fact is very logical: the difference between the means of two random samples from the same population should, averaged over many samples, equal zero. That is, the average difference score of an infinite number of random samples selected from the same population is zero. The standard error of the difference is calculated based on the size of the two samples and the variance in the population of raw scores; in this example, σ_{diff} = 1.4.[2]

To better understand the nature of the distribution of differences, consider a very simplified illustration using only eight samples (i.e., four difference scores) from the population of 1,500 students. The mean of all scores in the population is known to be μ = 83 (see Figure 4.6). Consider the two randomly selected samples of size N = 25 from above. The mean score for Sample One was $\overline{X}_1$ = 82 and the mean score for Sample Two was $\overline{X}_2$ = 86. The calculated difference score was d = 82 - 86 = -4.

The students in Samples One and Two are returned to the population of 1,500 students (sampling with replacement) and another two random samples of size N = 25 each are drawn and means for both samples are computed as follows:

Sample Three		Sample Four	
Student	Test Score	Student	Test Score
1. Ellen	78	1. Cameron	90
2. Chris	85	2. Maria	77
and so forth...		and so forth...	
25. Ed	80	25. Cassie	85
$\overline{X}_3 = 81$		$\overline{X}_4 = 84$	

The difference score computed for Samples Three and Four is d = 81 - 84 = -3.

Again, the students in Samples Three and Four are returned to the population and two more samples of size N = 25 are drawn from the population and a mean is computed for each sample:

Sample Five		Sample Six	
Student	Test Score	Student	Test Score
1. Barry	69	1. Max	88
2. Sonny	87	2. Sloane	80
and so forth...		and so forth...	
25. Grace	85	25. Josie	82
$\overline{X}_5 = 84$		$\overline{X}_6 = 83$	

The difference score computed for Samples Five and Six is d = 84 - 83 = +1.

The students in Samples Five and Six are returned to the population and two final random samples for this illustration are drawn from the population and means for both samples are computed:

Sample Seven		Sample Eight	
Student	Test Score	Student	Test Score
1. Wally	84	1. Christy	75
2. Shelly	86	2. Byron	82
and so forth...		and so forth...	
25. Ferris	81	25. Kelly	80
$\overline{X}_7 = 85$		$\overline{X}_8 = 79$	

The difference score computed for Samples Seven and Eight is d = 85 - 79 = +6.

The average of all eight sample means drawn from the same population is calculated as follows:

$$\mu = \frac{82 + 86 + 81 + 84 + 84 + 83 + 85 + 79}{8} = 83$$

The fact that the average of the eight sample means is identical to the mean of the population of 1,500 exam scores ($\mu = 83$) should not be surprising. Indeed, recall that the mean of the sampling distribution was equal to the mean of the population of raw scores because all raw scores are included in the sampling distribution, albeit in the form of sample means rather than individual raw scores.

The average of the four difference scores also can be computed as follows:

$$\mu_{diff} = \frac{(-4) + (-3) + (+1) + (+6)}{4} = 0$$

Notice that the average difference between randomly selected samples drawn from the same population is zero. That is, the mean of the distribution of differences is always zero. Although this simplified example includes only eight sample means (in reality there would be an infinite number of them), this illustration should clarify the nature of the means of the sampling distribution and the distribution of differences.

For the distribution of differences, z-scores and percentages function in exactly the same way as with the prior three normal distributions. Recall the general form of the equation for computing a z-score:

$$z = \frac{(\text{type of data in distribution}) - (\text{mean of distribution})}{\text{standard deviation of distribution}}$$

For the distribution of differences, it is not individual raw scores, X, or sample means, $\overline{X}$, that constitute the data points in the distribution but rather a difference between sample means, $\overline{X}_1 - \overline{X}_2$. The mean of the distribution of differences is $\mu_{\overline{X}_1-\overline{X}_2}$ or μ_{diff} and the standard deviation of the distribution of differences is $\sigma_{\overline{X}_1-\overline{X}_2}$ or σ_{diff}. Thus, the specific form of the z-score formula for the distribution of differences is the following:

$$z = \frac{(\overline{X}_1 - \overline{X}_2) - \mu_{\overline{X}_1-\overline{X}_2}}{\sigma_{\overline{X}_1-\overline{X}_2}}$$

or

$$z = \frac{(\overline{X}_1 - \overline{X}_2) - \mu_{\text{diff}}}{\sigma_{\text{diff}}}$$

Because the mean of the distribution of differences is always equal to zero ($\mu_{\text{diff}} = 0$), this formula can be shortened to the following:

$$z = \frac{(\overline{X}_1 - \overline{X}_2) - 0}{\sigma_{\text{diff}}} = \frac{\overline{X}_1 - \overline{X}_2}{\sigma_{\text{diff}}}$$

However, we suggest that you use the first formula, at least initially, in order to understand the fact that computing a z-score conceptually is identical regardless of the specific distribution being examined (sample, population, sampling, differences).

What is the z-score corresponding to a difference in sample means of -3.5? Referring to Figure 4.10, the difference of -3.5 is halfway between -2.8 (z = -2.00) and -4.2 (z = -3.00), so the z-score is z = -2.50. Using the z-score formula this z-score can be verified as follows:

$$z = \frac{(\overline{X}_1 - \overline{X}_2) - \mu_{\text{diff}}}{\sigma_{\text{diff}}} = \frac{(-3.5) - 0}{1.4} = -\frac{3.5}{1.4} = -2.50$$

Now consider deriving the percentage of differences in sample means that fall in various areas under the normal curve. As a review, consider the 68-95-99 rule applied to the distribution of differences (Figure 4.11). For the example exam scores, what percentage of differences between pairs of sample means is larger than ±2.8? The solution to this problem is depicted in Figure 4.12. A raw difference score of +2.8 corresponds to a z-score of z = +2.00 and a raw score difference of -2.8 corresponds to a z-score of z = -2.00. Using the 68-95-99 rule, 95% of all differences fall between z = -2.00 and z = +2.00. Thus, 5% of all differences fall outside of this 95% range. Because of the symmetrical property of the normal curve, 2.5% of differences are above z = +2.00 and 2.5% of differences are below z = -2.00.

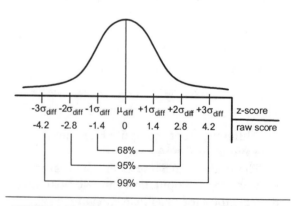

FIGURE 4.11: Distribution of differences with 68-95-99 rule

Summary

Four important normal distributions are the sample distribution, population distribution, sampling distribution, and distribution of differences. The sample distribution is a distribution of the raw scores from a sample or subset of a larger population. The population distribution is a distribution of the raw scores from all members of a population. The sampling distribution is a distribution of sample means obtained from computing an infinite number of sample means from randomly selected samples drawn from the same population. The distribution of differences is a distribution of differences between two sample means obtained from computing the difference between sample means of two randomly selected samples drawn from the same population. Both the sampling distribution and distribution of differences are theoretical distributions created using an infinite number of samples drawn from the same population and utilizing sampling with replacement. The standard deviation of the sampling distribution is called the standard error of the mean, and the standard deviation of the distribution of differences is called the standard error of the difference.

Normal distributions can be represented by either the original raw scores of the distribu

tion or z-scores which are an expression of the raw scores in standard deviation units. Raw scores are converted to z-scores by standardizing the raw score values based on the mean and standard deviation of the raw score distribution. Because of the property of symmetry and the constant relationship of the standard deviation with the normal curve, fixed percentages can be computed for a variety of scores on a normal distribution. The 68-95-99 rule is an approximation of the percentage of scores falling between ±1 standard deviation around the mean (68%), ±2 standard deviations around the mean (95%), and ±3 standard deviations around the mean (99%).

Key Terms

- distribution of differences
- population distribution
- raw score (X)
- sample distribution
- sampling distribution (distribution of sample means)
- sampling with replacement
- standard deviation unit
- standard error of the difference ($\sigma_{\bar{X}_1-\bar{X}_2}$ or σ_{diff})
- standard error of the mean ($\sigma_{\bar{X}}$)
- z-distribution
- z-score
- 68-95-99 rule

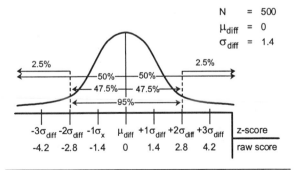

$$N = 500$$
$$\mu_{diff} = 0$$
$$\sigma_{diff} = 1.4$$

FIGURE 4.12: Deriving the percentage of differences beyond ±2.8

Problems

1. What type of distribution represents all of the individual scores of a sample?
   a. What is the symbol for the mean of these data?
   b. What is the symbol for the standard deviation of these data?
   c. What is the formula to compute a z-score for this distribution?
2. What type of distribution represents all of

the individual scores of a population?

a. What is the symbol for the mean of these data?

b. What is the symbol for the standard deviation of these data?

c. What is the formula to compute a z-score for this distribution?

3. What type of distribution represents sample means computed from an infinite number of random samples drawn from the same population?

a. What is the symbol for the mean of these data?

b. What is the symbol for the standard deviation of these data?

c. What is the formula to compute a z-score for this distribution?

4. What type of distribution represents differences between pairs of sample means that are computed from an infinite number of random samples drawn from the same population?

a. What is the symbol for the mean of these data?

b. What is the symbol for the standard deviation of these data?

c. What is the formula to compute a z-score for this distribution?

5. The term "statistic" is used to refer to means and standard deviations for a _____, whereas the term "parameter" is used to refer to means and standard deviations for a _____ .

6. Which of the four types of distributions (*sample, population, sampling,* or *differences*) use statistics? Which use parameters? Why do some distributions use statistics and others use parameters?

7. $\overline{X}$, μ, and μ_{diff} are symbols used to stand for the _____ as applied to different types of distributions.

8. SD, σ, $\sigma_{\overline{X}}$, and σ_{diff} are symbols used to stand for the _____ as applied to difference types of distributions.

9. What is another name for the standard deviation of the sampling distribution?

10. What is another name for the standard deviation of the distribution of differences?

11. Consider the following nine pairs of sample means:

11 and 3	9 and 13	11 and 11
8 and 12	8 and 16	14 and 10
16 and 12	5 and 5	9 and 9

a. Using the pairs given above, compute a difference score for each pair and draw a graph of these difference scores (use the first two samples as a pair, the second two samples as a pair, and so on until you exhaust all nine pairs of sample means).

b. What is the name of this distribution?

c. What is the mean of this distribution?

d. What is another name for the standard deviation of this distribution?

12. A z-score is the deviation of a score from the mean as expressed in _____ units.

13. For each of the following raw scores, indicate what the corresponding z-score would be:

a. a raw score that is 1.5 standard deviation units above the mean

b. a raw score that is 2 standard deviation units below the mean

c. a raw score that is equal to the mean

d. a raw score that is .66 standard deviation units below the mean

e. a raw score that is 2.75 standard deviation units above the mean

14. For each of the following sets of data (represented by the mean and standard deviation below), identify the end-points for six standard deviation units (that is between ±3SD around the mean – the range). Draw frequency polygons for each of the four distributions with the raw scores indicated for all six standard deviation units.

a. $\overline{X} = 15$ SD = 3
b. $\overline{X} = 1,000$ SD = 250
c. $\overline{X} = 75$ SD = 5
d. $\overline{X} = 150$ SD = 15

15. A test is administered to students and the resulting scores are normally distributed. The mean of this test is 75 and the standard deviation is 8.
   a. Draw the graph for the distribution of these data and label it both in terms of raw scores and z-scores (standard deviation units).
   b. Identify the z-score for each of the following raw scores on this distribution:
      i.   83
      ii. 63
      iii. 93
      iv. 75
      v.   60
   c. Identify the percentage of students who scored in the following ranges of raw scores:
      i.   between 67 and 83
      ii.   between 51 and 99
      iii. above 75
      iv.   above 83
      v.   below 67
      vi.   below 91
      vii. between 59 and 91
      viii. below 99
   d. Identify the appropriate raw score corresponding to each of the following z-scores:
      i.   z = +1.50
      ii. z = 0.00
      iii. z = -3.00
      iv. z = -0.25
      v.   z = +2.33
      vi. z = -1.75

16. Suppose you have a distribution of differences with a standard error of the difference, $\sigma_{diff} = 3$.
   a. Draw the normal distribution corresponding to this graph and label the raw difference scores corresponding to $\pm 1\sigma_{diff}$, $\pm 2\sigma_{diff}$, and $\pm 3\sigma_{diff}$.
   b. What raw score difference falls at $+1\sigma_{diff}$?
   c. What raw score difference falls at $-2\sigma_{diff}$?

17. Suppose a researcher is interested in the distribution of weights of football players in the National Football League. For simplicity, assume that there are 100 players per team in the NFL and there are 30 teams. Each team can be considered a sample from the larger population.
   a. What is the population of interest to this researcher?
   b. What are the appropriate symbols for the mean and standard deviation of the distribution of this population?
   c. Suppose the mean weight for the population of NFL players is 210 pounds with a standard deviation of 15 pounds. One Houston Oiler player, Tom, weighs 1.5 standard deviation units above the mean NFL weight. How much does Tom weigh?
   d. What type of distribution can be created using only the weights of players on the Dallas Cowboys' team?
   e. What are the appropriate symbols for the mean and standard deviation of this distribution?
   f. If the mean weight of players on the Dallas Cowboys' team is 208 pounds with a standard deviation of 10 pounds, how many standard deviations away from the mean is Dallas player Bob if he weighs 213 pounds?
   g. What percentage of Dallas Cowboys weigh between 198 and 218 pounds?
   h. What percentage of Dallas Cowboys weigh more than 228 pounds?
   i. Suppose a distribution is created from the means of the 30 teams (samples). The mean of the resulting distribution

is 200 pounds with a standard deviation of 5 pounds. What type of distribution is this?

j. How many standard deviations away
from the NFL mean weight is the Pitts-
burgh Steelers' team which has an average weight of 215 pounds?

k. What percentage of NFL teams (samples) weigh more than what the Pitts-
burgh Steelers' team weighs on average?

Notes

1 The standard error of the mean is a function of
the standard deviation of the population and the
sample size:

$$\sigma_{\bar{x}} = \frac{\sigma}{\sqrt{N}}$$

2 The standard error of the difference is a function
of the variance of the population and the two
sample sizes:

$$\sigma_{\bar{x}_1 - \bar{x}_2} = \sqrt{\frac{\sigma^2}{n_1} + \frac{\sigma^2}{n_2}}$$

Computer Section

Graphing and z-scores

After obtaining basic frequency and descriptive information from a set of data, it is frequently useful to graph the information in order to get a better overall sense of the data. Data can be displayed a number of different ways, including pie charts, bar graphs (histograms), and line graphs (frequency polygons). Graphs are frequently very useful for trying to communicate findings to people when making presentations and writing reports. Typically, graphs are produced on the computer by a graphing command which involves specifying: (1) the variable to be graphed, and (2) the type of graph to be produced (e.g., bar chart, line graph). Additionally, it may be useful to obtain standardized z-scores for some variables to aid in interpreting a distribution of data and to compare scores on different variables. Some type of descriptive command usually can be used on the computer to create a new variable that contains the z-score transformation of the original variable.

Sample Output for Pie Chart

A researcher distributed a survey on education and life satisfaction to 500 people. One of the items in the questionnaire asked respondents to rate the quality of their education on a five point scale from poor to excellent. The following pie chart displays the results of these data in graphical form.

Interpretation of Pie Chart Output

Based on a total of 100%, the pie chart is broken into segments like pie pieces that correspond with the percentage of students who

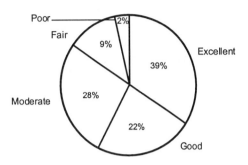

selected each response regarding the quality of their education. Based on the graph, a total of 39% (195 of the 500 respondents) indicated that their education was excellent, 22% indicated it was good, 28% indicated it was moderate, 9% indicated it was fair, and 2% indicated the quality of their education was poor.

Example Output for Bar Chart

Respondents to the education survey also were asked to indicate how exciting they perceived their lives to be with a forced-choice item that included the following three response options: routine, dull, and exciting. The following bar chart displays the results of this analysis:

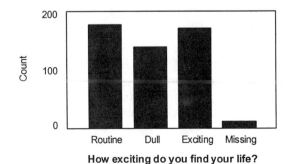

How exciting do you find your life?

Interpretation of Bar Chart Output

The results of this bar chart indicate the number of people (count) who selected each option. Bar charts also can be displayed using percentage as the basis for each bar rather than the total count. The results of this analysis revealed that 180 respondents felt their life was routine, 140 felt their life was dull, 174 felt their life was exciting, and 6 did not respond (i.e., had missing data).

Example Output for Line Graph

Finally, the researcher recorded the last level of education completed by each respondent. A line graph of these data follows:

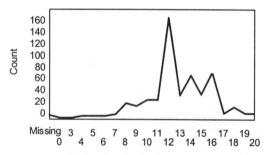

Highest year of school completed

Interpretation of Line Graph Output

As can be seen from the graph, the most frequently occurring score or count is 12 years of school, corresponding with a high school degree, completed by 145 of the respondents. A fairly high number of people also completed some college (about 40 completed one year of college, 60 completed two years of college, and so on). Frequency polygons are frequently useful for assessing whether a set of data are normally distributed.

Example Output for z-scores

A university campus health center official investigated how long (in days) students waited after they first became ill before they were examined by a doctor. These data were transformed from raw scores into standardized z-scores and the following output for 10 cases was obtained:

Number of valid observations (listwise) = 300.00						
Variable	Mean	Std Dev	Valid Minimum	Maximum	N	Label
TIME	6.72	4.85	1.00	21.00	300	Days to Dr Visit

TIME	ZTIME
10.00	.67575
3.00	-.76640
6.00	-.14833
7.00	.05769
8.00	.26371
16.00	1.91187
8.00	.26371
7.00	.05769
4.00	-.56038
22.00	3.14801

Number of cases read: 300
Number of cases listed: 10

Interpretation of z-score Output

Notice that only 10 of 300 cases were printed for illustration. Both the raw and standardized (z) scores are reported. The raw scores are the original variable TIME, and the z-scores are a new variable called ZTIME. Descriptive statistics on the variable TIME indicate that the mean is 6.72 and the standard deviation is 4.85. Notice that the z-score corresponding to each raw score is based on this mean and standard deviation. For example, the first respondent had a raw score of 10 days, which translates to a z-score of:

$$z = \frac{X - \overline{X}}{SD} = \frac{10 - 6.72}{4.85} = .67575$$

(Note: The computer only prints the mean and standard deviation to two decimal places, but uses the full calculated value to compute z-scores.)

One common reason researchers examine z-scores is to determine if there are cases that are substantially different from others in the population. If the z-score falls beyond the normal standard deviation range (-3 SD to +3 SD) this data value is often called an "extreme value" or "outlier" in the population from which it was drawn. Consequently, the score may be discounted or eliminated from future analyses. In the example above, the last case of a student who waited 22 days to visit the doctor ($z = 3.14801$) may be considered an outlier.

Computer Problems

1. Produce a pie chart showing the distribution of students in each class level (**CLSLVL**).
2. Create a pie chart illustrating the distribution of students' use of e-mail to provide feedback to their instructor (**FDBACK1**).
3. Create a bar chart for students' gender (**STDTSEX**).
4. Create a line graph that displays how fun students found e-mail (**FUN**). Are these data approximately normally distributed?
5. Examine how knowledgeable students found their instructor (**KNOW**).
   a. Create a bar graph of this distribution.
   b. Is this approximately a normal distribution?
   c. Create a bar graph for male students only.
   d. Create a bar graph for female students only.

6. Determine how comfortable students were in seeking advice/help from their instructor (**SEEK**).
   a. Create a line graph for students in the mediated class.
   b. Is this approximately a normal distribution?
   c. Create a line graph for students in the live class only.
7. Compute the z-scores for how well students think they did in the course (**OUTCOME**).
   a. What are the maximum and minimum z-scores within which 99% of all z-scores in a normal distribution fall?
   b. Do any of the z-scores for this variable fall beyond this 99% range? If so, how many?
8. Compute z-scores for how much students' interest in the subject matter increased as a result of taking the course (**MORELIKE**). Now examine only the raw scores and z-scores for this variable for the ten students enrolled with the female instructor in the cooperative and live class.
   a. Do these z-scores fall within ±3 SD?
   b. What are the maximum and minimum z-scores for this subset of students?
9. Compute z-scores for how dynamic students found their instructor to be (**DYN**). Now examine only the raw scores and z-scores for this variable for the ten students enrolled with the male instructor in the individualistic and mediated class.
   a. Do these z-scores fall within ±3 SD?
   b. What are the maximum and minimum z-scores for this subset of students?

Chapter 5 ❖ Hypothesis Testing and the z-test

Introduction to Inferential Statistics

This chapter introduces the foundation for inferential statistics and is a key chapter for understanding statistical reasoning. Recall that inferential statistics involves obtaining data from a subset of the population of interest and using the data from this sample as a basis for inferring what is likely true about the larger population. The concepts of hypothesis testing and probability are at the heart of inferential statistics. Hypothesis testing concerns the idea of testing a prediction or hypothesis to determine if it is true and either accepting or rejecting the hypothesis based on statistical probability. Thus, we will begin this chapter with a focus on understanding hypotheses and probability.

In Chapter 4 we introduced two very important normal distributions for inferential statistics: the sampling distribution of means and the sampling distribution of differences. In the latter part of this chapter, we will explain how these two distributions are used to test hypotheses.

What is a Hypothesis?

A *hypothesis* is a testable prediction about what is or is not true about a particular phenomenon. Hypotheses typically involve statements concerning the relationship among variables. Each of us formulates and tests hypotheses as a regular part of our daily lives. For example, Professor Peterson is teaching a statistics class similar to the one in which you are currently enrolled. Professor Peterson has taught this same statistics class for many years at her university. She has determined that the mean on the midterm exam she gives every semester is μ (mu) = 82 for the population, since across all students who have ever taken her class the average score has been an 82. This semester the university offered this course to 16 advanced high school students seeking college credit prior to admission to the university. Given that this is an unusual class, Professor Peterson believes that the students enrolled in this class will perform differently on her midterm exam than the historical average in this class of μ = 82. This prediction is Professor Peterson's hypothesis that she wishes to test. A common way that researchers state their prediction or hypothesis is in the following form:

> H: Students enrolled in this semester's class will score differently on the midterm exam than a mean of 82.

Such a hypothesis is called a *research hypothesis* because it is the researcher's prediction about what will happen or is true.

To test this hypothesis, Professor Peterson obtains the average midterm exam score for the students in this semester's class: $\overline{X}$ = 78. Based on this information, she might be tempted to conclude that students in this class do indeed score differently than a mean of μ = 82. However, she will need to conduct a statistical test of her hypothesis in order to determine whether the sample of 16 high school students is part of the same population that has a mean midterm exam score of μ = 82, and whether the observed 4 point difference in exam scores (78 - 82) reflects a true population difference or is due simply to chance.

As another illustration of a hypothesis, consider Joe who is a college sophomore enrolled in Professor Peterson's statistics class the following semester. Before the midterm exam, Professor Peterson distributes a review sheet to the class for them to use to study for the test. Joe is interested in whether using the review sheet aids in performance on the exam. He believes that students who study with the help of a review sheet will score differently, on average, than will students who do not study using the review sheet. However, Joe is not certain whether the review sheet is likely to help or hurt students' performance on the exam. Thus, he simply predicts that the review sheet will make some difference in students' exam scores:

> H: Students who use the review sheet to study will perform differently on the exam than will students who do not use the review sheet to study.

With this hypothesis Joe is predicting that there will be a relationship between the independent variable (use of the review sheet or not) and the dependent variable (exam scores).

Joe performs an experiment to test his hypothesis that students who use the review sheet will score differently on the exam than will students who do not use the review sheet. Joe solicits 12 of his friends who are enrolled in the class to serve as subjects for the experiment. Notice that Joe's 12 friends do *not* constitute a random sample. Joe puts all 12 names into a hat and randomly picks out six students to be those who will use the review sheet to study for the midterm exam and the other six students are randomly assigned not to use the review sheet. Notice that Joe *does* use random assignment to create two equivalent groups in his experiment.

After the midterm exam Joe computes the average grade for the six students who studied from the review sheet, $\overline{X}_{RevSh} = 88$, and for the six students who did not use the review sheet, $\overline{X}_{NoRevSh} = 80$. Based on these data, Joe is tempted to conclude that his hypothesis was confirmed: those who studied using the review sheet did indeed appear to score differently than those who did not study from the review sheet (in this case, the review sheet appeared to help test performance). Again, however, Joe will need to test this difference (8 points) using a statistical test to determine if the two groups truly represent different populations or if they represent the same population and scored differently purely due to chance.

Although we may not approach all problems and questions in life quite so systematically, hypothesis testing is a direct extension of the way people normally learn and interact with the world. Researchers formulate hypotheses based on reviewing what they already know and test those hypotheses by conducting research studies.

For example, a psychologist interested in the issue of learning environments might hypothesize that recall of information is greater if it occurs in the same location in which the material was initially learned than if recall occurs in a different location. A communication researcher examining the topic of pornography in society might hypothesize that men who are exposed to violent pornography will behave more aggressively toward women than will men who are exposed to nonviolent pornography.

An education researcher might hypothesize that students at a particular school are smarter than the average population, with an IQ greater than 100. A sociologist might hypothesize that women who are raised in families in which the mother worked outside of the home will be more likely to work outside the home themselves than will women raised in families in which the mother worked at home. An economist might hypothesize that there will be a difference in recovery rates following a recession in primarily agricultural states compared to primarily technological states.

Null and Alternative Hypotheses

The hypotheses that researchers formulate can be tested by collecting data utilizing a variety of research methods, including experiments, surveys, and content analysis. Recall from Chapter 2 that data can be measured at four different levels: nominal, ordinal, interval, and ratio. All of these types of data can be used for hypothesis testing. The remainder of this book focuses on different statistical tests that allow a researcher to test hypotheses based on the type of data collected and the number of independent variables being examined.

Consider again the hypothesis formulated by Professor Peterson: students in the current semester's class will perform differently on the midterm exam than a population whose mean is $\mu = 82$. In other words, this semester's class is hypothesized to not be a part of a population whose mean is 82 but rather to be a part of some other population whose mean is different from 82. Although this is the researcher's prediction (the research hypothesis), what is tested statistically is the opposite: that students in this semester's class perform the same as a population with a mean $\mu = 82$ (i.e., this semester's class is part of the same population whose mean is $\mu = 82$). Because the hypothesis that is tested statistically is one of no difference or no effect, it is called the *null hypothesis*, symbolized as H_0. For Professor Peterson's problem, the null hypothesis is:

$$H_0: \ \mu = 82$$

This statement says that the mean of the population (μ) from which this sample (this semester's statistics students) is drawn is equal to or not significantly different from a population with a known mean ($\mu = 82$).

The research hypothesis also can be presented notationally as:

$$H \text{ or } H_a: \ \mu \neq 82$$

This statement says that the mean of the population (μ) from which this sample is drawn is not equal to a population whose mean is 82 ($\mu \neq 82$). The research hypothesis is often represented as H_a, which stands for *alternative hypothesis*, because statistically this hypothesis is a logical alternative to the null hypothesis. Despite the fact that the alternative hypothesis is the one that Professor Peterson is interested in testing, statistical models of hypothesis testing are formulated such that she cannot directly test H_a. Rather, the null hypothesis is always the one which is tested statistically and either rejected or not rejected ("accepted").

If H_0 is rejected, then Professor Peterson can conclude within some margin of error that the alternative hypothesis is true. If H_0 is not rejected, then Professor Peterson cannot conclude that the alternative hypothesis is true. Remember that this reasoning is based on the fact that the null and alternative hypotheses are logical alternatives to one another, as illustrated in the following figure:

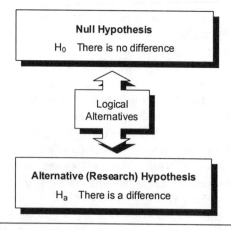

FIGURE 5.1: Logical Alternatives – null and alternative hypotheses

Usually the research and alternative hypotheses are the same because the most common questions asked are ones that examine differences among phenomena. However, occasionally a researcher actually might hypothesize that a sample is no different from a certain population. In this case the research hypothesis actually is equivalent to the null hypothesis. Usually, support for the researcher's hypothesis is found when the null hypothesis is rejected. In the above situation, however, support for the research hypothesis is found when the null hypothesis is not rejected.

Alternative hypotheses can be formulated as either directional or nondirectional. Professor Peterson advanced a *nondirectional hypothesis* (i.e., a difference statement) because she is not hypothesizing that students in her current class are from a population with a higher (>) or lower (<) mean than a population with a mean of $\mu = 82$. Rather, she is hypothesizing that this semester's students are part of a different ($\neq$) population than one whose mean is $\mu = 82$. In contrast, had Professor Peterson specified that students would score higher or lower than an 82, this would have been a *directional hypothesis*. If she predicted that these high school students were part of a population whose mean was less than 82, the corresponding null and alternative hypotheses would be the following:

$$H_0: \mu \geq 82$$
$$H_a: \mu < 82$$

Notice that between the null and alternative hypotheses, all possible relationships of the sample mean to a value of 82 are covered: greater than or equal to 82 (the null hypothesis) and less than 82 (the alternative hypothesis). Notice, too, that the alternative hypothesis still remains a logical alternative to the null hypothesis.

Null and alternative hypotheses also can be formulated to compare groups to each other to determine if they are part of the same or different populations. Consider Joe's example of two groups' scores on the statistics midterm exam: one group studied with a review sheet and the other group did not. Joe hypothesized that the two groups would score significantly different from one another (the research hypothesis). Thus, the null hypothesis tested statistically is that there is no difference between the two groups and the alternative hypothesis is that there is some significant difference between the two groups:

$$H_0: \mu_{RevSh} = \mu_{NoRevSh}$$
$$H_a: \mu_{RevSh} \neq \mu_{NoRevSh}$$

Notice that the null and alternative hypotheses are stated using the parameter μ to refer to the population means rather than the sample statistic $\overline{X}$ because these hypotheses are stating what is true in the populations of which the samples are a part. That is, the null hypothesis states that the true mean for a population that receives a review sheet is the same as the true mean for a population that does not receive a review sheet. In other words, these two groups are actually representative of the same population with the same midterm exam score. The alternative hypothesis states that the review sheet and no review sheet samples actually represent different populations with different midterm exam scores.

Instead of a nondirectional research hypothesis, Joe also might have formulated a directional hypothesis such as the following:

H: Students who use the review sheet to study will perform better on the exam than will students who do not use the review sheet to study.

In statistical notation, the corresponding null and alternative hypotheses are:

$$H_0: \mu_{RevSh} \leq \mu_{NoRevSh}$$
$$H_a: \mu_{RevSh} > \mu_{NoRevSh}$$

TABLE 5.1: Summary of Null and Alternative Hypotheses for a Two-Sample Problem

In Words	Symbolically Represented	Labeled	Test Used
1. There is a difference (H₀: There is no difference)	$H_0: \mu_1 = \mu_2$ $H_a: \mu_1 \neq \mu_2$	Nondirectional hypothesis	Two-tailed test
2. X is greater than Y (H₀: X is less than or equal to Y)	$H_0: \mu_1 \leq \mu_2$ $H_a: \mu_1 > \mu_2$	Directional hypothesis	One-tailed test
3. X is less than Y (H₀: X is greater than or equal to Y)	$H_0: \mu_1 \geq \mu_2$ $H_a: \mu_1 < \mu_2$	Directional hypothesis	One-tailed test

Example of a Hypothesis: Drivers Using Car Phones Are More Likely to Be Involved in Car Accidents

SOURCE: Jeffrey Kluger, "Distress Calls: A New Study Links Car Phones with Accidents," *Time*, February 24, 1997, p.C52.

Imagine if every time you took to the road, 35 million of your fellow drivers were legally drunk. That's not likely, but it *is* possible they're doing something nearly as dangerous as drinking: talking on a cellular phone.

According to a study published last week in the *New England Journal of Medicine*, drivers using car phones are four times as likely to be involved in an accident as those minding only the road – about the same rate found among motorists driving at the legal blood-alcohol limit. The study, conducted by a Canadian research team, relied on a large sample group of cell-phone owners who had been involved in road mishaps and agreed to release their phone records. As suspected, subjects often had their collisions within minutes of initiating a call. Surprisingly, drivers with speakerphones fared no better than those using at least one hand to make a call.

The cell-phone industry is treading cautiously. One trade group conceded the findings but stressed that phones could also enhance road safety by allowing drivers in distress to call for help. Even the *Journal* study did not say the phones were responsible for the accidents, but that they were merely associated with them. And Michael Goodman, a researcher with the National Highway Traffic Safety Administration, concurred, pointing out that the nature of a call – an argument, say – could be more distracting than the call itself.

Next month the NHSTA will try to settle the question, issuing a two-year review of research on the problem. And well it might, since things are only likely to get worse. In 1995, according to the study, the number of Americans who signed up for new cell-phone service exceeded the national birthrate.

Statistically, nondirectional hypotheses are tested by a two-tailed test and directional hypotheses are tested by a one-tailed test. These two variations of statistical hypothesis testing will be addressed in subsequent sections of this chapter.

Probability and Hypothesis Testing

With hypothesis testing there are two possible hypotheses to be considered, only one of which can be correct: (1) the alternative hypothesis is correct (e.g., people who used the review sheet scored differently than people who did not use the review sheet), or (2) the null hypothesis is correct (e.g., people who used the review sheet did not score any differently than people who did not use the review sheet). How does a researcher determine which one of these two possibilities is correct? Statistical hypothesis testing is always conducted with respect to the null hypothesis and is used to determine whether to: (1) reject the null hypothesis and conclude that the alternative hypothesis is true, or (2) not reject the null hypothesis and conclude that the null hypothesis is true. Remember that the null and alternative hypotheses are logical alternatives to one another (see Figure 5.1); rejecting H_0 means that H_a is true and not rejecting H_0 means that H_0 is true, within some margin of error in making this decision.

To clarify the idea of hypothesis testing, consider a statistics class where the room is divided in half down the middle and the grade point average of students on the left side of the room is calculated ($\overline{X}_{left}$ = 3.14) and compared with the GPA of students on the right side of the room ($\overline{X}_{right}$ = 3.12). Is the left half of the room really, truly more intelligent than the right half of the room? The answer is probably not. This difference (3.14 - 3.12 = .02) is most likely due purely to random chance because of how students happened to sit down on that particular day.

Suppose instead that the left half of the room had a GPA of $\overline{X}_{left}$ = 3.60 and the right half of the room had a GPA of $\overline{X}_{right}$ = 2.40. In this case, it is much more likely that the observed difference (3.60 - 2.40 = 1.20) is probably not due to chance but rather is a true, significant (nonchance) difference. There is something truly different about the right and left halves of the room (e.g., all the heavy partiers decided to sit on the right side of the room and stare out the window and all the Phi Beta Kappa students decided to sit on the left side of the room and pay attention). The right and left halves of the room truly represent two different groups or populations with respect to GPA.

In the first case, the observed difference (.02) was due purely to chance and not to any true difference between the two groups; the null hypothesis should not be rejected. In the second case, the observed difference (1.20) was not due to chance and was due to true differences between the groups; the null hypothesis should be rejected.

Probabilistic criteria are used to determine whether to reject the null hypothesis. Generally, researchers are more concerned about claiming that a difference or effect exists when in fact it does not (rejecting a true null hypothesis and incorrectly accepting the alternative hypothesis as true) than they are about concluding that there is no effect or difference when there actually is (not rejecting a false null hypothesis and incorrectly accepting the null hypothesis as true). Thus, very strict criteria have been established that must be met in order to reject the null hypothesis. In fact, the default assumption researchers make is that the null hypothesis is true; that is, the alternative hypothesis is considered to be false until evidence strongly suggests otherwise. If H_0 can be rejected with a great deal of certainty, then

H_a can be accepted as true with that same level of certainty since the two hypotheses are logical alternatives.

In order to reject the null hypothesis, researchers have decided that they must be at least 95% certain that the null hypothesis is false before it is rejected. Consequently, there is a 5% chance or less (probability less than .05, $p \leq .05$) that the conclusion is drawn that an effect or difference exists (accepting the alternative hypothesis) when in fact there actually is no effect (the null hypothesis actually is true). The significance level required to reject the null hypothesis (e.g., .05) is termed the *alpha level*.

Consider, for example, a new flu shot that costs $500 and is very painful to receive. How confident would you want to be that this new shot actually does prevent colds and flus before you spend the money and suffer the pain to receive it? Would you want to be 50% confident that it is effective (produces a difference in likelihood of getting the flu versus receiving nothing at all)? 75% confident? 95% confident? 99% confident? Before rejecting the null hypothesis that your likelihood of getting the flu is no different with or without the flu shot and accepting the alternative hypothesis that your likelihood of getting the flu is significantly less with the flu shot than without it, you probably would want to be very confident that you are correct in rejecting the null hypothesis.

By setting the alpha level at .05, the null hypothesis will not be rejected unless the probability that H_0 is true is $p \leq .05$, with a 95% chance that H_0 is false and the alternative hypothesis is true. Perhaps in this case, considering the money and pain involved in getting the flu shot, an even more stringent criteria might be applied such as setting the alpha level at .01. In order to reject the null hypothesis, the probability has to be $p \leq .01$ that H_0 is actually true, with a 99% chance that H_0 is false and H_a is true.

When the null hypothesis is rejected at $p \leq .05$ (or $p \leq .01$), the alternative hypothesis is accepted and the difference or effect stated in the alternative hypothesis is presumed to be true with only a $p \leq .05$ chance of being incorrect (that H_0 actually is true and was incorrectly rejected). When the null hypothesis is rejected and an effect is identified, it is called a *significant* effect because the effect or difference is assumed to be not due to chance. On the other hand, if the null hypothesis cannot be rejected at $p \leq .05$, the null hypothesis is assumed to be true (H_0 is not rejected) and any observed effect or difference is assumed to have occurred purely due to chance or random factors and is not a true effect in the population.

Of course, even using such stringent criteria as $p < .05$ and $p < .01$, there is always the possibility for an incorrect decision. Consider again the difference in GPA between the left and right sides of the statistics class. It is possible that a difference in GPA of .02 (3.14 - 3.12) in the first case actually might be indicative of a true difference in the left and right sides of the room, but the statistical decision was made that there was no difference (H_0 was not rejected). If the null hypothesis is not rejected when in fact there truly is a difference, an error occurred. Similarly, there is the possibility that a 1.20 difference in GPA (3.60 - 2.40) in the second case is due purely to chance and does not reflect true differences in the left and right sides of the room. However, the statistical decision was made that there truly was a difference (H_0 was rejected). If the null hypothesis is rejected when in fact there truly is no difference, an error was made. In general, there are two types of errors that can be made with hypothesis testing: Type I (alpha) error and Type II (beta) error.

Type I error or *alpha error* is when a true null hypothesis is incorrectly rejected. That is, the researcher claims that a difference or effect exists in the population when in fact it does not. The Type I error is equivalent to the alpha level set in testing the null hypothesis. For instance, if the null hypothesis is rejected at the $p \leq .05$ level, the alpha level used in testing this hypothesis is .05. Thus, the Type I error is less than or equal to .05. This means that the probability of incorrectly rejecting a true null hypothesis is .05 or less. There is a 5% chance or less that the observed effect is due purely to chance rather than any true difference in the population.

The second type of error that can be made is a *Type II error* or *beta error*, which occurs when a false null hypothesis is incorrectly not rejected. That is, there truly is a difference not due to chance, but the researcher does not detect this effect in hypothesis testing and so does not reject the null hypothesis when in fact it should be rejected. Type II error is a function of a variety of factors including the magnitude of the treatment effect the researcher is interested in detecting and the standard deviation of the population. Although both types of error are of concern to researchers, it is considered somewhat less problematic to not detect a true effect (Type II error) than to incorrectly claim that an effect does exist (Type I error). Type I and Type II errors can be summarized in the following figure:

		Researcher's Decision	
		Reject H_0	Do Not Reject H_0
In Reality	H_0 True	Type I Error	No Error
	H_0 False	No Error	Type II Error

FIGURE 5.2: Decisions regarding Type I and Type II errors

In general, researchers consider a .05 or less alpha level as an acceptable risk in determining whether there is a significant effect. How does one determine, then, when a difference is significant ($p \leq .05$) and when it is simply due to error, chance, or random factors? This is the fundamental notion of hypothesis testing. How far away from a mean of 82 do Professor Peterson's high school students need to score in order to conclude that those students represent a fundamentally different population than a group with a mean of 82? Is an 81 enough to conclude the high school students represent a different population? an 80? a 79? How different do Joe's review sheet and no review sheet groups need to score in order to conclude that using a review sheet causes students to score differently than not using a review sheet? Is a 1 point difference enough? 5 points? 10 points? These are questions that can be answered by the most basic statistical test used for hypothesis testing: the z-test.

The One Sample z-test

Consider Professor Peterson's question regarding the high school students enrolled in her university statistics course. Historically, the average score on her midterm exam in this class has been $\mu = 82$ with a standard deviation of $\sigma = 6$. She suspects that the high school students currently enrolled in her class are not part of this same population, so she advances the following hypothesis:

H: Students enrolled in this semester's class will score differently on the midterm exam than a mean of 82.

The null and alternative hypotheses for this problem are:

$$H_0: \mu = 82$$
$$H_a: \mu \neq 82$$

The mean midterm exam score for the 16 high school students enrolled in Professor

Peterson's statistics class was $\overline{X}$ = 78. How likely is it (what is the probability) that this sample of students who scored a 78 is part of a population with a mean of 82? Can H_0 be rejected at $p < .05$ and the conclusion drawn that this sample is part of some other population that scores different than an 82? To answer this question, one of the important distributions described in Chapter 4 becomes relevant: the sampling distribution of means. The following sampling distribution of means can be produced based on a sample size of 16, a population mean of $\mu = 82$, and a population standard deviation of $\sigma = 6$:

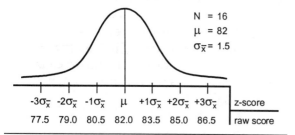

FIGURE 5.3: Sampling distribution of midterm scores

Notice that the standard deviation of the population is known in this problem, $\sigma = 6$. Using the formula from Chapter 4 (Note 1), the standard error of the mean was computed as a known value for the sampling distribution of means, $\sigma_{\overline{x}} = 1.5$.[1]

The problem Professor Peterson is attempting to solve is the following: how likely is it that a sample mean of $\overline{X} = 78$ would be obtained from a sample that is part of a population whose mean is 82? Using the sampling distribution of means and the z-score formula from Chapter 4, the raw score of 78 can be translated into a z-score as follows:

$$z = \frac{\overline{X} - \mu}{\sigma_{\overline{x}}} = \frac{78 - 82}{1.5} = -2.66$$

Applying the 68-95-99 rule, since 95% of all scores fall between ±2 standard deviations around the mean, the calculated z of -2.66 falls beyond this range. Thus, the probability of obtaining a sample mean of $\overline{X}$ = 78 from a population whose true mean is $\mu = 82$ is $p < .05$. This is a very low probability that, purely by chance, such a low mean would be obtained from a sample that is part of a population whose mean is $\mu = 82$. Instead, it is much more likely that this sample is part of some other population whose mean is not equal to 82. For this problem, then, the null hypothesis is rejected and the alternative hypothesis is determined to be true with a very small chance of having made an incorrect decision to reject H_0 (Type I error is less than .05).

To summarize this procedure for hypothesis testing, a *calculated value*, a z-score, is computed based on the observed sample mean. This calculated value is compared to a *critical value*, z = ±2.00, beyond which less than 5% of all sample means fall in the sampling distribution. If the calculated value is larger (in absolute terms) than the critical value, then the null hypothesis is rejected at $p < .05$. For this problem, since the calculated value of -2.66 was larger than the critical value of -2.00 (in absolute terms), H_0 was rejected at the $p < .05$ level. Thus, the decision rule for determining whether to reject the null hypothesis is based on whether the calculated value is larger than the critical value:

Reject H_0 ⟶ Z calculated ≥ Z critical

Do not reject H_0 ⟶ Z calculated < Z critical (accept H_0)

FIGURE 5.4: Decision rules for rejecting H_0

With hypothesis testing it is necessary to be as accurate as possible in determining whether to reject the null hypothesis. According to the 68-95-99 rule, approximately 95% of all scores fall between ±2 standard deviations around the mean. More precisely, 95% of all scores fall within ±1.96 standard deviations around the mean. Thus, ±1.96 not ±2.00 is the critical value beyond which the calculated value must fall in order to reject the null hypothesis at $p < .05$ (see Figure 5.5). Since the calculated value of -2.66 exceeds the critical value of -1.96, the correct statistical decision is to reject H_0 at the $p < .05$ level. If the calculated value is exactly equal to the critical value (±1.96), then the null hypothesis is rejected at $p = .05$. This is the most basic form of hypothesis testing and is called the *one-sample z-test* because it involves comparing one sample mean to some known population value and uses z-scores to determine whether to reject the null hypothesis.

Notice that because the alternative hypothesis was nondirectional, hypothesis testing was conducted with respect to both the left and right tails of the sampling distribution. That is, the null hypothesis would have been rejected if the high school students scored either beyond +1.96 standard deviations above the mean in the upper 2.5% of the distribution or beyond -1.96 standard deviations below the mean in the lower 2.5% of the distribution. Such a nondirectional test is called *two-tailed* because both tails of the sampling distribution are considered in determining whether to reject the null hypothesis.

In this example, Professor Peterson rejected the null hypothesis at $p < .05$ and concluded that her sample of high school students is not part of a population whose average midterm exam score is $\mu = 82$, with less than a 5% chance of being wrong in this decision (Type I error is less than .05). Although researchers consider the .05 significance level acceptable in determining whether to reject the null hypothesis, rejecting at a more stringent probability level is certainly better, if possible, since the likelihood of making an incorrect decision in rejecting H_0 is lower (i.e., Type I error is

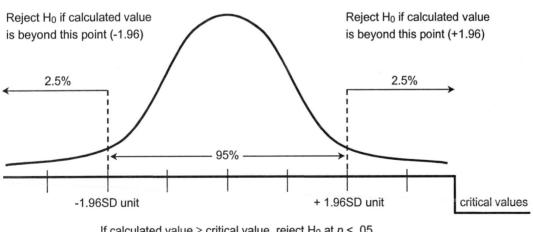

If calculated value ≥ critical value, reject H_0 at $p < .05$

If calculated value < critical value, do not reject H_0

FIGURE 5.5: Rejecting H_0 at $p < .05$, 2-tailed test

lower). With the 68-95-99 rule, approximately 99% of all scores fall between ±3 standard deviations around the mean. More precisely, 99% of all scores fall within ±2.58 standard deviations of the mean. Thus, if a calculated value falls beyond the critical value of ±2.58 for a two-tailed test, the null hypothesis can be rejected at $p < .01$ (see Figure 5.6).

Professor Peterson's calculated value was $z = -2.66$ which is larger (in absolute terms) than the critical value of $z = -2.58$. Thus, she can be even more confident about her decision to reject the null hypothesis by using the .01 alpha level. H_0 is rejected at $p < .01$ and the researcher is 99% confident that the high school students in her class are from a different population than one whose average midterm exam score is $\mu = 82$. Notice that, again, because this was conducted as a two-tailed test, Professor Peterson could have rejected H_0 if her calculated value was above +2.58 (in the upper 0.5% of the sampling distribution) or below -2.58 (in the lower 0.5% of the sampling distribution). If the calculated value was

exactly equal to the critical value of +2.58 or -2.58, then the null hypothesis is rejected at $p = .01$. Notably, the .05 and .01 alpha levels are most common, but any alpha level can be used for hypothesis testing. For instance, a researcher might reject H_0 at $p = .027$, which is better than $p < .05$ but not as good as $p < .01$. The Type I error in this example exactly equals .027; there is a 2.7% chance H_0 is incorrectly rejected. When statistical tests are performed on the computer, the exact alpha level typically is given.

Professor Peterson's problem above involved a nondirectional, two-tailed hypothesis test. Suppose that, instead of hypothesizing that the students in her class were different from a population whose mean was $\mu = 82$, Professor Peterson made the following directional prediction:

H: Students enrolled in this semester's class will score lower on the midterm exam than a mean of 82.

In this case, the null and alternative hypothe-

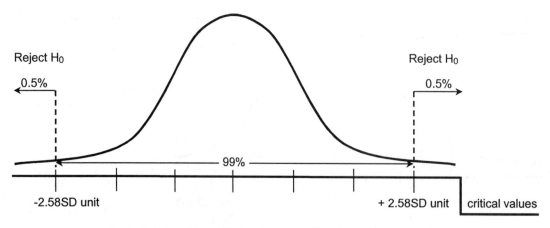

If calculated value ≥ critical value, reject H_0 at $p < .01$

If calculated value < critical value, do not reject H_0

FIGURE 5.6: Rejecting H_0 at $p < .01$, 2-tailed test

ses for this problem are:

$$H_0: \mu \geq 82$$
$$H_a: \mu < 82$$

Hypothesis testing for this problem proceeds in much the same way as it did with the nondirectional, two-tailed test. A calculated value is compared with a critical value and the null hypothesis is rejected if the calculated value exceeds the critical value. However, there are two major differences between a directional and a nondirectional hypothesis test. First, because a directional prediction was advanced, only means that are consistent with the alternative hypothesis are considered. In this example, only means smaller than 82 are of interest because this was the researcher's hypothesis. A sample mean larger than 82, no matter how much larger, must automatically lead to not rejecting the null hypothesis. Thus, the first step in conducting a directional test is to verify that the sample mean is in the hypothesized direction. If it is not, the null hypothesis is automatically not rejected.

Since only sample means falling in the hypothesized direction are considered, a second major difference of a directional vs. a nondirectional test is that only the left or the right tail of the sampling distribution is utilized in testing the null hypothesis, whichever is consistent with the alternative hypothesis. For instance, Professor Peterson hypothesized that the high school students would score below an 82. Consequently, only the left tail of the sampling distribution, corresponding with negative z-scores, is considered in hypothesis testing since only raw scores below 82 can produce negative z-scores. Any raw score above 82 will produce a positive z-score and lead to automatic nonrejection of H_0. Because we are now looking at only one tail of the sampling distribution, the 5% error that was previously distributed in both the left and right tails (2.5% error in each tail) is now con-

centrated in only the left or right tail.

The critical value is determined by that z-score which excludes the outermost 5% of the distribution in either the left or the right tail. In this example, only the left tail, corresponding to negative z-scores, is being considered. Thus, the critical value is that z-score below which 5% of all scores fall and above which 95% of all scores fall. This critical value is -1.65. Given that a z-score of -1.96 excludes the bottommost 2.5% of the sampling distribution, it should make sense that a smaller z-value (in absolute terms), -1.65, excludes a larger percentage of the distribution (5%). Such a directional test is called *one-tailed* because only the left or right tail of the sampling distribution is considered in determining whether to reject the null hypothesis.

For the current problem, if the calculated value exceeds the critical value of -1.65, being certain that the sample mean falls in the predicted direction, then the null hypothesis is rejected at $p < .05$. If the calculated value equals -1.65, H_0 is rejected at $p = .05$. As previously computed, the z-score corresponding with a raw score of 78 for this problem is -2.66. Since 78 is less than 82, consistent with the alternative hypothesis, and since the calculated value of -2.66 is larger (in absolute terms) than the critical value of -1.65, H_0 is rejected at $p < .05$. Had the alternative hypothesis been that the mean for the population of which this sample is a part is larger than 82, then only the right tail of the sampling distribution, corresponding with positive z-scores, would be considered.

In sum, conducting a directional, one-tailed test involves: (1) verifying that the observed mean is in the predicted direction, consistent with the alternative hypothesis, and (2) examining only the left or right tail of the sampling distribution, whichever is appropriate, to determine the critical value and conduct the hypothesis test. At the .05 level, hypothesis testing for the one-tailed test can be visualized as shown in Figure 5.7.

As with the two-tailed test, rejecting at a lower probability level is preferable, if possible, because the likelihood of making an incorrect decision (committing a Type I error) in rejecting H_0 is smaller. Since Professor Peterson rejected H_0 at the $p < .05$ level, the next step is to determine if she can be even more than 95% certain that her decision is correct by comparing the calculated value to the critical value at the $p < .01$ level. The critical value that excludes the outermost 1% of the distribution in either the left or the right tail is +2.33 or -2.33.

Since this problem involves only the left tail, the critical value used is -2.33. Since the calculated value of -2.66 exceeds the critical value of -2.33 (in absolute terms), Professor Peterson can reject H_0 at the $p < .01$ level and be 99% confident she is making the correct decision. Again, if the calculated value exactly equals the critical value of -2.33, H_0 is rejected at $p = .01$. Critical values for the .01 significance level with a one-tailed, directional test can be visualized as shown in Figure 5.8.

So what is the advantage in conducting a one-tailed test over a two-tailed test, since in this example both tests led to the same statisti-

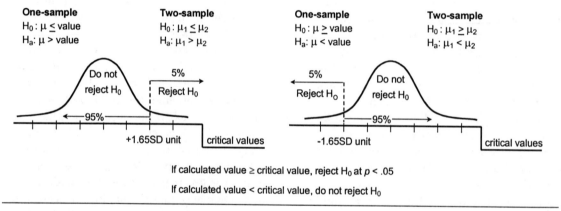

FIGURE 5.7: Rejecting H_0 at $p < .05$, 1-tailed test

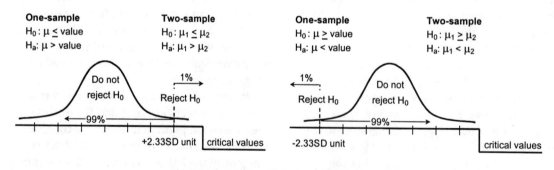

FIGURE 5.8: Rejecting H_0 at $p < .01$, 1-tailed test

cal decision: reject H_0 at $p < .01$? To answer this question, consider if the statistics class had an observed mean of $\overline{X} = 79.5$. This raw score corresponds with a calculated z-score of -1.66. The statistical decision for this problem would be to not reject H_0 if this were conducted as a two-tailed test (since -1.66 is not larger than -1.96, in absolute terms), but the statistical decision would be to reject H_0 at $p < .05$ if this were conducted as a one-tailed test (since -1.66 is larger than -1.65 in absolute terms). Thus, a one-tailed test has greater ability to reject the null hypothesis than does a two-tailed test, a concept termed *power*.

Researchers typically are interested in detecting significant differences, so having a powerful statistical test is very important. However, the power that is gained by use of a one-tailed rather than a two-tailed test comes with a price: the ability to test differences in the opposite than predicted direction, no matter how large. Had this example problem been conducted using a one-tailed test (H_a: $\mu < 82$) and the statistics class had a mean of $\overline{X} = 99$, the only decision would be to not reject the null hypothesis since the sample mean is not in the hypothesized direction. As a two-tailed test, however, this effect would have been highly significant. Thus, a researcher needs to carefully consider whether to conduct the statistical test as one-tailed or two-tailed. Generally, if a directional prediction is advanced, a one-tailed test is appropriate.

The Two-Sample z-test

Just as the z-test was used to determine if Professor Peterson's statistics class is part of a population whose mean midterm exam score is $\mu = 82$, so too can the z-test be used to determine if Joe's two experimental groups are part of the same population. This type of hypothesis test is called a *two-sample z-test* because the means for two samples are being compared to

each other rather than the mean from one sample being compared to a known population value. The two-sample z-test is conducted in virtually an identical way to the one-sample z-test, except that instead of referring to the sampling distribution of means for testing the null hypothesis, the sampling distribution of differences described in Chapter 4 is used.

Joe advanced the following nondirectional research hypothesis:

H: Students who use the review sheet to study will perform differently on the exam than will students who do not use the review sheet to study.

The corresponding null and alternative hypotheses for this problem are:

$$H_0:\ \mu_{RevSh} = \mu_{NoRevSh}$$
$$H_a:\ \mu_{RevSh} \neq \mu_{NoRevSh}$$

The six students Joe randomly assigned to use the review sheet to study for the exam achieved a mean score on the midterm of $\overline{X}_{RevSh} = 88$ and the six students Joe randomly assigned not to use the review sheet achieved an average of $\overline{X}_{NoRevSh} = 80$ on the midterm exam. Is this difference (88 - 80 = 8 points) large enough to conclude with greater than 95% certainty that these two groups represent different populations? Joe talks to Professor Peterson and finds out that the average score for students who have ever taken this statistics class is $\mu = 82$ with a standard deviation of $\sigma = 6$. Based on these values in the population and a sample size of $N = 6$, Joe produces the distribution of differences shown in Table 5.9.

Again, notice for this problem that the standard deviation of midterm exam scores is known for the population, $\sigma = 6$. Using the formula in Chapter 4 (Note 2), the standard error of the difference is computed as $\sigma_{diff} = 3.5$.[2]

Joe is now interested in answering the following question: do the two groups in his study represent the same population with the same mean? Based on the sampling distribution of differences, a z-score can be calculated for the observed difference in means (8 points) from Joe's study:

$$z = \frac{\left(\overline{X}_1 - \overline{X}_2\right) - \mu_{\overline{X}_1 - \overline{X}_2}}{\sigma_{\overline{X}_1 - \overline{X}_2}} = \frac{(88 - 80) - 0}{3.5} = +2.29$$

Is this calculated z-score large enough to reject the null hypothesis and conclude there is a significant difference in means? Since this is a two-tailed test, the calculated value of +2.29 must exceed the critical value of ±1.96 in order to reject H_0 at $p < .05$, which it does (see Figure 5.5). Can the null hypothesis be rejected at the .01 level? Since the calculated value of +2.29 is not larger than the critical value of ±2.58, H_0 cannot be rejected at $p < .01$ (see Figure 5.6). Thus, the final statistical decision is to reject H_0 at the $p < .05$ level and conclude that the two groups do represent different populations with a Type I error or chance of being wrong in rejecting H_0 of less than .05.

This problem could have been conducted as a one-tailed z-test had Joe advanced a directional hypothesis:

H: Students who use the review sheet to study will perform better on the exam than will students who do not use the review sheet to study.

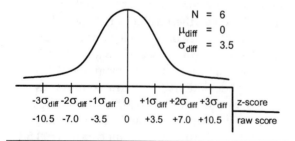

FIGURE 5.9: Distribution of differences for midterm scores

The null and alternative hypotheses for this problem are:

$$H_0: \mu_{RevSh} \leq \mu_{NoRevSh}$$
$$H_a: \mu_{RevSh} > \mu_{NoRevSh}$$

With the one-tailed z-test, the means must first be examined to ensure that they are in the hypothesized direction. Since the review sheet mean of $\overline{X}_{RevSh} = 88$ is indeed larger than the no review sheet mean of $\overline{X}_{NoRevSh} = 80$, Joe can proceed to test the null hypothesis using the right tail of the sampling distribution of differences (only positive z-scores are of interest in this problem). And, since the calculated value of +2.29 exceeds the critical value of +1.65, Joe can reject H_0 at the $p < .05$ level (see Figure 5.7). However, the calculated value of +2.29 does not exceed the critical value of +2.33 at the .01 level, so H_0 cannot be rejected at $p < .01$ (see Figure 5.8). The final statistical decision is to reject H_0 at $p < .05$ and conclude that using the review sheet causes students to score significantly higher on the midterm exam than not using the review sheet, with the probability of making a Type I error of less than .05.

Summary

Researchers are interested in testing hypotheses, which are formal statements about an effect or phenomenon. Such hypotheses are called research hypotheses because they are the researcher's statements about what will occur or is true about a phenomenon. Hypothesis testing refers to assessing two logical alternatives to determine which one is most likely to be true: the null hypothesis, H_0 (no difference or effect exists with respect to the phenomenon) vs. the alternative hypothesis, H_a (some difference or effect exists). Statistical hypothesis testing is always conducted with respect to the null hypothesis which is assumed to be true unless there is a very small probability that it is not true. If the probability that a null hypothesis is true is very small ($p \leq .05$), then H_0 is rejected and H_a is concluded to be true, with the chance of being wrong in this decision equal to the alpha level (called Type I error). If the probability that the null hypothesis is true is not very small ($p > .05$), then H_0 is not rejected and H_0 is concluded to be true, with some chance of being wrong in this decision (called Type II error).

When one sample mean is compared to a known population value to determine if the sample is part of the same population whose mean value is given, the appropriate statistical test is the one-sample z-test using the sampling distribution of means. When two sample means are compared to each other to determine if the samples represent the same population with the same mean, the appropriate statistical test is the two-sample z-test using the sampling distribution of differences.

The z-test involves calculating a z-value based on the observed sample mean(s) and comparing this calculated value to a critical z-value beyond which 5% (or 1%) or less of all z-scores fall. If the calculated value is greater than or equal to the critical value, the null hypothesis is rejected and a significant effect or difference is concluded to exist. When a nondirectional hypothesis is advanced, a two-tailed z-test is conducted using critical values in both the left and right tails of the sampling distribution. When a directional hypothesis is advanced, a one-tailed z-test is employed using critical values in either the left or the right tail of the sampling distribution, whichever is consistent with the alternative hypothesis. A one-tailed test is more powerful than a two-tailed test because the critical values needed to reject H_0 are lower with a one-tailed test making it easier to reject the null hypothesis and conclude that a significant effect exists.

Key Terms

- alpha level
- alternative hypothesis (H_a)
- calculated value
- critical value
- directional hypothesis
- hypothesis
- nondirectional hypothesis
- null hypothesis (H_0)
- one-sample z-test
- one-tailed test
- power
- research hypothesis
- significance
- two-sample z-test
- two-tailed test
- Type I (alpha) error
- Type II (beta) error

Problems

1. Define the null hypothesis (H_0) and the alternative hypothesis (H_a).
2. Which hypothesis (*null* or *alternative*) is usually the researcher's prediction (i.e., the research hypothesis)?
3. Which hypothesis (*null* or *alternative*) is tested statistically?
4. For each of the following symbolic representations, state which hypothesis (*null* or *alternative*) is represented below. In addition, state which statistical test is relevant (*one-tailed* or *two-tailed*):
   a. $\mu_1 > \mu_2$
   b. $\mu \neq 100$
   c. $\mu_1 \leq \mu_2$
   d. $\mu < 50$
   e. $\mu_1 = \mu_2$
   f. $\mu \geq 5$
5. For each of the following, indicate whether

the statement represents a null hypothesis or an alternative hypothesis:

a. Women will be more likely to show support to a distressed stranger than will men.

b. There will be no difference between younger and older children's hand-eye coordination.

c. Cartoons will have more than 25 violent acts on average per 30 minute program.

d. College seniors will express a different opinion on the issue of a tuition increase than will college freshman.

e. There will be fewer sensational stories published in the New York Times than in the Washington Post.

f. Residents of New York City will have the same mean family income as the national average of $30,000 per year.

g. There will be no difference among employees' and managers' knowledge of company goals.

6. For each of the following, formulate an appropriate null hypothesis and alternative hypothesis. State each hypothesis both verbally and symbolically:

a. A researcher wants to examine whether there is a difference between university students' and professors' preferences for a semester system.

b. A researcher wants to determine whether families living in poverty have more than the national average of 2.5 children.

c. A researcher wants to examine whether there is a difference in the number of crimes committed by men versus women.

d. A researcher wishes to determine if students at private universities assume college loan debt that is different from the $15,000 which public university students have.

7. For questions 5a-g and 6a-d, identify whether a one-sample or two-sample z-test should be conducted for hypothesis testing.

8. For each of the following pairs of weather forecasts, identify which weather condition is the *least* likely to occur (the probability values represent how likely it is that the weather condition will occur)?

a. rain, $p = .08$ or snow, $p = .01$

b. windy, $p = .45$ or overcast, $p = .25$

c. foggy, $p = .50$ or sunshine, $p = .80$

9. For each of the following sets of three horses, identify which horse is *most* likely to win its race (the probability value represents the likelihood of that horse winning)?

a. Lucky Shot, $p = .44$; Royal Blue, $p = .12$; French Admiral, $p = .51$

b. Nobility, $p = .25$; Sapphire, $p = .70$; Gone with the Wind, $p = .68$

c. Majestic Prince, $p = .99$; Good Fortune, $p = .81$; Victory, $p = .40$

10. What are the two most common alpha levels used in hypothesis testing? Describe what these alpha levels mean.

11. Which test (*one-tailed* or *two-tailed*) should be conducted if the researcher cannot predict the direction of the effect?

12. Which test (*one-tailed* or *two-tailed*) should be conducted if the researcher can predict the direction of the effect?

13. For each of the following hypotheses indicate whether a one-tailed or a two-tailed z-test should be conducted:

a. Students with GPAs over 3.5 will study more hours than will students with GPAs below 3.5.

b. There will be a difference in the number of freeway deaths on highways where the speed limit is 55 mph compared to freeways where the speed limit is 65 mph.

c. Voters will be more likely to vote for

male political candidates than for female political candidates.

d. Adults aged 21-30 will drink a different number of cups of coffee per day than the national average of 2 cups.

14. What are the critical values for deciding whether to reject the null hypothesis for a normal sampling distribution when the following z-tests are conducted:
   a. two-tailed z-test at the $p < .05$ level
   b. two-tailed z-test at the $p < .01$ level
   c. one-tailed z-test at the $p < .05$ level
   d. one-tailed z-test at the $p < .01$ level

15. When the calculated value is larger than the critical value the researcher should (*reject* or *not reject*) the null hypothesis.

16. For each of the following calculated z-scores, indicate whether the null hypothesis should be rejected or not rejected assuming a $p < .05$ rejection criterion and a two-tailed hypothesis:
   a. +1.65
   b. -2.01
   c. +1.50
   d. +2.68
   e. +1.33
   f. -0.75
   g. -3.00

17. For each of the following z-scores, indicate whether the null hypothesis should be rejected or not rejected assuming a $p < .05$ rejection criterion and a one-tailed hypothesis such that H_a: $\mu > 100$ or H_a: $\mu_1 > \mu_2$:
   a. +1.85
   b. -0.50
   c. -4.00
   d. +2.00
   e. +0.75
   f. -1.90
   g. +1.75

18. Which error is committed when the researcher rejects the null hypothesis when in fact it should have not been rejected

(i.e., when H_0 is really true)?

19. If a researcher concludes that two samples are really from the same population (not significantly different from one another) when in fact the two samples really are from different populations, which error has the researcher committed?

20. What is the Type I error if the null hypothesis is rejected at the $p < .05$ level? At the $p < .01$ level?

21. Greater power means that the researcher has (*more* or *less*) ability to reject the null hypothesis?

22. A principal at a local high school believes students at his school are more intelligent, on average, than the general population, which has a known mean IQ score of $\mu = 100$ with a standard deviation of $\sigma = 15$. The principal draws a random sample of 25 students from his high school and finds that their mean IQ is $\overline{X} = 108$. With a sample size of $N = 25$ and a population standard deviation of $\sigma = 15$, the standard error of the mean for this problem is $\sigma_{\overline{X}} = 3$. Formulate the appropriate null and alternative hypotheses for this problem and conduct a z-test to determine whether H_0 should be rejected.

23. A principal at another high school assumes that his students' intelligence, in general, is not different from the average population with a mean IQ score of $\mu = 100$ with a standard deviation of $\sigma = 15$. However, she is interested in whether a new teaching method she has read about causes students to obtain different IQ scores compared with using the old, standard method of teaching. The principal obtains a random sample of 200 students from her school and randomly assigns half of them to classes utilizing the new teaching method whereas the other 100 students are randomly assigned to classes using the standard teaching

method. At the end of the school year, she gives all 200 students an IQ test and obtains the following means: $\overline{X}_{NewMethod}$ = 102 ; $\overline{X}_{OldMethod}$ = 99. Based on a sample size of N = 100 and a population standard deviation of σ = 15, the standard error of the difference for this problem is σ_{diff} = 2.12. Formulate the appropriate null and alternative hypotheses for this problem and conduct a z-test to determine whether H_0 should be rejected.

Notes

1 Based on the formula for computing the standard error of the mean:

$$\sigma_{\overline{X}} = \frac{\sigma}{\sqrt{N}} = \frac{6}{\sqrt{16}} = \frac{6}{4} = 1.5$$

2 Based on the formula for computing the standard error of the difference:

$$\sigma_{diff} = \sqrt{\frac{\sigma^2}{n_1} + \frac{\sigma^2}{n_2}} = \sqrt{\frac{6^2}{6} + \frac{6^2}{6}} = \sqrt{\frac{36}{6} + \frac{36}{6}} = \sqrt{6+6} = \sqrt{12} = 3.5$$

Computer Section

Devising Hypotheses

Because hypothesis testing is one of the most critical concepts in statistics, the computer section of this chapter will focus on generating hypotheses from the instructional technology study introduced in Chapter 2. Beginning with the statistical test covered in the next chapter (Chapter 6: the t-test), the computer will be used to test hypotheses. Thus, it is essential to understand the nature of research hypotheses and the formulation of the corresponding null and alternative hypotheses used in statistical hypothesis testing.

As an example of formulating hypotheses for a study, consider a researcher who wishes to examine the use of music therapy as a method for stress management. The researcher recruits 30 individuals to participate in his study. What types of hypotheses could be formulated to test the researcher's question of interest?

On one hand, a nondirectional research hypothesis such as the following could be generated:

H: There will be a difference in average stress levels between people who participate in a music therapy program vs. those who do not.

The corresponding null and alternative hypotheses, where μ represents average level of stress, are:

$$H_0: \mu_{Music} = \mu_{NoMusic}$$
$$H_a: \mu_{Music} \neq \mu_{NoMusic}$$

On the other hand, a directional research hypothesis also could be advanced:

H: People exposed to music therapy will experience less stress than will those not exposed to music therapy.

The corresponding null and alternative hypotheses are:

$$H_0: \mu_{Music} \geq \mu_{NoMusic}$$
$$H_a: \mu_{Music} < \mu_{NoMusic}$$

Computer Problems

Note: Reread the instructional technology study introduced in Chapter 2 and refer to the student evaluation survey as you answer the following questions.

1. Devise two research hypotheses, one directional and one nondirectional, pertaining to differences that might be expected between those students in the live vs. mediated classrooms. For each research hypothesis, provide the corresponding null and alternative hypotheses.
2. Devise two research hypotheses, one directional and one nondirectional, pertaining to differences that might be expected between those students who have the male vs. female instructors. For each research hypothesis, provide the corresponding null and alternative hypotheses.

Chapter 6 ❖ The t-test

From z to t

The statistical test covered in this chapter, the t-test, is a very simple extension of the z-test discussed in Chapter 5. In fact, the t-test is used to answer the same types of questions as the z-test. That is, does a particular sample represent a population with a given mean? Do two samples represent the same population with the same mean? Although the t-test can be used to solve either one- or two-sample problems, the most common application of the t-test is to determine if two groups differ significantly from one another. Thus, in this chapter, we will focus only on the two-sample t-test.

The two-sample situation involves the comparison of two groups, each of which is considered to be one of two levels of a single independent variable. For instance, in the review sheet example presented in the previous chapter, there was one independent variable, presence of a review sheet, with two levels: review sheet or no review sheet. One group of subjects received the review sheet and the other group did not receive the review sheet. Both the two-sample z-test and the two-sample t-test presented in this chapter involve a single independent variable with two levels. The dependent variable (e.g., exam score) must be measured at the interval- or ratio-level in order to calculate means for each of the two groups.

With the z-test, a critical assumption necessary in conducting the statistical test is that the standard deviation in the population is known. Recall in the example discussed in the prior chapter that Professor Peterson had been administering her midterm exam for many years in her statistics class. As a result, she knew the exact mean ($\mu = 82$) and standard deviation ($\sigma = 6$) in the population of students. The standard intelligence or IQ test is another example where the population standard deviation is known, $\sigma = 15$ IQ points. However, it is highly unusual to know the exact standard deviation in a population, since this would involve having data on most or all members of the population. Without knowledge of the exact standard deviation in the population, an exact sampling distribution of differences (a z-distribution) cannot be created. Consequently, the z-test cannot be conducted and an alternative statistical procedure called the t-test must be used. The two-sample *t-test* is similar to the two-sample z-test in that it involves testing the difference between two group means except that the population standard deviation is not a known value.

When the standard deviation of the population (σ) is unknown, the standard deviation from the two samples, s_1 and s_2, are used to estimate the unknown population standard deviation ("s" refers to the unbiased sample standard deviation, as discussed in Chapter 3). These sample estimates of the population standard deviation are used to compute an estimated *standard error of the difference*, s_{diff}. Suppose Joe conducts the same review sheet experiment described in Chapter 5 except that the population standard deviation is unknown. Joe hypothesizes that students who use the review sheet will score differently than will those who do not use the review sheet (a nondirectional prediction). A total of $N = 20$ subjects participate in his study, 10 in each group (n_{RevSh} = 10; $n_{NoRevSh}$ = 10).[1] At the end of the class, all students take an exam to measure their comprehension of the course material. The group that used the review sheet had a mean of $\overline{X}_{RevSh}$ = 86 on the exam with a standard deviation of s_{RevSh} = 4; the group that did not use the review sheet had a mean of $\overline{X}_{NoRevSh}$ = 79 with a standard deviation of $s_{NoRevSh}$ = 5. Based on the two unbiased sample standard deviations obtained, an estimate (s_{diff}) of the true standard error of the difference (σ_{diff}) is computed: s_{diff} = 2.02.[2]

With this estimate for the standard error of the difference, a standardized score for the difference between the two sample means can be produced, just as was done with the z-test. Recall that to conduct the two-sample z-test, the actual difference between two sample means was standardized by dividing the difference in means by the standard error of the difference, yielding a z-score on the distribution of differences:

$$z = \frac{\left(\overline{X}_1 - \overline{X}_2\right) - 0}{\sigma_{diff}} = \frac{\overline{X}_1 - \overline{X}_2}{\sigma_{diff}}$$

Similarly, when the standard error of the difference is unknown, a standardized score can still be produced using the same z-score formula except substituting the estimated standard error of the difference (s_{diff}) for the actual standard error of the difference (σ_{diff}). To distinguish this latter standardized score from a z-score produced with a known standard error of the difference, the standardized score based on the estimated standard error of the difference is referred to as a *t-score*:

$$t = \frac{\left(\overline{X}_1 - \overline{X}_2\right) - 0}{s_{diff}} = \frac{\overline{X}_1 - \overline{X}_2}{s_{diff}}$$

For Joe's review sheet problem, the t-score is

calculated as follows:

$$t = \frac{\left(\overline{X}_{RevSh} - \overline{X}_{NoRevSh}\right) - 0}{s_{diff}} = \frac{86 - 79}{2.02} = 3.47$$

Once a t-score is calculated, representing the standardized difference between two sample means, this score must be compared with a critical value in order to decide whether to reject the null hypothesis and conclude that the two groups really are significantly different from one another. Recall that with the z-test, the calculated z-score was compared with a critical z-value based on excluding the outermost 95% or 99% of the z-distribution (a distribution of differences). With a t-score, the critical value cannot be based on the z-distribution because the z-distribution is derived from the actual standard error of the difference. Instead, the critical values are based on a series of distributions that use the estimated standard error of the difference and are known as t-distributions.

The t-distributions

Once an estimated standard error of the difference is calculated, a distribution of differences can be created. However, the resulting distribution of differences produced with the estimated standard error of the difference is not exactly the same shape as the distribution of differences produced with the actual standard error of the difference (the z-distribution). The problem with estimating the standard error of the difference from sample standard deviations rather than using a known population standard deviation is that the resulting sampling distribution is not normally distributed, particularly when small samples are involved. That is, the sampling distribution of differences created using sample standard deviations is somewhat flatter in shape (platykurtic) compared to a normal distribution. Sampling distributions based on sample standard deviations do not exhibit the important property of normal distributions in which the range has a constant relationship with the standard deviation (R ≈ 6SD). The sampling distribution obtained using an estimated standard error of the difference is called a *t-distribution* rather than a z-distribution since it is not normally distributed:

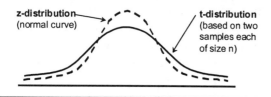

FIGURE 6.1: z-distribution vs. t-distribution

In fact, there is not a single t-distribution for all sample sizes like there is one z-distribution for all sample sizes. Rather, there are many t-distributions possible, depending upon the sample sizes used in computing the standard error of the difference. The smaller the sample sizes are, the flatter the t-distribution is; the larger the sample sizes are, the more the t-distribution approaches a normal distribution. Once the samples used to estimate the standard error of the difference are fairly large (e.g., several hundred observations per sample), the samples themselves are fairly representative of the larger population. Consequently, the t-distribution produced from large sample estimates will very closely approximate the z-distribution. Figure 6.2 provides examples of several t-distributions for different size samples compared with the z-distribution. Notice that the distribution of differences that was created using two samples each of size n = 10 is quite flat and spread out (i.e., platykurtic). The t-distribution created using two samples of size n = 20 each and n = 50 each are closer in shape to the normal distribution. A

t-distribution with several hundred cases per sample yields a t-distribution that is shaped virtually identically to the z-distribution.

To help understand why the t-distribution more closely approximates the z-distribution as sample sizes increase, consider two t-distributions created with samples of two different sizes: n = 2 each and n = 10 each. As discussed above, the t-distribution created with samples of size n = 2 will be less like the normal curve (more platykurtic) than will the t-distribution based on samples of size of n = 10. That is, the range and standard error of the difference of the t-distribution using samples of size n = 2 will be larger (the distribution will be more spread out) than will the range and standard error of the difference of the t-distribution with samples of size n = 10.

Why will the range and standard deviation be larger with smaller sample sizes, yielding a flatter distribution of differences? To help conceptualize this answer, recall that the theoretical distribution of differences is a plot of an infinite number of differences between sample means based on samples of some particular size drawn randomly from the same population. Consider a major league baseball player, Bob, who plays for the Anaheim Angels and weighs 425 pounds. If a distribution of differences is created using samples of size n = 2, the following difference might be created when

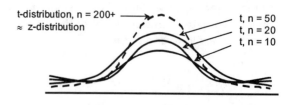

FIGURE 6.2: t-distributions with increasing sample size

Bob is included in one of the samples:

Sample One		Sample Two	
Player	Weight	Player	Weight
Bob	425 lbs.	Brad	235 lbs.
Rich	215	Art	200
$\overline{X}_1 =$	320	$\overline{X}_2 =$	217.5

The difference between these two sample means is $d = \overline{X}_1 - \overline{X}_2 = 320 - 217.5 = 102.5$. Notice that a player with a very extreme weight (Bob) has a large impact on the mean for a sample with a small size such as n = 2. Such extreme individual scores, therefore, will produce rather large differences between sample means (e.g., d = 102.5). These large differences when graphed onto a distribution of differences will yield a very spread out, flat distribution of differences with a relatively large standard error of the difference.

In contrast, consider how the distribution of differences would be shaped if extreme scores such as Bob's were averaged in with many other scores using larger sample sizes such as n = 10:

Sample One		Sample Two	
Player	Weight	Player	Weight
Bob	425 lbs.	Brad	235 lbs.
Rich	215	Art	200
Alec	175	B.B.	265
Chris	220	Blake	170
Andy	235	Randy	225
Mike	210	Kalid	230
Ben	240	James	215
Walt	210	Achim	215
Will	190	Calvin	220
Herb	200	Bud	205
$\overline{X}_1 =$	232	$\overline{X}_2 =$	218

The difference between these two sample

means is much smaller: d = 232 - 218 = 14. A graph of the differences between sample means produced using a larger sample size such as n = 10 will produce much smaller differences because extreme scores have less impact on sample means. Thus, the resulting distribution of differences will be more closely shaped to the normal distribution as sample size increases.

Critical Values and the t-distributions

Recall that conducting the z-test involved comparing the calculated z-score to a critical z-value which excluded the outermost 95% or 99% of the z-distribution. For example, in order to reject the null hypothesis or hypothesis of no difference at the $p < .05$ level, the calculated z-score needed to be larger than the critical z-score of ±1.96:[4]

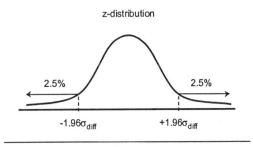

z-distribution

FIGURE 6.3: Reject H_0 at $p < .05$, two-tailed with the z-distribution

The t-test is conducted exactly the same way: a calculated t-score is compared with a critical t-value in order to determine whether H_0 should be rejected. These critical t-values are those t-scores which exclude the outermost 5% or 1% of the t-distribution that is the distribution of differences for the size of the samples being compared.[3] The appropriate t-distribution must be used to determine the critical values rather than the z-distribution because use of the critical z-values would yield too liberal of a test, particularly with small sample sizes. That is, critical z-values of ±1.96 exclude the outermost 5% of the z-distribution, but for t-distributions based on small sample sizes, critical values of ±1.96 exclude more than the outermost 5% of the t-distribution. Thus, using the critical z-values for a t-test might incorrectly lead to rejection of H_0 at $p < .05$ when in fact the probability level is .08, .10, or even higher.

To help clarify the error with using critical z-values for a t-test problem, consider the following diagram:

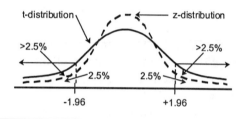

FIGURE 6.4: Exclusion regions for a z-distribution and t-distribution based on a critical value of ±1.96

Critical values of ±1.96 exclude the outermost 5% of the z-distribution, but these same values exclude more than the outermost 5% of t-distributions. And, the smaller the sample size the more of the t-distribution is excluded by these critical values. How, then, can one conduct a t-test at the .05 or .01 levels, which is common for statistical hypothesis testing? The answer may be obvious by looking at Figure 6.4. If ±1.96 excludes the outermost 5% of the z-distribution, then the critical values for the t-test will be whatever t-values exclude the outermost 5% of the appropriate t-distribution. For instance, with a very small sample size, such as n = 2 per sample, the critical values needed to exclude the outermost 5% of the relevant t-distribution are ±4.303:

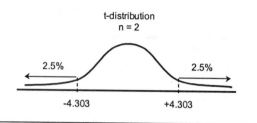

FIGURE 6.5: Critical values to reject H_0 with t-distribution based on samples of size n=2

Notice in Figure 6.5 how much more difficult it is to reject H_0 with a t-distribution based on samples of size n = 2 each than it is to reject H_0 using the z-distribution. A calculated z-score of larger than ±1.96 is sufficient to reject H_0 at $p < .05$ with the z-distribution whereas a t-score larger than ±4.303 is needed in order to reject H_0 at $p < .05$ with a t-distribution based on samples of size n = 2.

As the sample sizes increase and the t-distributions come closer and closer to the z-distribution (normal), the critical values needed to reject H_0 gets smaller and smaller, approaching the critical z-values (e.g., ±1.96 for a two-tailed hypothesis test at $p < .05$). For instance, a t-distribution based on samples of size n = 10 each looks like the following:

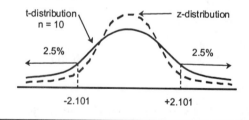

FIGURE 6.6: Critical values to reject H_0 with t-distribution based on samples of size n=10

With a t-distribution based on two samples of size n = 10, the critical values needed to reject H_0 is ±2.101, which is closer to the critical z-values of ±1.96 than were the critical values of ±4.303 with a t-distribution based on two samples of size n = 2.

Since the critical values needed in order to reject H_0 with the t-test get smaller as the sample size increases, a large sample t-test is more powerful than a small sample t-test. Recall from Chapter 5 that power refers to the ability to reject H_0. We discussed another way to increase the power of a z-test (or a t-test): conduct a one-tailed test rather than a two-tailed test because the critical value needed to reject H_0 is lower with a one-tailed test. Similarly, the critical value needed to reject H_0 with a t-test is lower with large sample sizes, yielding a more powerful statistical test.

Degrees of Freedom, Critical Values, and the t-table

Because of the importance of the z-distribution as a standard theoretical distribution, we believe knowing the critical values for the normal curve are important, as discussed in Chapter 5 (±1.96 for a two-tailed z-test at the .05 level, ±2.58 for a two-tailed z-test at the .01 level, +1.65 or -1.65 for a one-tailed z-test at the .05 level, and +2.33 or -2.33 for a one-tailed z-test at the .01 level). However, given the large number of t-distributions, it would certainly be an unwieldy task to memorize four critical values for each t-distribution. And, what if the critical value for a probability level other than .05 or .01 is desired (e.g., .001)? Fortunately, statisticians have already addressed this question by calculating the critical values for most standard probability levels for t-distributions based on different sample sizes. These critical values are supplied in a *t-table* such as the one located in Appendix A. The t-table in this book provides the critical values at the .05 and .01 probability levels for the one-tailed and two-tailed t-tests.

One important aspect to using the t-table is the fact that it does not identify t-distributions

according to sample size (e.g., two samples of size n = 2 or n = 10 each), but rather by a related concept called degrees of freedom. Use of degrees of freedom allows greater flexibility in defining t-distributions than does sample size, such that the same t-table can be used whether conducting a one- or two-sample t-test with equal or unequal sample sizes. *Degrees of freedom* refers to how many scores are free to vary in a group of scores in order to obtain the observed mean. Consider a sample with five scores and a mean of $\overline{X} = 80$. In this situation, there are four degrees of freedom because four of the five scores can vary to be any value; however, once these four values are set, the fifth score is automatically predetermined in order to obtain the specified mean of 80. For example, consider the following four exam scores for students Ben, Sue, Johann, and Marcy:

Example One	
Ben	81
Sue	73
Johann	90
Marcy	88
Merle	?
	$\overline{X} = 80$

In order to obtain a mean of 80 there is only one possible value that Merle's score can be, and that value is 68. If Merle had any other score than 68, the mean for all five students would not equal 80. Thus, there are four degrees of freedom, or N - 1 = 5 - 1 = 4, for this problem. With a sample size of 20, there are N - 1 = 20 - 1 = 19 degrees of freedom. Thus, the formula for computing degrees of freedom in general is the total sample size (N) minus one:

$$df = N - 1$$

Because the two-sample t-test covered in

this chapter always involves two samples, a total of two degrees of freedom are lost, one for each sample. The formula for computing degrees of freedom for a two-sample t-test is the following:

$$df = (n_1 - 1) + (n_2 - 1) = N - 2$$

For instance, if a t-test is conducted with two samples each of size n = 2 (i.e., $n_1 = 2$, $n_2 = 2$), the degrees of freedom for this problem are $df = (n_1 - 1) + (n_2 - 1) = (2 - 1) + (2 - 1) = 1 + 1 = 2$ degrees of freedom. Alternatively, this same value can be calculated by subtracting 2 (one df lost for each sample) from the total number of subjects in the study: $df = N - 2 = 4 - 2 = 2$. For a problem with one sample of size n = 9 and the other sample of size n = 11 the degrees of freedom are $df = (n_1 - 1) + (n_2 - 1) = (9 - 1) + (11 - 1) = 8 + 10 = 18$.

Once the degrees of freedom are determined, this value can then be used to locate the critical values for the appropriate t-distribution. A two-tailed t-test with 2 degrees of freedom conducted at the $p < .05$ level yields a critical value of $t_{(2).05} = \pm 4.303$. A one-tailed t-test with 18 degrees of freedom at the $p < .01$ level yields a critical value of $t_{(18).01} = +2.552$ or -2.552 depending on the direction of the alternative hypothesis. These critical values are then used to determine whether to reject the null hypothesis. If the calculated t-score is greater than or equal to the critical t-value, then H_0 is rejected at that probability level.

For Joe's review sheet problem, the degrees of freedom are calculated as:

$$df = (n_1 - 1) + (n_2 - 1) = (10 - 1) + (10 - 1) = 9 + 9 = 18$$

Since Joe had a nondirectional hypothesis, the appropriate critical values are for a two-tailed t-test, $t_{(18).05} = \pm 2.101$. Since the calculated value of t = 3.47 is larger than the critical value of +2.101, the null hypothesis is rejected at the

$p < .05$ level. Joe can reduce the Type I error even further by rejecting H_0 at the $p < .01$ level, since the critical value is $t_{(18).01} = +2.878$. Joe concludes that there is a significant difference in exam performance between those who use the review sheet vs. those who do not use the review sheet.

One final point concerning t-distributions can be observed in the t-table when the degrees of freedom are infinite (∞), which is around sample sizes of several hundred or more. Do these critical values look familiar? They should – they are the critical values for the z-distribution! Recall that t-distributions are approximations for the theoretical z-distribution for different sample sizes. Once sample sizes become very large, the t-distributions become less and less platykurtic so that they are virtually the normal distribution, with the same critical values as the z-distribution. Notice on the t-table how as sample size (degrees of freedom) increases, the critical values needed to reject H_0 get smaller and closer to the critical z-values. Clearly, then, the family of t-distributions and the z-distribution are closely related.

An Example of the t-test

A statistics professor wishes to test the effectiveness of a new teaching guide she has designed to help students understand statistics better. She hypothesizes that using the study guide will improve students' exam performance. Thus, the researcher's hypothesis is:

H: Students who use the study guide will score higher on an exam than will students who do not use the study guide.

The population of interest is all students taking an introductory statistics class. Because the professor's current statistics class is convenient, she decides to use it to conduct her study (an experiment). She randomly assigns half of the class, $n_E = 12$, to use the study guide (the experimental group) and randomly assigns the other half of the class, $n_C = 12$, to not use the study guide (the control group). At the end of the class, the researcher calculates the mean score on the final exam for those students in the experimental group ($\overline{X}_E = 90$) and those students in the control group ($\overline{X}_C = 82$). The estimated standard error of the difference (the estimated standard deviation for the distribution of differences), which is calculated based on the sample size and standard deviation for each of the two groups (see Note 2) is computed to be $s_{diff} = 3$.

QUESTION: Did use of the study guide cause students to score significantly (not due to chance) higher on the final exam than students who did not use the study guide?

ANSWER:

Step 1: Identify the hypotheses for this study.

Since conducting a t-test involves testing the null hypothesis and either not rejecting H_0 or rejecting H_0 in favor of the alternative hypothesis, both the null and alternative hypotheses should be clearly identified for the problem. In this example, the professor is predicting that use of the study guide will cause students to score higher on the final exam than will not using the study guide. Since the researcher is predicting that the means will fall in a particular direction, with the study guide group scoring higher than the control group, a directional research hypothesis is predicted:

H_a: Students who use the study guide will score higher on the final exam than will students who do not use the study guide.

The corresponding null hypothesis is:

H_0: Students who use the study guide will score the same as or lower on the final exam than will students who do not use the study guide.

These hypotheses can be stated symbolically as:

$$H_a: \quad \mu_E > \mu_C$$
$$H_0: \quad \mu_E \leq \mu_C$$

Step 2: Calculate the value for t.

Since this problem involves comparing two group means, the dependent measure must involve interval- or ratio-level data. Further, since this problem has one independent variable (type of study technique) with two levels (study guide, no study guide), either a two-sample z-test or a two-sample t-test is required. The decision about which statistical test is appropriate is determined by whether the standard deviation in the population and the standard error of the difference are known (a z-test) or whether the standard deviation in the population is unknown and the standard error of the difference must be estimated from the two sample standard deviations (a t-test). This problem involves estimating the standard error of the difference so a t-test is the appropriate statistical test.

As discussed at the beginning of this chapter, calculating a standardized score for a t-test problem is exactly the same as for a z-test problem except the t-score formula involves substituting the estimated standard error of the difference (s_{diff}) for the actual standard error of the difference (σ_{diff}). Using the t-score formula, the calculated value for this problem is:

$$t = \frac{\overline{X}_E - \overline{X}_C}{s_{diff}} = \frac{90 - 82}{3} = \frac{8}{3} = +2.67$$

With a calculated value of $t = +2.67$ representing the standardized difference between the two sample means, the question now becomes:

is this difference significant? That is, can the professor reject H_0 and conclude that those who used the study guide scored significantly higher on the final exam than did those who did not use the study guide?

Step 3: Calculate the degrees of freedom.

Because this calculated t-value needs to be compared with a critical t-value using the t-table, the next step is to determine which of the family of t-distributions should be referred to for the critical values by calculating the degrees of freedom. Recall that one degree of freedom is lost for each of the two samples, so the degrees of freedom for this problem are:

$$df = (n_1 - 1) + (n_2 - 1) = (12 - 1) + (12 - 1) = 11 + 11 = 22$$
or
$$df = N - 2 = 24 - 2 = 22$$

Step 4: Look up the critical value from the t-table at the .05 level.

Since this is a directional hypothesis, the t-test will be conducted using critical values obtained from the t-table for a one-tailed test. At the .05 level, the critical value for a t-distribution with 22 degrees of freedom for a one-tailed t-test is: $t_{(22).05} = +1.717$ or -1.717, depending upon the direction predicted for the means. Because the researcher predicted that the first mean ($\overline{X}_E$) would be larger than the second mean ($\overline{X}_C$) in this problem, the critical value is positive: $t_{(22).05} = +1.717$.

Step 5: Compare the calculated t to the critical t at the .05 level.

To conduct the t-test, the calculated value of t is compared to the critical value of t. If the calculated value is greater than or equal to the critical value, H_0 is rejected, else H_0 is not rejected. For this directional test, only when the difference between the experimental and control group means falls in the upper 5% of the t-distribution, at or beyond +1.717 where the experimental mean is larger than the control mean, will the null hypothesis be rejected. The calculated t-value was +2.67, with the experimental group mean being larger than the control group mean. This calculated value of +2.67 is larger than the critical value of +1.717; therefore, the null hypothesis is rejected at the $p < .05$ level. With a Type I error of .05 (i.e., less than a 5% chance of being wrong), the researcher can conclude that using the study guide causes students to score better on an exam than does not using the study guide. However, the researcher should not stop at this decision until she determines if she can be even more certain (i.e., have a lower Type I error) in rejecting H_0.

Step 6: If H_0 was rejected at $p < .05$, look up the critical value from the t-table at the .01 level.

Looking at the one-tailed section of the t-table under the .01 rejection level, the corresponding critical value for 22 degrees of freedom is $t_{(22).01} = +2.508$ or -2.508. Since this problem predicts the first mean ($\overline{X}_E$) will be larger than the second mean ($\overline{X}_C$), the critical value is $t_{(22).01} = +2.508$.

Step 7: If H_0 was rejected at $p < .05$, compare the calculated t to the critical t at the .01 level.

We already ascertained that the difference in sample means is in the predicted direction when the t-test was conducted at the .05 level (the experimental group mean is larger than the control group mean). To conduct the t-test at the .01 level, the calculated t-value of +2.67 is compared with the critical t-value of +2.508 to determine if the calculated t-score falls in the extreme outermost 1% of the upper part of the t-distribution. Since +2.67 is larger than +2.508, the null hypothesis can be rejected at the $p < .01$ level. The researcher can conclude that the experimental group scored significantly higher than the control group with a

Type I error, or chance of being wrong, of less than .01.

Step 8: State the final conclusion both statistically and in words.

Statistically, the final decision for this problem is to reject H_0 (the null hypothesis) at the $p < .01$ level. In words, the researcher concludes that the experimental group scored significantly higher than the control group with a Type I error (or chance of being wrong) of less than .01. The researcher is more than 99% confident that use of the study guide causes students to perform better on a statistics exam than does not using the study guide. There is less than a 1% chance that the study guide either does not help students at all or actually hurts their performance on exams. As a result of her findings for this study, the researcher decides to use her study guide in all of her future statistics classes.

t-test Flowchart

The flowchart on the following page (in Figure 6.7) summarizes the steps necessary for conducting a t-test.

Summary

The two-sample t-test is a simple extension of the two-sample z-test. The two-sample t-test involves one independent variable having two levels, a dependent variable measured with interval- or ratio-level data, and an unknown population standard deviation. A t-score is computed identically to a z-score except that the estimated standard error of the difference, based on the two sample standard deviations, is used in place of the actual standard error of the difference. The calculated t-score is compared with a critical t-value that is determined from the appropriate t-distribution.

The t-distributions are a family of distributions corresponding with different sample sizes or degrees of freedom. Degrees of freedom refers to how many scores are free to vary in order to obtain a particular mean in a group of scores. The t-distributions approach the z-distribution as degrees of freedom increase. A t-table is used to determine the appropriate critical values for the different t-distributions. The null hypothesis is rejected if the calculated t-value is larger than the critical value.

Key Terms

- degrees of freedom
- estimated standard error of the difference (s_{diff})
- t-distributions
- t-score
- t-table
- t-test

Problems

1. For each of the following research problems, identify: (1) the independent variable, (2) the levels of the independent variable, and (3) the dependent variable.
   a. A researcher is interested in whether caffeine influences learning. He randomly assigns 20 subjects to drink four cups of caffeinated coffee in an hour and randomly assigns another 20 subjects to drink four cups of decaffeinated coffee in an hour. After consuming the coffee, subjects are asked to memorize 30 words and then recall as many words as possible. The mean number of words recalled by each group are compared.
   b. A student wants to determine whether her friends like her better when she dresses up. She randomly assigns half of her friends (unbeknownst to them) to go to a party with her while she is

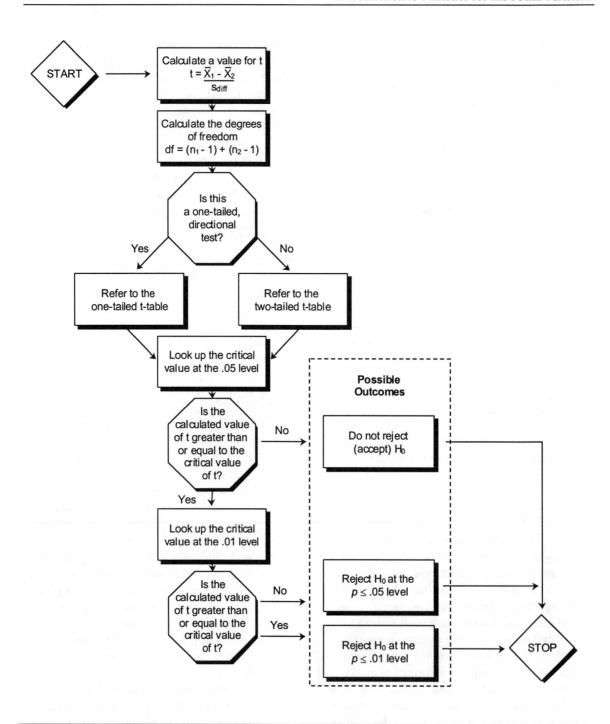

FIGURE 6.7: t-test flowchart

wearing a fancy dress. She randomly assigns the other half of her friends to go to a party with her while she is wearing sweat pants. She videotapes her friends interacting with her at the party and later counts the number of seconds each friend smiles at her during the party. She compares the mean number of seconds of smiling for each of the two groups.

c. A researcher is interested in whether loud music causes anxiety. He randomly assigns 30 subjects to hear a piece of music at a loud volume and randomly assigns another 30 subjects to hear the same piece of music at a soft volume. After listening, subjects are given a standard anxiety test scored on a scale from 1 to 100, with higher scores indicating greater anxiety. The mean anxiety score for each group is compared.

2. What is the formula used for calculating a t-score, the standardized difference between two sample means using an estimated standard error of the difference?

3. What is the formula for finding the degrees of freedom for conducting a two-sample t-test?

4. Which distribution (*sample, population, sampling,* or *differences*) is used to conduct a two-sample t-test?

5. What three pieces of information do you need in order to look up the correct critical value in the t-table?

6. When there is enough of a probability (.95 or higher) that two groups do not represent the same population, the researcher (*rejects* or *accepts*) the null hypothesis at the $p < .05$ level.

7. When there is enough probability (.95 or higher) that two groups do not represent the same population, the conclusion is that the two groups are (*significantly* or *not*

significantly*) different from one another at the $p < .05$ level.

8. Describe two ways to increase the power of the t-test.

9. For each of the following calculated t-values and sample sizes, indicate the degrees of freedom and whether you should reject or accept the null hypothesis (if you reject H_0, indicate whether it is at the .05 or .01 significance level). Conduct each of these t-tests using a two-tailed hypothesis.

a. $t = +2.18$ $n_1 = 5$ $n_2 = 5$
b. $t = -2.05$ $n_1 = 12$ $n_2 = 10$
c. $t = +2.18$ $n_1 = 15$ $n_2 = 15$
d. $t = -2.05$ $n_1 = 16$ $n_2 = 16$

10. Look at your four answers in question #9. What can you conclude about the relationship between sample size and rejecting the null hypothesis (i.e., is the t-test more powerful with smaller or with larger sample sizes)?

11. How many subjects are there in each sample of these studies if the following degrees of freedom are obtained for a two-sample t-test with equal sample sizes?

a. 46 df
b. 120 df
c. 28 df
d. 14 df
e. 22 df
f. 40 df

12. As a political consultant you hypothesize that people will react differently to a political ad that attacks the opposing party vs. an ad that supports the sponsoring party. You obtain a total of 20 voters to watch one of two political commercials produced by the Democratic party. Ten people are randomly assigned to watch a commercial slandering Republicans (an attack ad) whereas the other 10 people are randomly assigned to see a commercial that expounds the virtues of the Democratic party (support ad). After watching

the appropriate commercial, voters indicate their degree of liking for the commercial on a scale ranging from 1 to 7 with 1 as the lowest liking score and 7 as the highest liking score. You collect the following data:

Attack Ad	Support Ad
$n_{Attack} = 10$	$n_{Support} = 10$
$\overline{X}_{Attack} = 4$	$\overline{X}_{Support} = 6.5$

Based on the two sample sizes and the two standard deviations for the two samples, the estimated standard error of the difference is calculated as $s_{diff} = 1.20$.

a. Is this a one-tailed or a two-tailed problem?
b. Formulate appropriate null and alternative hypotheses.
c. Calculate the value for t.
d. Find the critical t-value at the $p < .05$ and $p < .01$ levels.
e. Conduct a t-test for this problem and state your final decision both statistically and in words.
f. If you were recommending which ad the Democratic party should show in order to achieve the highest degree of voter liking for the ad, which of the two ads would you suggest be aired?
g. Suppose instead you hypothesized that voters who viewed the attack ad would like it less than would voters who viewed the support ad. What would be the appropriate null and alternative hypotheses in words and in appropriate notation?
h. What would your statistical decision be for the problem in part g?

13. A sociology researcher is interested in whether a certain hour-long film portraying the effects of racial prejudice will affect attitudes toward a minority group. Two groups of 21 subjects each were randomly assigned to one of two conditions. The first group of subjects watched the hour-long movie whereas the second group spent an hour playing cards. At the end of the hour, both groups were given a racial attitude test, with high scores representing a higher level of prejudice. The data from this study are as follows:

Film Viewing Group	Card Playing Group
$n_{Film} = 21$	$n_{Cards} = 21$
$\overline{X}_{Film} = 42.60$	$\overline{X}_{Cards} = 38.62$

Based on the two sample sizes and the two standard deviations for the two samples, the estimated standard error of the difference is calculated as $s_{diff} = 1.36$.

a. Is this a one-tailed or a two-tailed problem?
b. Formulate appropriate null and alternative hypotheses using appropriate notation.
c. Conduct a t-test for this problem.
d. State your final decision both statistically and in words.

14. A clinical researcher is interested in discovering whether a six-week, nondirective, individual therapy program affects levels of measured anxiety among delinquent boys. A clinical sample of 122 delinquent boys was selected and randomly assigned to two groups. The boys in the first group received the six-week therapy (experimental group), whereas the boys in the second group did not receive the therapy (control group). At the end of six weeks, both groups were given an anxiety test with high scores indicating a greater level of anxiety. The following data were obtained from this study:

Experimental Group	Control Group
$n_E = 61$	$n_C = 61$
$\overline{X}_E = 98.06$	$\overline{X}_C = 102.35$

Based on the two sample sizes and the two standard deviations for the two samples, the estimated standard error of the difference is calculated as $s_{diff} = 2.45$.

a. Is this a one-tailed or a two-tailed problem?

b. Formulate appropriate null and alternative hypotheses.

c. Conduct a t-test for this problem.

d. State your final decision both statistically and in words

15. A researcher hypothesizes that people who watch the *Brady Bunch* will want to have larger families than will people who watch *Three's Company*. The researcher randomly assigns 31 people to watch the *Brady Bunch* every night for one month and randomly assigns 31 other people to watch *Three's Company* every night for the same month. At the end of the month the participants are asked how many children they would like to have. The following data are collected:

Brady Bunch	Three's Company
$n_{BradyBunch} = 31$	$n_{Three'sCompany} = 31$
$\overline{X}_{BradyBunch} = 3.9$	$\overline{X}_{Three'sCompany} = 1.8$

Based on the two sample sizes and the two standard deviations for the two samples, the estimated standard error of the difference is calculated as $s_{diff} = 0.82$.

a. Is this a one-tailed or a two-tailed problem?

b. Formulate appropriate null and alternative hypotheses.

c. Conduct a t-test for this problem.

d. State your final decision both statistically and in words

16. A researcher hypothesizes that men will initiate a conversation with a woman more quickly than they will initiate a conversation with another man. The researcher randomly assigns 13 men to be placed alone in a room with a woman (the same woman is used with each of the 13 men). Another 13 men are randomly assigned to be alone in a room with a man (the same man is used with each of the 13 men). The researcher monitors the sound in the room and determines how long (in seconds) it takes male subjects to initiate a conversation with the other person in the room. The following means are the length of time, in seconds, before the subjects initiated a conversation with the other person in the room. A smaller number indicates that a conversation was initiated more quickly.

With Female in Room	With Male in Room
$n_F = 13$	$n_M = 13$
$\overline{X}_F = 18$	$\overline{X}_M = 12$

Based on the two sample sizes and the two standard deviations for the two samples, the estimated standard error of the difference is calculated as $s_{diff} = -1.45$.

a. Is this a one-tailed or a two-tailed problem?

b. Formulate appropriate null and alternative hypotheses.

c. Can you conduct this t-test? Why or why not?

d. Instead, assume that the following data was obtained: $\overline{X}_F = 5$, $\overline{X}_M = 9$, $s_{diff} = 2.30$. Conduct a t-test for this problem.

e. State your final decision for the problem in part d both statistically and in words.

Notes

1 "N" refers to all subjects participating in a study whereas "n" refers to a subset of the larger group, such as each of the two individual samples n_1 and n_2.

2 To compute the estimated standard error of the difference (s_{diff}), replace the population standard deviation (σ) in the standard error of the difference formula:

$$\sigma_{\bar{x}_1-\bar{x}_2} = \sqrt{\frac{\sigma^2}{n_1} + \frac{\sigma^2}{n_2}}$$

with the two unbiased sample standard deviations (s_1 and s_2):

$$s_{\bar{x}_1-\bar{x}_2} = \sqrt{\frac{s_1^2}{n_1} + \frac{s_2^2}{n_2}}$$

In this example, the estimated standard error of the difference is calculated as follows:

$$s_{\bar{x}_1-\bar{x}_2} = \sqrt{\frac{s_1^2}{n_1} + \frac{s_2^2}{n_2}} = \sqrt{\frac{4^2}{10} + \frac{5^2}{10}} = \sqrt{\frac{16}{10} + \frac{25}{10}} = \sqrt{1.6+2.5} = \sqrt{4.1} = 2.02$$

3 The t-test can be conducted with both equal and unequal sample sizes, although calculation of the estimated standard error of the difference is somewhat more complex than shown in Note 2 when sample sizes are unequal.

4 Recall that if the calculated z-score exactly equaled +1.96 or –1.96 the null hypothesis is rejected at p = .05.

Perceptual Factors Affecting the Accuracy of Ball and Strike Judgments from the Traditional American League and National League Umpiring Perspectives

Adapted from article by same title, Ford, G., Goodwin, F., & Richardson, J. (1995). *International Journal of Sport Psychology, 27*, 50-58.

THIS STUDY investigated perceptual factors affecting the accuracy of umpires' ball-strike judgments by comparing the traditional positions of American League and National League home plate umpires. Currently, all major league umpires today use the National League position behind home plate even though no empirical test of the accuracy of judgments between the two positions has been undertaken. Traditionally, American League umpires were positioned behind the catcher with his head directly above the catcher's head, whereas National League umpires also were positioned behind the catcher but a little lower with his head over the catcher's shoulder (the shoulder closer to the batter). These researchers wanted to empirically test the judgmental superiority of the National League position and proposed the following general hypothesis:

(continued on page 120)

Perceptual Factors Affecting the Accuracy of Ball and Strike Judgments from the Traditional American League and National League Umpiring Perspectives (continued)

Specifically, we investigated whether the home plate umpiring position employed in professional baseball today provides the optimal perceptual perspective for making accurate ball and strike judgments.

Thirty nonumpires (16 female and 14 male undergraduates) evaluated a set of 30 videotaped pitches (all fastballs) from each of the two perspectives (i.e., the same pitches were viewed from two different positions). Part of the results obtained from this study are reported below:

Participants were significantly more accurate in calling strikes (M=74.2% correct) than balls (M=63.6% correct) from both umpiring perspectives, $t(29)$ =3.39, p < .01.

The National League perspective yielded significantly greater overall accuracy in ball-strike judgments (M=70.34 vs. M=65.95, $t(29)$ =-2.18, p < .05). This result can be accounted for in large part by the greater accuracy of the National League perspective in making outside calls: Two-thirds of the pitches viewed were on the outside area of home plate, reflecting the typical pitching strategy employed in professional baseball today.

The National League perspective yielded significantly less accurate judgments on low pitches (M=68.80 vs. M=74.24, $t(29)$ =2.02, p < .05)..[and] less accurate judgments of inside pitches (M=62.22 vs. M=82.23, $t(29)$ =2.90, p < .01) ... [whereas] the American League perspective ... was significantly less accurate in judging outside pitches (M=62.92 vs. M=73.33, $t(29)$ =-4.38, p < .001) ... [and] mid-height pitches (M=55.00 vs. M=71.67, $t(29)$ =-4.47, p < .001).

The study is an initial effort to determine the optimal home plate umpiring position for accuracy of ball and strike judgments. The National League position proved superior for judging pitches on the outside corner of home plate, but poorer for low pitches and inside pitches. Thus, the practical implications of this study suggests that umpires may need special training in overcoming the perceptual difficulties associated with calling low and inside corner pitches from their current position behind the plate.

Comprehension of Arithmetic Word Problems: A Comparison of Successful and Unsuccessful Problem Solvers

Adapted from article by same title, Hegarty, M., Mayer, R., & Monk, C. (1995). *Journal of Educational Psychology, 87*, 18-32.

THE QUESTION of why some students are successful in solving word problems whereas others are unsuccessful was explored in this study. Potentially, people's problem solving strategies may account for individual differences in performance. The researchers proposed the following two general hypotheses in their investigation:

> We hypothesize that when confronted with an arithmetic story problem, unsuccessful problem solvers begin by selecting numbers and keywords from the problem and base their solution plan on these (direct-translation strategy). In contrast we hypothesize that successful problem solvers begin by trying to construct a mental model of the situation being described in the problem and plan their solution on the basis of the model (problem model strategy).

Three dependent variables were measured to test the hypotheses: number of errors, response times (length of time to complete problems), and scoring of eye-fixation data (the words students fixated their eyes on as they solved math problems such as "4" or "less than"). Successful problem solvers were expected to make fewer errors, take less time to solve problems and fixate their eyes more on variable names when they reexamine a problem, whereas unsuccessful problem solvers were expected to make more errors, take more time to solve a problem and look at numbers and relational terms more when they reread a math problem. In the first of two studies conducted, 38 participants were given a series of problems to solve. The materials consisted of four sets of 48 arithmetic word problems, 16 target and 32 filler problems. The language varied by consistency: in half of the problems the relational term (e.g., "less than," "more than") was consistent with the operation to be performed (e.g., subtraction , addition) and in the other half it was inconsistent (e.g., the problem contained "less than" and addition was required). The results from the t-tests are reported below:

> **Errors.** We recorded the time to specify a solution plan and whether or not each participant made an error in specifying a solution plan on each of the 15 target problems. Unsuccessful problem solvers committed four or more errors on the 16 target problems, and successful problem solvers committed 0 or 1 errors. As in previous

(continued on page 122)

Comprehension of Arithmetic Word Problems: A Comparison of Successful and Unsuccessful Problem Solvers (continued)

studies unsuccessful problem solvers generated a higher proportion of errors on inconsistent than consistent problems, (Ms = .62 and .24 respectively), $t(7) = 5.69$, $p < .01$, whereas successful problem solvers by definition produced almost no errors.

Response times. An analysis of response times revealed that unsuccessful problem solvers tended to spend more time solving the problems than did successful problem solvers, although the difference was significant only by a directional test (Ms = 21.7 s and 14.6 s, respectively), $t(14) = 1.78$, $p = .05$, one-tailed. These data indicate that there was no speed-accuracy tradeoff. Because of the differences in accuracy between the two groups of participants for different problem types, the response-time data are difficult to interpret and were not analyzed further.

Scoring of eye-fixation data. Consistent with our predictions, unsuccessful problem solvers reexamined numbers and relational terms significantly more often than did successful problem solvers, $t(14) = 2.37$, $p < .05$. More specifically, unsuccessful problem solvers reexamined numbers an average of 16.3 times per problem as compared with 11.2 times for successful problem solvers, $t(14) = 2.06$, $p = .059$, and they reexamined relational terms an average of 2.3 times per problem as compared with 1.3 times for the successful problem solvers, $t(14) = 2.07$, $p = .058$. In contrast, unsuccessful and successful problem solvers did not differ significantly in how often they reexamined the names of the variables in the problem. In all of these analyses the data are collapsed over presentation order, because order did not have any significant effects on reexamination or any significant interactions with problem-solving success ($p > .10$ in all cases).

Overall, the hypotheses were supported in that successful problem solvers were more likely to comprehend by building a *problem model* whereas unsuccessful problem solvers were more likely to comprehend by *direct translation*. However, the authors are careful to note that strategy selection is likely to be based on both individual and situational factors and that they are not concluding that all unsuccessful problem solvers use one strategy or that all successful problem solvers use another strategy on all story problems. The researchers conclude that successful and unsuccessful problem solvers differ in their tendencies to use one strategy versus another.

Computer Section

Overview of the t-test

The t-test is used to determine whether there is a significant difference in means between two levels of a single independent variable. Conducting a t-test on the computer involves using a t-test command and specifying: (1) the independent variable and the levels of the two groups being compared, and (2) the dependent measure on which means are computed.

Example Output for the t-test

A study was conducted to compare patients' perceptions of the quality of care given in public and private health facilities. As patients checked out of the hospital they filled out a questionnaire and rated the quality of their care on a scale from 1 to 4. A t-test was conducted to determine if patients from public vs. private hospitals differed in their perceptions of the quality of care they received. The following output was obtained:

t-tests for Independent Samples of HEALTHFAC

Variable	Number of Cases		Mean	SD	SE of Mean
QUALITY OF CARE					
Public	1	148	1.7838	.761	.063
Private	2	174	2.0402	.835	.063

Mean Difference = -.2564

Levene's Test for Equality of Variances: F= .659 P= .418

t-test for Equality of Means 95%

Variances	t-value	df	2-Tail Sig	SE ofDiff	CI for Diff
Equal	-2.86	320	.005	.090	(-.433,-.080)
Unequal	-2.88	318.49	.004	.089	(-.432,-.081)

Interpretation of t-test Output

The independent variable in this study was the type of health facility (HEALTHFAC), with two levels (conditions or groups): 1 = Public and 2 = Private. The dependent variable was patients' assessment of the quality of care received (QUALITY OF CARE).

The first part of the output provides some basic frequency and descriptive information about the two groups. A total of 148 patients from public hospitals responded and 174 patients from private hospitals answered the questionnaire. The mean rating of those from public hospitals was $\bar{X}_{public}$ = 1.7838 and the mean rating of those from private hospitals was $\bar{X}_{private}$ = 2.0402. The t-test involved computing the difference between the two means and dividing this difference by the estimated standard error of the difference to create a standardized t-score:

$$t = \frac{\bar{X}_{public} - \bar{X}_{private}}{s_{diff}} = \frac{1.7838 - 2.0402}{.090} = \frac{-.2564}{.090} = -2.86$$

(Note: the computer output only gives results to a few decimal places, but the full calculated value is used in all computations).

The bottom part of the output depicts the results of the t-test. Frequently, t-test output will involve two different sets of results: one set for when the variances (square of the standard deviation) of the two groups are approximately equal and a second set of results for when the variances of the two samples are unequal. Levene's test is used to test the null hypothesis that the variances of the two groups are equal. Usually, the two sample variances will be approximately equal and the t-test is conducted as described in the text. If the two variances are significantly different (as indicated by a probability value equal to .05 or less for Levene's test), then the degrees of freedom used in conducting the t-test are modified somewhat.

For this example, Levene's test is nonsignificant (p = .418) so the equal variances results are used. The calculated t-value was t = -2.86 based on a mean difference of d = -0.2564 and an estimated standard error of the difference of s_{diff} = .09. The degrees of freedom were calculated as df = $(n_1 - 1) + (n_2 - 1)$ = (148 - 1) + (174 - 1) = 147 + 173 = 320. The results of the t-test reveal that there is a significant difference between means at the $p < .01$ level (or $p = .005$ to be exact). Patients evaluated the quality of care received in private hospitals to be significantly better than the quality of care received in public hospitals. These results are for a two-tailed test; a one-tailed test can sometimes be conducted by specifying this option on the computer or by looking up the one-tailed critical values using a t-table.

Computer Problems

1. Conduct t-tests to examine the following hypotheses regarding differences between class levels (**CLSLVL**), and indicate whether the null hypothesis should be rejected or not rejected in each case. Remember to check the direction of the hypothesis (one-tailed vs. two-tailed) and to give the appropriate t-value and significance level.

  a. Freshmen are less comfortable than seniors in seeking help/advice from their instructor (**SEEK**).
  b. Sophomores put more effort into the course (**EFFORT**) than do seniors.
  c. There is a difference between juniors' and sophomores' self perception in how well they performed in the class (**OUTCOME**).
  d. Freshmen find the class more intellectually challenging (**CHALL**) than will juniors.

2. Conduct t-tests to examine the following hypotheses regarding differences between the live vs. mediated classrooms (**CONDIT**), and indicate whether the null hypothesis should be rejected or not rejected in each case. Remember to check the direction of the hypothesis (one-tailed vs. two-tailed) and to give the appropriate t-value and significance level.

  a. Students in the live classroom evaluate the instructor as more interesting (**INTEREST**) than do students in the mediated classroom.
  b. Students in the live vs. mediated classrooms will differ in their perceptions of how qualified (**QUAL**) the instructor is.
  c. Students in the mediated classroom will indicate being more interested in the subject matter of the course (**LIKECLAS**) than will those in the live classroom.

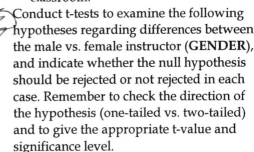

3. Conduct t-tests to examine the following hypotheses regarding differences between the male vs. female instructor (**GENDER**), and indicate whether the null hypothesis should be rejected or not rejected in each case. Remember to check the direction of the hypothesis (one-tailed vs. two-tailed) and to give the appropriate t-value and significance level.

  a. Students will indicate that the female instructor showed a greater interest in them as students (**CARE**) than did the male instructor.
  b. Students will differ in their perceptions of how confident (**CONFID**) the male vs. female instructors are.
  c. Students will differ in their perceptions of how well they think they are able to apply the course content (**APPLY**) when they had the course with the male vs. female instructor.

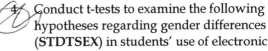

4. Conduct t-tests to examine the following hypotheses regarding gender differences (**STDTSEX**) in students' use of electronic

mail, and indicate whether the null hypothesis should be rejected or not rejected in each case. Remember to check the direction of the hypothesis (one-tailed vs. two-tailed) and to give the appropriate t-value and significance level.

a. Male and female students differ in their perceptions of e-mail as threatening (**THREAT**).

b. Male and female students differ in their frequency of e-mail use to contact their professor (**TEACH1**).

c. Male and female students differ in their frequency of e-mail use to contact their classmates (**STUDENT1**).

Chapter 7 ❖ Single-Factor Analysis of Variance (ANOVA)

From t to F

Having reached this part of the book involves a major achievement. The last few chapters have required mastering some of the most difficult material involved in learning statistics – hypothesis testing and statistical significance. The remainder of this book, beginning with ANOVA in the present chapter, primarily will build upon the concepts developed in the first part of this text. Indeed, we already have covered much of what is needed to understand the next statistical test, single-factor analysis of variance (ANOVA), because it is an extension of the t-test from Chapter 6.

Throughout the remainder of this book, we will emphasize the importance of identifying the correct statistical test to use for different types of data and research problems. The three primary considerations for determining the appropriate statistical test to conduct are: (1) the level of measurement of the dependent variable – nominal, ordinal, or interval/ratio, (2) the number of independent variables, and (3) the number of levels for each independent variable (i.e., the total number of groups or conditions). For instance, the indications for a t-test are: (1) the dependent variable is measured at the interval/ratio level, (2) there is one independent variable, and (3) the independent variable has only two levels or groups. The t-test example presented in detail in the previous chapter involved comparing means on exam scores between a group that received a study guide and a group that did not receive a study guide.

In this chapter, we will see how the study guide problem from Chapter 6 can be extended to a situation in which there are more than two groups. Suppose the same statistics professor also is interested in testing whether extra help sessions she holds with her students help them to understand course material better and score higher on exams. This is now a situation in which there are three groups – a study-guide group, a help-session group, and a control group which receives neither a study guide nor extra help sessions. This revised experiment has two experimental conditions and one control condition, which constitute the levels of the independent variable, type of study technique. The statistical test used to analyze these data is the single-factor ANOVA: (1) the dependent variable is measured at the interval/ratio level, (2) there is one independent variable, and (3) the independent variable has more than two levels or groups.

The professor conducts this study technique experiment using the 45 students (N) enrolled in her statistics class. She randomly assigns one third of the class to use the study guide during the course ($n_{StudyGuide} = 15$), one third of the class to go to extra help sessions ($n_{HelpSession} = 15$), and one third of the class to have no study guide or extra help ($n_{Control} = 15$). At the end of the semester, the professor finds the average final exam score for students in each of the three groups: the study-guide group had a mean $\overline{X}_{StudyGuide} = 85$, the help-session group had a mean $\overline{X}_{HelpSession} = 88$, and the control group had a mean $\overline{X}_{Control} = 82$. The question the professor is trying to answer is the following: is there a difference in final exam scores among the three groups?

One possible solution to this problem is to utilize the t-test covered in Chapter 6. Since the t-test allows the comparison of only two sample means at a time, each of the groups could be compared with every other group through three separate t-tests. That is, one t-test would compare the study-guide and help-session groups to see if they differed significantly, a second t-test would compare the study-guide and control groups, and the third t-test would compare the help-session and control groups. Although this may seem reasonable at first, there is a fundamental flaw to this approach. Because each statistical test is conducted at the .05 significance level, there is a 5% chance of making an incorrect decision when the null hypothesis is rejected for any individual test, which is an acceptable error rate for most circumstances. However, when multiple statistical tests are conducted, each at the .05 level, the overall Type I error rate is compounded when the null hypothesis is rejected multiple times for the set of three t-tests. That is, the probability of making an incorrect decision when H_0 is rejected for three t-tests is not .05 but almost .15.[1] Thus, the t-test approach does not provide a satisfactory solution for determining if there are significant differences among the three groups in the problem.

To compare means among more than two groups, a statistical test known as the *F-test* or analysis of variance (ANOVA) is conducted. In general, analysis of variance is used when interval- or ratio-level data is collected from a single dependent measure to compare means among more than two groups. In this chapter we will present the simplest form of the F-test, single-factor analysis of variance, and in the following chapter we will describe the more complete form of the F-test, multiple-factor analysis of variance. The distinction between single- and multiple-factor ANOVA refers to the number of independent variables in the problem. A *factor* is another term for an independent variable. If there is one independent variable, as with the t-test in Chapter 6 and the example in the present chapter, then the problem is *single factor*. If there is more than one independent variable, then the problem is *multiple factor*.

As with the t-test, *single-factor analysis of variance (ANOVA)* involves examining differences in means among levels of a single independent variable. For the example concerning techniques to improve exam performance, there is one independent variable: type of study technique. In the t-test problem presented earlier, this factor had two levels: study guide or no study guide (control). For the single-factor ANOVA problem in the present chapter, this factor has three levels: study guide, help session, or no technique (control). Because the single-factor ANOVA involves only one independent variable, this statistical test is also sometimes referred to as a *one-way analysis of variance*.

Conducting the F-test involves testing the null hypothesis that all group means are equal and rejecting H_0 if the differences between the groups are large enough to conclude with probability .05 or less that the groups truly are significantly different from one another. Both nondirectional and directional hypotheses can be formulated for the F-test and are simple extensions of the hypotheses described for the t-test. Recall that the nondirectional research and null hypotheses for the t-test study technique problem were:

H_a: $\mu_{StudyGuide} \neq \mu_{Control}$
H_0: $\mu_{StudyGuide} = \mu_{Control}$

Extended to the single-factor ANOVA study technique problem, the nondirectional research and null hypotheses are:

H_a: $\mu_{StudyGuide} \neq \mu_{HelpSession} \neq \mu_{Control}$
H_0: $\mu_{StudyGuide} = \mu_{HelpSession} = \mu_{Control}$

Directional hypotheses also can be proposed for the F-test (e.g., H_a: $\mu_{StudyGuide} > \mu_{HelpSession} > \mu_{Control}$); however, the nature of the F-test is such that only positive F-values will ever exist, in contrast to the t-test which could yield either positive or negative t-scores. Thus, both nondirectional and directional hypotheses are tested in the same way with the F-test.

Overview of Single-Factor Analysis of Variance

Analysis of variance involves comparing group means by *analyzing the variance* in scores. Presumably, not every single person will obtain exactly the same score on a given dependent measure. For instance, all students in a statistics class will probably not score identically on a final exam. The total variability in scores is measured by looking at how each individual subject's score varies from the grand mean of all scores. When subjects are part of different groups (e.g., a study-guide group, a help-session group, and a control group), this total variability in scores can be partitioned into two different sources: (1) differences between the group means and the grand mean, and (2) differences between the individual subjects' scores and the subjects' own group means.

The study technique problem involves three groups (study guide, help session, control) with n = 15 participants per group. The following data are collected:

Study-Guide Group		Help-Session Group		Control Group	
1. Barb	90	16. Tom	94	31. Mark	78
2. Warren	82	17. Burt	90	32. Chris	80
3. Andy	86	18. Cliff	86	33. Betsy	84
.....		.....		.....	
15. Corinne	82	30. Claire	85	45. Rudy	83

$\overline{X}_{StudyGuide} = 85$ $\overline{X}_{HelpSession} = 88$ $\overline{X}_{Control} = 82$

Grand Mean for all 45 students = $\overline{X}_{Grand} = 85$

Although some students (e.g., participant 30, Claire) scored exactly the grand mean $\overline{X}_{Grand} = 85$, most students varied to some extent around this grand mean. For instance, Barb scored a 90, 5 points above the grand mean, whereas Warren scored an 82, 3 points below the grand mean. By computing a difference between each individual student's score (X) and the grand mean ($\overline{X}_{Grand}$), a measure of the total variability in scores can be obtained:

Student	Difference $(X - \overline{X}_{Grand})$
1. Barb	90 - 85 = +5
2. Warren	82 - 85 = -3
.....	.....
45. Rudy	83 - 85 = -2

To express the total variability for all students in a single number, the sum of all of these differences could be computed: (+5) + (-3) + ... + (-2). Unfortunately, the problem with this approach is that some differences are positive and some differences are negative. By summing these differences, the positive and negative values cancel each other out and the resulting sum is zero! Obviously, there is not zero variability in scores. In order to prevent positive and negative differences from negating each other, each computed difference is squared to produce a positive value. These positive values are then summed, yielding a measure of the total variability in scores:

Student	Difference $(X - \overline{X}_{Grand})$	Squared Difference $(X - \overline{X}_{Grand})^2$	
1. Barb	90 - 85 = +5	$(+5)^2$ =	25
2. Warren	82 - 85 = -3	$(-3)^2$ =	9
.....	.....	.....	
45. Rudy	83 - 85 = -2	$(-2)^2$ =	4
		Sum (Σ) =	1476

This sum of squared differences between each individual score and the grand mean of all scores is called *sum of squares total (SS$_{Total}$)*:

$$SS_{Total} = \sum (X - \overline{X}_{Grand})^2$$

The larger SS$_{Total}$, the greater variability there is in the individual scores; the smaller SS$_{Total}$, the more homogeneous the individual scores are. This concept should look familiar because SS$_{Total}$ is a fundamental component of standard deviation and variance covered in Chapter 3. Recall that sum of squares (SS) divided by the total number of scores (N) *is* variance.[2]

Total sum of squares can be partitioned into two components: sum of squares between (SS$_{Between}$) and sum of squares within (SS$_{Within}$). First, part of the overall variability in scores can be observed in the difference between each group mean and the grand mean ($\overline{X}_{Grand} = 85$): $\overline{X}_{StudyGuide} = 85$, $\overline{X}_{HelpSession} = 88$, and $\overline{X}_{Control} = 82$. The means for each of the three groups are not always identical to the grand mean. This is variability between groups and is represented in a value called *sum of squares between (SS$_{Between}$)*. SS$_{Between}$ represents variability in the dependent variable (exam score) that is due to the independent variable (type of study technique). The remaining part of the total variability in scores can be observed in the difference between each individual score and its own group mean. For instance, in the help-session group, not everyone scored the group mean of $\overline{X}_{HelpSession} = 88$: Tom had a 94, Burt had a 90, and so on. This is variability within groups and is represented in a value called *sum of squares within (SS$_{Within}$)*.

By analyzing these two sources of variability, between and within groups, we can determine whether the three group means are significantly different from one another, or whether the observed differences between groups is due purely to chance. Recall that if a nonsignificant result is obtained, any observed difference between groups is due to random factors, such as how people happened to be assigned to groups, rather than to true differences caused by the manipulated variable, type of study technique. A test statistic, the F, is computed as the ratio of the two sources of variability which are transformed into two variance measures. This process essentially averages each of the sum of squares values, similar to the formula used to calculate variance. We will now examine each of the two sources of variability more closely for the example problem in this chapter and discuss the meaning of the ratio of the two variances in the F statistic.

First, to measure the variability between groups, differences are calculated between each of the three group means ($\overline{X}_k$) and the grand mean ($\overline{X}_{Grand} = 85$). Since there are a total of K = 3 groups, three differences are computed:

Group	Difference $(\overline{X}_k - \overline{X}_{Grand})$
Study Guide	85 - 85 = 0
Help Session	88 - 85 = +3
Control	82 - 85 = -3

Once again, simply summing these differences would not provide an accurate measure of the overall deviation of the group means from the grand mean, (0) + (+3) + (-3) = 0. Clearly, the variability between groups is not zero. As with the calculation of total variability (SS$_{Total}$), these differences are squared in order to prevent positive and negative differences from canceling each other out:

Group	Difference $(\overline{X}_k - \overline{X}_{Grand})$	Squared Difference $(X - \overline{X}_{Grand})^2$
Study Guide	85 - 85 = 0	$0^2 = 0$
Help Session	88 - 85 = +3	$(+3)^2 = 9$
Control	82 - 85 = -3	$(-3)^2 = 9$

Before these squared differences are summed, there is one additional step required which was not done with the computation of sum of squares total. With SS_{Total}, each subject was involved in producing a squared difference. However, differences for $SS_{Between}$ involve group means which aggregate across many subjects per group. Consequently, to reflect the number of subjects actually in every group, each squared difference is weighted by the number of subjects per group (n_k). For example, the squared difference between the help-session group mean and the grand mean ($d^2 = 9$) is multiplied or "weighted" by the 15 subjects in the help-session group in order to provide a representation of the overall variability for this group. By weighting each squared difference by the number of subjects per group, groups with a large number of subjects are weighted more heavily in the calculation of sum of squares between than are groups with a small number of subjects. This weighting process is completed with each of the groups in the study and then the weighted squared differences are summed to produce sum of squares between:

Group	Difference $(\overline{X}_k - \overline{X}_{Grand})$	Squared Difference $(\overline{X}_k - \overline{X}_{Grand})^2$	Weighted by Subjects $n_k(\overline{X}_k - \overline{X}_{Grand})^2$
Study Guide	85 - 85 = 0	$0^2 = 0$	15(0) = 0
Help Session	88 - 85 = +3	$(+3)^2 = 9$	15(9) = 135
Control	82 - 85 = -3	$(-3)^2 = 9$	15(9) = 135
			Sum (Σ) = 270

Overall, then, the sum of squares between is calculated as:

$$SS_{Between} = \sum n_k (\overline{X}_k - \overline{X}_{Grand})^2$$

To help understand the meaning of the sum of squares between value computed for this problem ($SS_{Between} = 270$), consider this same example with groups that differ even more substantially from one another: the study-guide group still has a mean $\overline{X}_{StudyGuide} = 85$, but the help-session group has a mean $\overline{X}_{HelpSession} = 90$ (instead of 88) and the control group has a mean $\overline{X}_{Control} = 80$ (instead of 82). The grand mean is still $\overline{X}_{Grand} = 85$ and there are still 15 subjects per group. Sum of squares between for this revised problem is computed as follows:

Group	Difference $(\overline{X}_k - \overline{X}_{Grand})$	Squared Difference $(\overline{X}_k - \overline{X}_{Grand})^2$	Weighted by Subjects $n_k(\overline{X}_k - \overline{X}_{Grand})^2$
Study Guide	85 - 85 = 0	$0^2 = 0$	15(0) = 0
Help Session	90 - 85 = +5	$(+5)^2 = 25$	15(25) = 375
Control	80 - 85 = -5	$(-5)^2 = 25$	15(25) = 375
			Sum (Σ) = 750

The calculated $SS_{Between} = 750$ for this second set of data is larger than the $SS_{Between} = 270$ computed for the first set of data, reflecting the fact that the group means are more variable or different in the second data set than in the first data set.

The variability between the individual scores and the group means, sum of squares within, is calculated very similarly to the two sums of squares measures described above (total and between). Each individual score (X) is compared to its own group mean ($\overline{X}_k$); these differences are squared, and then summed across all subjects:

$$SS_{Within} = \sum (X - \overline{X}_k)^2$$

In the present problem, this computation involves summing 45 squared differences because there are 45 individual scores:

Study-Guide Group		Difference $(X - \bar{X}_{SG})$	Squared Difference $(X - \bar{X}_{SG})^2$
1. Barb	90	90 - 85 = +5	$+5^2 =$ 25
2. Warren	82	82 - 85 = -3	$-3^2 =$ 9
3. Andy	86	86 - 85 = +1	$+1^2 =$ 1
....		....	....
15. Corinne	82	82 - 85 = -3	$-3^2 =$ 9
$\bar{X}_{StudyGuide} =$	85		Sum = 413

Help-Session Group		Difference $(X - \bar{X}_{HS})$	Squared Difference $(X - \bar{X}_{HS})^2$
16. Tom	94	94 - 88 = +6	$+6^2 =$ 36
17. Burt	90	90 - 88 = +2	$+2^2 =$ 4
18. Cliff	86	86 - 88 = -2	$-2^2 =$ 4
....		....	....
30. Claire	85	85 - 88 = -3	$-3^2 =$ 9
$\bar{X}_{HelpSession} =$	88		Sum = 389

Control Group		Difference $(X - \bar{X}_C)$	Squared Difference $(X - \bar{X}_C)^2$
31. Mark	78	78 - 82 = -4	$-4^2 =$ 16
32. Chris	80	80 - 82 = -2	$-2^2 =$ 4
33. Betsy	84	84 - 82 = +2	$+2^2 =$ 4
....		....	....
45. Rudy	83	83 - 82 = +1	$+1^2 =$ 1
$\bar{X}_{Control} =$	82		Sum = 404

Sum (Σ) across groups = 1206

Notice that the computation of sum of squares within does not involve directly weighting each squared difference, since each difference is computed for a single subject – the weighting always equals one.

Sum of squares total ($SS_{Total} = 1476$), then, is the sum of the two sources of variability in scores: sum of squares between groups

($SS_{Between} = 270$) and sum of squares within groups ($SS_{Within} = 1206$):

$$SS_{Total} = SS_{Between} + SS_{Within}$$

These sum of squares values are listed in the first part of an *ANOVA table*, which depicts the computations involved in calculating the F statistic. The first part of the ANOVA table shows the source of variability (between groups, within groups, and total) and the sum of squares computed for each of the sources of variability:

Partial ANOVA Table	
Source	SS
Between	270
Within	1206
Total	1476

Before we describe the other components necessary to finish the ANOVA table and compute the F statistic, we believe it is worthwhile taking a closer look at $SS_{Between}$ and SS_{Within} with respect to detecting significant differences among groups. Recall that $SS_{Between}$ represents how much of the total variability in the dependent variable (i.e., how scores differ from the grand mean) is explained by the independent variable (which group a person is in). Ideally, the differences between groups should be very large and the differences within groups should be very small, as depicted in Figure 7.1. That is, the best scenario for observing significant differences among groups is when there are large differences between group means, indicating that the groups are very different from one another, and small differences within group scores, indicating that the individuals within any particular group are very similar to one another.

Study Guide Group   Help Session Group   Control Group

When variability between groups is large and variability within groups is small, the sample groups represent *different* populations

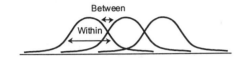

Study Guide Group Help Session Group Control Group

When variability between groups is small and variability within groups is large, the sample groups represent the *same* population

FIGURE 7.1: Analyzing variance between and within groups

To illustrate, consider a small example of three groups with five people per group and a dependent measure of people's weight. The null hypothesis is that the three groups are part of the same population with the same mean weight (i.e., the three group means are equal). In contrast, the alternative hypothesis predicts that the three groups do not represent the same population (i.e., the three group means are not equal). Comparison of the following two sets of data, each with the same mean weights for each of the three groups, illustrates the importance of between-groups vs. within-groups variability:

Set One:

Group 1		Group 2		Group 3	
Ben	155	Tom	195	Art	130
Sam	155	Joe	195	Jon	130
Abe	160	Bif	200	Al	135
Sid	165	Dan	205	Ed	140
Les	165	Sal	205	Hal	140
$\overline{X}_1 =$	160	$\overline{X}_2 =$	200	$\overline{X}_3 =$	135

$$\overline{X}_{Grand} = 165$$

Set Two:

Group 1		Group 2		Group 3	
Ben	95	Tom	115	Art	80
Sam	125	Joe	155	Jon	110
Abe	160	Bif	200	Al	135
Sid	195	Dan	245	Ed	150
Les	225	Sal	285	Hal	200
$\overline{X}_1 =$	160	$\overline{X}_2 =$	200	$\overline{X}_3 =$	135

$$\overline{X}_{Grand} = 165$$

In both data sets, the between-groups variability is exactly the same because the group means, grand mean, and number of subjects per group are identical. However, the within-groups variability is much larger in the second set of data than in the first set because the individual scores in the second data set are more spread out within each group. Because of the lack of consistency in scores within groups in the second set of data, it is less likely that the observed differences in group means are due to true weight differences among the groups and more likely that these differences are due to random factors affecting the people within each group. In contrast, for the first set of data, the people in Group 2 appear to truly weigh more on average than do the people in Group 3, since there is very little fluctuation within each group but a lot of variation between the groups. In sum, the best case for detecting significant differences between groups is when the differences between groups is large (the groups differ as much as possible from each other) and the differences within groups is small (the individual scores within each group are as similar as possible).

Degrees of Freedom

As with the t-test, an F-test is conducted with a certain number of degrees of freedom (the number of scores that are free to vary). In general, one degree of freedom is lost for each of the objects being examined, such as groups or subjects. For instance, the t-test involves a loss of one degree of freedom for each of the two groups: $df = (n_1 - 1) + (n_2 - 1)$. Overall for any set of data, there are N - 1 total degrees of freedom. The three-group example in the present chapter involves a total of 45 subjects in the entire study. Thus, there are N - 1 = 45 - 1 = 44 degrees of freedom: 44 of the scores can vary and assume any value, but the final score is fixed in order to obtain the grand mean of $\overline{X}_{Grand} = 85$. These 44 degrees of freedom are divided between the between-groups variability and the within-groups variability.

The degrees of freedom for between-groups variability is calculated as the total number of groups in the study (K) minus one degree of freedom:

$$df_{Between} = K - 1$$

In the present example, one degree of freedom is lost from the three groups: $df_{Between} = 3 - 1 = 2$.

Degrees of freedom for within-groups variability is calculated similar to degrees of freedom for the t-test, with one degree of freedom lost for each of the groups in the study ($n_k - 1$). For instance, for the study-guide group, there are a total of 15 individual scores with a loss of one degree of freedom: $n_{StudyGuide} - 1 = 15 - 1 = 14$. With one degree of freedom lost for each of the three groups, within-groups degrees of freedom is calculated as: $df_{Within} = (n_{StudyGuide} - 1) + (n_{HelpSession} - 1) + (n_{Control} - 1) = (15 - 1) + (15 - 1) + (15 - 1) = 14 + 14 + 14 = 42$. In general, degrees of freedom for within-groups variability is equal to the sum of the number of scores in each individual group minus one degree of freedom for each group:

$$df_{Within} = (n_1 - 1) + (n_2 - 1) + \text{.......} + (n_k - 1)$$

This formula can be simplified as the total number of subjects in the study minus one degree of freedom lost for each of the groups in the study:

$$df_{Within} = N - K$$

In this example, $df_{Within} = N - K = 45 - 3 = 42$.

Notice that the sum of the between-groups and within-groups degrees of freedom is equal to the total degrees of freedom in the study: $df_{Total} = 2 + 42 = 44 = N - 1$:

$$df_{Total} = df_{Between} + df_{Within} = N - 1$$

One additional point worth noting about degrees of freedom is that the formulas described above are exactly those used with the t-test, although we did not present degrees of freedom in this way previously. Since there are two groups involved with a t-test, the between-groups degrees of freedom is always: $df_{Between} = K - 1 = 2 - 1 = 1$. Because $df_{Between}$ always equals one for the t-test, this value is not displayed. Only the degrees of freedom associated with within-groups variability is calculated for the t-test based on the general ANOVA formula: $df_{Within} = N - K = (n_1 - 1) + (n_2 - 1) + ... + (n_k - 1)$. In the two group case this formula is $df_{Within} = N - 2 = (n_1 - 1) + (n_2 - 1)$, which is exactly the t-test degrees of freedom formula presented in Chapter 6. What this example illustrates is that the t-test is nothing but a very specific case of analysis of variance with two groups. In fact, if a calculated t-value is squared, the result is the test statistic for ANOVA: $F = t^2$. Because the differences computed in deriving the sum of squares for analysis of variance were squared, the t-value also must be squared to yield the equivalent F-value.

The ANOVA table can now be modified to include the degrees of freedom associated with each source of variability:

Partial ANOVA Table

Source	SS	df
Between	270	2
Within	1206	42
Total	1476	44

Calculating the F-Statistic

With the sums of squares and degrees of freedom computed, the next step is to obtain a measure of variance, which is equivalent to the average variability for each source. To calculate the "mean" variability for between- and within-groups, each sum of squares is divided by its corresponding degrees of freedom to produce the *mean square*:

$$MS = \frac{SS}{df}$$

Notice how similar this formula is to the formula presented in Chapter 3 for the unbiased estimator of the population variance:

$$V = \frac{SS}{N-1}$$

In fact, since total degrees of freedom for a set of data is df = N -1, another way to write the formula for variance is:

$$V = \frac{SS}{df}$$

Thus, mean square is equal to variance. By applying the general mean square formula to the present problem, the *mean square between groups* is calculated by taking the sum of squares between groups ($SS_{Between}$ = 270) and dividing by the associated degrees of freedom ($df_{Between}$ = 2):

$$MS_{Between} = \frac{SS_{Between}}{df_{Between}} = \frac{270}{2} = 135$$

Similarly, the *mean square within groups* is computed by taking the sum of squares within groups (SS_{Within} = 1206) and dividing by the corresponding degrees of freedom (df_{Within} = 42):

$$MS_{Within} = \frac{SS_{Within}}{df_{Within}} = \frac{1206}{42} = 28.71$$

A mean square value is not computed for the total source of variability, as only the mean square for between- and within-groups are used in the computation of the F statistic. Adding the mean square values to the ANOVA table yields the following:

Partial ANOVA Table

Source	SS	df	MS
Between	270	2	135
Within	1206	42	28.71
Total	1476	44	

The last step in determining the calculated value of the test statistic, F, is to compare the mean square between groups to the mean square within groups. The resulting F-value is the ratio of between-groups variance to within-groups variance:

$$F = \frac{MS_{Between}}{MS_{Within}}$$

This calculated F-value provides a measure of how much groups differ from one another. If there is a lot of difference between groups, mean square between groups will be large and so, too, will F. A large F-value means a greater chance of concluding a significant difference among more than two groups, just as a higher t-value meant a greater chance of concluding a significant difference between two groups. If there is a lot of difference or variability among the scores within groups, then mean square within groups will be large and F will be small. A small F-value means a lower chance of concluding there is a significant difference among groups. Computing the F-value for the present problem yields the following:

$$F = \frac{MS_{Between}}{MS_{Within}} = \frac{135}{28.71} = 4.70$$

With the calculated F-value added, the ANOVA table is complete:

ANOVA Table

Source	SS	df	MS	F
Between	270	2	135	4.70
Within	1206	42	28.71	
Total	1476	44		

Critical Values and the F-table

Once a calculated F is obtained, this F-value must be compared with a critical value to determine whether there is a significant difference in means, just as with the t-test. The critical values for the F-test are obtained from a family of distributions called the *F-distributions*, which are theoretical distributions created from the ratio of two variances for different degrees of freedom. In order to reject the null hypothesis, the calculated F-value must fall in the outermost 5% of the F-distribution. Since the F-statistic is always computed as the ratio of mean square between to mean square within, only those critical values in the upper 5% (or 1%) of the F-distribution are of interest, that is, where the variance in the numerator is larger than the variance in the denominator. The critical values for the F-test are given in the *F-table* (see Appendix A) and are determined based on the numerator or between-groups degrees of freedom and the denominator or within-groups degrees of freedom.

The present problem involves testing the calculated F = 4.70 using an F-distribution with 2 and 42 degrees of freedom. The critical F-value from the F-table that corresponds with 2 and 42 degrees of freedom at the .05 significance level is $F_{(2,42).05} = 3.22$. The F-test is conducted by comparing the calculated F-value with the critical F-value. Since the calculated F = 4.70 is larger than the critical $F_{(2,42).05} = 3.22$, the null hypothesis is rejected at the $p < .05$ level. The conclusion is that there is a significant difference among groups; some of the three groups differ significantly from some other of the three groups.

By rejecting H_0 at p < .05, there is a Type I error of less than .05, representing less than a 5% chance that H_0 was incorrectly rejected and in fact there is no significant difference among groups. As with the t-test, the next question becomes whether confidence in rejecting H_0 can be even higher than just over 95%. Again referring to the F-table, the critical value for F at the .01 level is $F_{(2,42).01} = 5.15$. Since the calculated F = 4.70 is not larger than the critical $F_{(2,42).01} = 5.15$, H_0 cannot be rejected at the $p < .01$ level. The final decision must be to reject H_0 at the $p < .05$ level and conclude that there is some significant difference among the three groups, accepting a Type I error of less than .05 but more than .01.

Since a significant F was obtained, the question arises as to exactly which of the groups differ from which other groups. Did the help session cause students to score significantly higher ($\overline{X}_{HelpSession} = 88$) than the control group ($\overline{X}_{Control} = 82$) and the study-guide group

($\overline{X}_{StudyGuide}$ = 85)? Did the help-session group score significantly higher than the control group but not the study-guide group? Did the study-guide group score significantly higher than the control group? To answer these questions about which groups differ from which other groups it is necessary to use a post-hoc test. A *post-hoc test* is conducted after an overall or primary statistical test such as the F-test is found to be significant. The post-hoc test identifies exactly which groups differ significantly from which other groups. Post-hoc comparisons following a significant F typically involve the comparison of each group mean with every other group mean. This is somewhat akin to a series of t-tests except that the post-hoc test controls the Type I error obtained by conducting the overall F-test initially. There are several different types of post-hoc tests, such as Scheffé and Tukey, which can be used to determine which groups differ significantly from which other groups. Many popular statistical packages compute post-hoc tests automatically once a significant F is obtained. Other more advanced statistics books cover the computations involved in these post-hoc procedures in detail.

An ANOVA (F-Test) Example

A sociologist is interested in the effects of having regular family meetings on children's delinquent behavior. Based on his review of the literature in the area of children and delinquency, the researcher hypothesizes that:

H: Children who receive positive reinforcement from their family will exhibit less delinquent behavior than will children who do not receive positive reinforcement from their families

The researcher locates 100 children who have behavioral problems and randomly assigns 25 of the children to attend one-hour meetings once a week with their families to talk about positive achievements in the child's life. Another 25 of the children are randomly assigned to have one-hour meetings twice a week with their families. Twenty-five other children are randomly assigned to have one-hour meetings with their families four times per week. And, the final 25 children are randomly assigned to have no meetings with their families. After a period of two months the researcher goes to the children's schools and obtains ratings from teachers regarding the amount of delinquent behavior each child exhibits. Children are rated on a scale from 0 to 10, with 0 indicating no delinquent behavior and 10 indicating frequent delinquent behavior. The researcher calculated the following means for the four groups in this study, where the subscript on each mean indicates the number of family meetings per week: $\overline{X}_0$ = 9.3; $\overline{X}_1$ = 8.2; $\overline{X}_2$ = 8.0; $\overline{X}_4$ = 6.9. The mean behavioral rating for all 100 children is $\overline{X}_{Grand}$ = 8.1.

QUESTION: Does increased interaction with family members through family meetings reduce the amount of negative behavior exhibited by delinquent youths?

ANSWER:

Step 1: Identify the hypotheses for this study.

The researcher is predicting that an increased number of weekly family meetings will reduce the amount of children's delinquent behavior. The independent variable, the variable that the researcher manipulates, is the frequency of family meetings per week. There are four levels to this independent variable: 0 times per week (the control), 1 time per week, 2 times per week, and 4 times per week. The dependent variable is the teacher ratings of each child's delinquent behavior on a scale from 0 to 10. For the purposes of this problem we will assume that this Likert-type scale is interval-level data. Given one independent variable with more than two levels and interval-level data for the dependent measure, the appropriate statistical test is a single-factor analysis of variance (F-test).

The researcher is predicting that children who are involved in a higher number of family meetings per week will exhibit a lower mean delinquent behavioral score than will those who are involved in a fewer number of weekly family meetings, yielding the following alternative hypothesis:

$$H_a: \quad \mu_4 < \mu_2 < \mu_1 < \mu_0$$

The corresponding null hypothesis indicates that the four means are no different from one another or are in the opposite than predicted direction:

$$H_0: \quad \mu_4 \geq \mu_2 \geq \mu_1 \geq \mu_0$$

Although this is a directional hypothesis, there is no one-tailed F-test that is conducted. With analysis of variance the concept of one-tailed and two-tailed does not exist because only the upper part of the F-distribution is used for the F-test. That is, only ratios where the numerator (mean square between) is larger than the denominator (mean square within) are of interest, so only the upper tail of the F-distribution is considered, regardless of whether a directional or nondirectional hypothesis is predicted.

Step 2: Begin the ANOVA table and compute the sums of squares.

The sum of squares between groups is calculated using the four group means ($\overline{X}_0 = 9.3$; $\overline{X}_1 = 8.2$; $\overline{X}_2 = 8.0$; $\overline{X}_4 = 6.9$) and the overall grand mean ($\overline{X}_{Grand} = 8.1$) for the 100 children in the study:

Group	Difference	Squared Difference	Weighted by S's
0 meetings	9.3 - 8.1 = +1.2	$+1.2^2 = 1.44$	1.44 * 25 = 36
1 meeting	8.2 - 8.1 = +0.1	$+0.1^2 = .01$	.01 * 25 = .25
2 meetings	8.0 - 8.1 = -0.1	$-0.1^2 = .01$	.01 * 25 = .25
4 meetings	6.9 - 8.1 = -1.2	$-1.2^2 = 1.44$	1.44 * 25 = 36

Sum of squares between = 72.5

Although we will not show the entire calculation here, deriving the sum of squares within groups involves computing a difference between each individual score and the subject's own group mean, squaring these differences, and summing these squared differences across all subjects:

$$SS_{Within} = \sum (X - \overline{X}_k)^2$$

For this problem, sum of squares within is $SS_{Within} = 954.5$. Filling in the ANOVA table with the sum of squares values yields the following:

Source	SS
Between	72.5
Within	954.5
Total	1027.0

Step 3: Compute the degrees of freedom.

There are two sets of degrees of freedom for analysis of variance: one df-value is associated with the between-groups variability and the other df-value is associated with the within-groups variability. For between groups, one degree of freedom is lost across the total number of groups in the study: $df_{Between} = K - 1 = 4 - 1 = 3$ degrees of freedom. For within groups, one degree of freedom is lost from the total number of subjects in a group for each group in the study: $df_{Within} = (n_1 - 1) + (n_2 - 1) + (n_3 - 1) + (n_4 - 1) = (25 - 1) + (25 - 1) + (25 - 1) + (25 - 1)$

$= 24 + 24 + 24 + 24 = 96$, or $df_{Within} = N - K = 100 - 4 = 96$ degrees of freedom. The total number of degrees of freedom for this study is $df_{Total} = df_{Between} + df_{Within} = 3 + 96 = 99$, or $df_{Total} = N - 1 = 100 - 1 = 99$ degrees of freedom. Adding the degrees of freedom to the ANOVA table yields the following:

Source	SS	df
Between	72.5	3
Within	954.5	96
Total	1027	99

Step 4: Compute the mean squares.

The mean squares is a value that represents the average variability in scores around the mean and is calculated using the sum of squares and the degrees of freedom for each source of variability. For between groups, the mean squares represents the average variability in group means around the grand mean:

$$MS_{Between} = \frac{SS_{Between}}{df_{Between}} = \frac{72.5}{3} = 24.17$$

For within groups, the mean squares represents the average variability of the individual scores around their own group means:

$$MS_{Within} = \frac{SS_{Within}}{df_{Within}} = \frac{954.5}{96} = 9.94$$

Adding the mean squares values to the ANOVA table yields the following:

Source	SS	df	MS
Between	72.5	3	24.17
Within	954.5	96	9.94
Total	1027	99	

Step 5: Compute the F-value.

The F-value is calculated by comparing the variance between groups (mean squares between) to the variance within groups (mean squares within):

$$F = \frac{MS_{Between}}{MS_{Within}} = \frac{24.17}{9.94} = 2.43$$

The completed ANOVA table now looks like the following:

Source	SS	df	MS	F
Between	72.5	3	24.17	2.43
Within	954.5	96	9.94	
Total	1027	99		

Step 6: Look up the critical value at the .05 level.

In order to reject the null hypothesis, the calculated F must equal or exceed the critical F with 3 and 96 degrees of freedom at the .05 significance level. The F-table is used to obtain the critical values; however, no value is listed for 96 degrees of freedom in the denominator. The closest denominator degrees of freedom are 80 and 100, yielding the following critical values:

$$F_{(3,80).05} = 2.72$$
$$F_{(3,100).05} = 2.70$$

Researchers have several different methods for determining the critical value to use when the exact critical value is not listed. One method is to choose the highest critical value, corresponding with the lower degrees of freedom because it is a conservative estimate of the actual critical value. As a result, it is more difficult to reject the null hypothesis, and the Type I error set for the statistical test (e.g., .05) will not be exceeded by using the larger critical value for hypothesis testing. This method is certainly a reasonable approach, though it tends to yield overly conservative critical values. A second method for choosing the critical value for unlisted degrees of freedom is to estimate or extrapolate the critical value based on the two nearest critical values. Although exact formulas for extrapolation are available, we will use a more crude estimation procedure for illustration. Since 96 is quite close to 100, the critical value we will use is 2.70.

Step 7: Compare the calculated F to the critical F at the .05 level.

Since the calculated F of 2.43 is not larger than the critical F of 2.70, the problem is solved and the final decision is to not reject the null hypothesis. There is no significant difference among the four group means.

Step 8: Look up the critical value at the .01 level.

This step is not applicable for this problem, since the null hypothesis could not be rejected at the .05 level. However, if H_0 had been rejected at the .05 level, steps 8 and 9 would be performed using a critical value at the .01 level

of approximately 3.99 for 3 and 96 degrees of freedom.

Step 9: Compare the calculated F to the critical F at the .01 level.

Again, this step is not applicable for the current example, since H_0 was not rejected when tested at the .05 level.

Step 10: State the final conclusion both statistically and in words.

The final conclusion stated statistically is to not reject H_0. In words, the conclusion is that there is no significant difference among the four groups. Increased family meetings did not cause a significant reduction in delinquent behavior among troubled children. If H_0 had been rejected, the next step at this point would be to conduct a post-hoc test, such as a Scheffé, in order to determine which groups were significantly different from which other groups.

ANOVA Formula Summary

Table 7.1 provides a summary of the formulas used for completing the single-factor or one-way ANOVA table.

TABLE 7.1: Single-Factor ANOVA Summary Table

Source of Variation (Source)	Sum of Squares (SS)	Degrees of Freedom (df)	Mean Square (MS)	Calculated F-value (F)
Between	$\sum n_k (X - \bar{X}_k)^2$	$K - 1$	$\dfrac{SS_{Between}}{df_{Between}}$	$F = \dfrac{MS_{Between}}{MS_{Within}}$
Within	$\sum (\bar{X}_k - \bar{X}_{Grand})^2$	$N - K$	$\dfrac{SS_{Within}}{df_{Within}}$	
Total	$\sum (X - \bar{X}_{Grand})$	$N - 1$		

Summary

ANOVA, short for ANalysis Of VAriance, is used to test differences in means among more than two groups. The single-factor analysis of variance involves a single independent variable with three or more levels. The test statistic for the ANOVA is the F, which is the ratio of the variance between groups compared to the variance within groups. When the variance between groups is large and the variance within groups is small, there is a greater likelihood that the observed difference between means is significant and not due to chance. The critical values for the F-test are obtained from a series of distributions of the ratios of two variances called the F-distributions. F-distributions are referenced by the two degrees of freedom values in the numerator and denominator of the variances ratio (for between- and within-groups). The F-table contains the critical values which exclude the uppermost 5% or 1% of the F-distribution. If the F-test is significant, a post-hoc test is used to determine exactly which groups differ significantly from which other groups.

Key Terms

- ANOVA table
- F-distributions
- F-table
- F-test
- factor
- mean square
- mean square between groups
- mean square within groups
- multiple factor
- post-hoc test
- single factor
- single-factor (one-way) analysis of variance (ANOVA)
- sum of squares between groups ($SS_{Between}$)
- sum of squares within groups (SS_{Within})
- sum of squares total (SS_{Total})

Problems

1. To compare the difference between sample means for only two groups, a(n) _____ test is conducted, whereas to compare the differences among sample means for more than two groups a(n) _____ test is used.

2. What is another name for an independent variable?

3. In order to detect significant differences among groups, which should be larger: *between-group differences* or *within-group differences*?

4. A(n) _____ test indicates that there is a significant difference among some of the group means, whereas a(n) _____ test indicates which groups in particular differ from one another.

5. Can a t-test be used as a post-hoc test? Why or why not?

6. When should a post-hoc test be conducted?

7. Can both one-tailed and two-tailed F-tests be conducted as with the t-test? Why or why not?

8. For each of the following, indicate what the appropriate statistical decision is: reject H_0 at $p < .05$, reject H_0 at $p < .01$, do not reject (accept) H_0, or cannot be determined from the information given.

a. F = 2.91   4 groups   10 subjects per group

b. F = 2.70 $df_{Between} = 9$ $df_{Within} = 80$

c. F = 3.00   5 groups   15 subjects in the first group

d. F = 3.67   3 groups   17 total subjects in the study

e. F = 2.40   13 groups   32 subjects per group

9. Given the partial ANOVA table below, answer the following questions:

Source	SS	df	MS	F
Between	82.8	3	27.60	
Within	69.2	16	4.32	
Total	152.0	19		

a. How many groups or conditions were in this study?
b. How many total subjects participated in this study?
c. Conduct an F-test.
d. State your final decision both statistically and in words.

10. Given the partial ANOVA table below, answer the following questions:

Source	SS	df	MS	F
Between	50	5	10	
Within	25	5	5	
Total	75	10		

a. How many groups or conditions were in this study?
b. How many total subjects participated in this study?
c. Compute the F-value.
d. State your decision both statistically and in words.

11. A researcher hypothesizes that children who watch different types of *Star Trek* programs will have different beliefs about the possibility of life on other planets. Forty children are taken from a 5th grade classroom and an equal number are randomly assigned to watch one of four different versions of *Star Trek*: the original *Star Trek* program, *Star Trek: The Next Generation* (TNG), *Star Trek: Deep Space Nine*

(DS9), or *Star Trek: Voyager*. After children view the appropriate program they are asked how possible it is for life to exist on other planets on a scale ranging from 1 to 5, where 1 represents "not at all possible" and 5 represents "very, very possible." The data yield the following partial ANOVA table and group means:

Source	SS	df	MS	F
Between	55			
Within	140			
Total	195			

$\overline{X}_{Original} = 2.34 \quad \overline{X}_{TNG} = 4.56 \quad \overline{X}_{DS9} = 1.44$
$\overline{X}_{Voyager} = 1.69$

a. State the null and research hypotheses.
b. How many children watched *Star Trek: Deep Space Nine*?
c. Complete the ANOVA table and conduct an F-test.
d. State your final decision both statistically and in words.
e. Basing your answer on your analysis, which group(s) are significantly more likely to believe that life exists on other planets?

Suppose instead that the ANOVA table and group means for this problem was as follows:

Source	SS	df	MS	F
Between	25			
Within	85			
Total	110			

$\overline{X}_{Original} = 4.44 \quad \overline{X}_{TNG} = 4.20 \quad \overline{X}_{DS9} = 4.35$
$\overline{X}_{Voyager} = 4.10$

f. Complete the ANOVA table and conduct an F-test.

g. State your decision both statistically and in words.

h. Basing your answer on your analysis, which group(s) are significantly more likely to believe that life on other planets is possible?

12. An experimenter hypothesizes that factory workers will differ in their productivity according to how much positive reinforcement they receive from their supervisors. The researcher randomly assigns 10 employees to receive, unbeknownst to them, 5 minutes of positive reinforcement per day from their immediate supervisors. Ten additional employees are randomly assigned to receive 10 minutes of praise per day, and 10 more employees are assigned to receive 15 minutes of praise per day. One month later the researcher returns and measures the employees' productivity rates in terms of the number of Widgets produced per hour. The data obtained from this study were the following:

Source	SS	df	MS	F
Between	180			
Within	800			
Total	980			

$\overline{X}_{5\,minutes} = 836$　$\overline{X}_{10\,minutes} = 884$
$\overline{X}_{15\,minutes} = 912$

a. State the null and research hypotheses.

b. How many total employees participated in this study?

c. Complete the ANOVA table and conduct an F-test.

d. State your decision both statistically and in words.

e. Basing your answer on your analysis, how many minutes per day would you recommend that supervisors praise

their employees to obtain significantly higher productivity rates?

Instead of 10 employees per condition, suppose there had been 20 employees per condition, with the remainder of the information identical from above:

Source	SS	df	MS	F
Between	180			
Within	800			
Total	980			

$\overline{X}_{5\,minutes} = 836$　$\overline{X}_{10\,minutes} = 884$
$\overline{X}_{15\,minutes} = 912$

f. Complete the ANOVA table and conduct an F-test.

g. State your decision both statistically and in words.

h. Basing your answer on your analysis, how many minutes per day would you recommend that supervisors praise their employees to obtain significantly higher productivity rates?

13. A researcher is interested in whether people's enjoyment of pop music is affected by how tired they are. In particular, she hypothesizes that pop music is more enjoyable the more tired one is when he or she hears it. The researcher solicits 15 subjects to participate in a study. Of these, 5 are randomly assigned to sleep 8 hours every night for one week; another 5 are randomly assigned to sleep 6 hours every night for one week, and the remaining 5 subjects are randomly assigned to sleep only 4 hours per night for one week. At the end of one week, all participants listen to a popular Rolling Stones' song and are then asked to rate how much they enjoyed listening to the song on a 7-point scale, where 1 = "did not enjoy at all" and 7 =

"enjoyed very much." The following ratings are obtained for the 15 participants:

4 hours	6 hours	8 hours
6	5	3
5	6	2
7	5	2
6	4	5
6	5	3

Complete the ANOVA table for this problem, including calculating the sum of squares values, and conduct the F-test. Be sure to indicate your final answer for this problem both statistically and in words. Based on the results, is there a relationship between tiredness and enjoyment of pop music?

Notes

1 The actual probability of a Type I error is .14 when the null hypothesis is rejected for three tests: $\alpha = 1 - (1 - \alpha)^p$, where p = the number of tests for which the null hypothesis is rejected. With three t-tests, $\alpha = 1 - (1 - \alpha)^p = 1 - (1 - .05)^3 = 1 - .86 = .14$

2 As described in Chapter 3, the variance is calculated based on the sum of squared deviations of each individual score around the group mean:

$$V = \frac{SS}{N} = \frac{\sum (X - \overline{X})^2}{N}$$

and the standard deviation is the square root of the variance:

$$SD = \sqrt{\frac{SS}{N}} = \sqrt{\frac{\sum (X - \overline{X})^2}{N}}$$

The Impact of Disputants' Expectations on Mediation: Testing an Interventionist Model

Adapted from article by same title, Burrell, N. A., Donohue, W. A, & Allen, M. (1990). *Human Communication Research, 17,* 104-139.

THIS STUDY examined factors influencing the mediation of a dispute between roommates when a mediator intervened in the dispute. Specifically, the researchers were interested in how roommates' expectations about reaching an agreement in a dispute influenced the mediation process compared with other variables, and how the different participants viewed the mediation process. Participants in the study were undergraduate roommates. Students were randomly assigned to one of three expectation conditions: low expectation of resolution, moderate expectation of resolution, or high expectation of resolution. Level of expectation was manipulated by having students attempt to resolve a series of conflicts with a confederate or cohort of the researcher. Students in the low expectation condition were unable to resolve any of the conflicts with the confederate whereas those in the high expectation condition were able to resolve all of the conflicts. Students in the moderate expectation condition were able to resolve half of the conflicts and unable to resolve the other half.

(continued on page 143)

The Impact of Disputants' Expectations on Mediation: Testing an Interventionist Model (continued)

In order to study the influence of level of expectation on the mediation process, the researchers needed to ascertain that, indeed, their manipulation of level of expectation was successful. That is, did students who resolved none of the conflicts with the confederate in the low expectation condition actually have a lower expectation of later resolving a conflict with their roommate than did those subjects in either the moderate or high expectation conditions? To answer this question, the researchers conducted a "manipulation check" to verify that their manipulation of the variable "level of expectation" was successful:

> The second manipulation check focused on whether or not participants' expectations were altered regarding the likelihood of resolving disputes successfully. Three separate one-way ANOVAs were performed using level of expectation (low, moderate, and high) for resolving disputes as the independent variable with dependent variables related to the likelihood of resolution (percentage of success in resolving the next dispute, ability to reach an agreement based on the past, and prediction of success in future conflicts). The following results indicate clear differences between the three groups when predicting their ability to resolve disputes.
>
> First, participants were asked what percentage chance they believed that they had in resolving the next roommate conflict. The results showed a difference (F = 1103.51, df = 2/179, p < .05, eta = .92) between the low (M = 14.08, SD = 9.56, n = 62), moderate (M = 49.52, SD = 9.57, n = 62) and high (M = 90.48, SD = 7.29, n = 58) expectation groups. Second, participants were asked to what degree they were able to reach an agreement in previous conflicts. These results also indicate a difference (F = 818.08, df = 2/179, p < .05, eta = .90) between the low (M = 1.27, SD = .45, n =62), moderate (M = 3.91, SD = .96, n = 62), and high (M = 6.64, SD = .67, n = 58) level of expectation groups. Finally, participants asked to what extent they anticipated reaching an agreement in future conflicts. Results show a difference (F = 569.69, df = 2/179, p < .05, eta = .86) between the low (M = 1.82, SD = .50, n = 62), moderate (M = 4.21, SD = .83, n = 62), and high (M = 6.17, SD = .75, n = 58) groups. Thus, the manipulation for inducing levels of expectations was successful.

The researchers had indeed successfully manipulated students' expectations of conflict resolution. [Note that the "eta" reported with each F-test refers to the size of the effect observed. A higher number indicates a larger effect size, meaning that more of the variation in the dependent variable observed across the groups is explained by the independent variable rather than by other factors.]

Self-Esteem of Persons Seeking Dates via Bars, Singles Clubs, and Personal Advertisements

Adapted from article by same title, Yelsma, P., & Wienir, P. (1996). *Sociological Spectrum, 16,* 27-41.

THE LEVEL of satisfaction of single adults seeking dates or mates in three date-meeting environments – bars, singles clubs, and personal advertisements in newspapers – was examined in this study. One of three hypotheses proposed by the researchers was:

> Date seekers who utilize bars will have the highest self-esteem; those who attend singles clubs will have intermediate self-esteem – a level between bar users and newspaper advertisers; and newspaper advertisers will have the lowest self-esteem.

Three sets of data were collected using identical questionnaires in the same geographic region. People advertising in local daily newspapers were mailed a questionnaire whereas people who were club participants and bar patrons had questionnaires distributed to them at the club or bar. Although the data were collected deliberately in one dating environment, approximately half of the date-seekers employed more than one method of meeting people. In an attempt to avoid the effect of multiple environmental influence on date seekers, participants were reclassified into seven distinct categories: advertisers, bar, club, advertisers plus bar, advertisers plus club, bar plus club, and advertisers plus bar plus club. The questionnaire contained several questions on dating satisfaction, biographical information, and Coopersmith's (1967) 50-item Self-Esteem Inventory. The results were reported as follows:

> One-way analysis of variance on the self-esteem scale revealed a significant main effect between the seven categories of date seekers ($F[6, 141]=2.60$, $p < .02$), indicating that respondents' self-esteem varied significantly across the seven methods of meeting people. Post hoc tests of comparison revealed significant differences in the self-esteem of respondents between four combinations of methods of meeting people. No differences in self-esteem were found among those who used only one type of date-seeking method. Those seekers who employed all three methods at one time or another revealed lower self-esteem than those who socialized only in clubs. Respondents who utilized newspaper advertising and clubs had significantly lower self-esteem scores than date seekers who utilized clubs only, bars only or clubs plus bars. Although our first hypothesis was not supported, there were significant differences among people who used single or combined methods for seeking dates.

(continued on page 145)

Self-Esteem of Persons Seeking Dates via Bars, Singles Clubs, and Personal Advertisements (continued)

The researchers found that self-esteem does not appear to be associated with the types of environments people choose for seeking dates when they use only one environment. However, they discovered that people who utilized more than one environment for meeting people had significantly lower self-esteem than did those who used only one environment. The researchers observe that this finding may be explained in one of two ways: (1) those with lower self-esteem may select multiple ways to meet people, or (2) those who use multiple environments to meet people develop lower self-esteem. A summary of the researcher's findings were provided via the following table:

Means, Standard Deviations, and Numbers of Respondents Who Utilized Seven Methods for Meeting Dates (only data pertaining to H1 were reported below; adapted from original article)

Group Number	Methods Utilized	Mean Self-Esteem	SD	N
2	Club	78.7	13.8	29
1	Advertiser	74.2	14.4	11
5	Advertiser + Bar	74.0	16.0	25
3	Bar	72.5	13.9	42
6	Club + Bar	69.2	20.3	18
7	Club + Bar + Advertiser	63.5	18.7	15
4	Advertiser + Club	58.3	26.6	8
S	Single Method	74.9	14.1	82
M	Multiple Methods	68.4	19.6	66

Note: Significant differences ($p < .05$) occurred in self-esteem between groups 1 and 4; 2 and 4; 3 and 4; 5, 2 and 7. Also, self-esteem of single-method date seekers was significantly different ($p < .02$) from the multiple-method date seekers.

Computer Section

Interpretation of Single-Factor ANOVA Output

This single-factor ANOVA examined differences in means for the dependent variable LIFESAT (General Life Satisfaction) across three groups or levels of the independent variable LAUGH (Frequency of Laughter). The output depicts the major computational steps in the form of a summary ANOVA table. The sum of squares for each source of variability is given along with the corresponding degrees of freedom. The between-groups degrees of freedom equals the number of groups minus one, $df_{Between} = K - 1 = 3 - 1 = 2$; the within-groups degrees of freedom equals the total number of subjects in the study minus the total number of groups, $df_{Within} = N - K = 318 - 3 = 315$; and the total degrees of freedom equals the sum of the between- and within-groups degrees of freedom or the total number of subjects in the study minus one, $df_{Total} = N - 1 = 318 - 1 = 317$. The mean square values equal the sum of squares divided by the degrees of freedom. For example:

$$MS_{Between} = \frac{SS_{Between}}{df_{Between}} = \frac{18.5630}{2} = 9.2815$$

Finally, the F-value equals the mean square between divided by the mean square within:

$$F = \frac{MS_{Between}}{MS_{Within}} = \frac{9.2815}{.6020} = 15.4182$$

The calculated F-value is tested at 2 and 315 degrees of freedom and is significant at $p = .0000$. Thus, there is a highly significant difference in mean life satisfaction ratings among the three groups.

Following the significant F-test findings on the computer output are the results of Scheffé's post-hoc test, indicating which of the three groups differ significantly from which of the other three groups. Scheffé's test compares each group with every other group and those

Overview of Single-Factor ANOVA

Single-factor analysis of variance involves assessing whether there is a significant difference in means among three or more levels of a single independent variable. Conducting a single-factor analysis of variance on the computer involves using an ANOVA command and specifying: (1) the independent variable on which mean differences among groups are to be compared, (2) the levels of the independent variable (e.g., 1-3 for three groups), and (3) the dependent variable. A variety of options exist for the printed output, including the means of each of the groups and the results of a post-hoc test such as the Scheffé if a significant F is obtained.

Example Output for Single-Factor ANOVA

Studies have suggested that laughter may contribute to people's overall sensation of well-being in the same way that exercise does. A researcher randomly assigned a total of 318 people from a large corporation to three different conditions. The groups consisted of 106 people each and differed by the number of times per day they pause for laughter and merrymaking: 25 times (group 1), 15 times (group 2), or 5 times per day (group 3). At the end of one week all subjects completed a questionnaire regarding their general sense of life satisfaction on a scale from 1 to 4, with a 4 indicating a higher level of life satisfaction. Table 7.2 shows the results that were obtained from the one-way ANOVA.

TABLE 7.2

O N E W A Y

Variable LIFESAT   GENERAL LIFE SATISFACTION
By Variable LAUGH   FREQUENCY OF LAUGHTER

Analysis of Variance

Source	D.F.	Sum of Squares	Mean Squares	F Ratio	F Prob.
Between Groups	2	18.5630	9.2815	15.4182	.0000
Within Groups	315	189.6256	.6020		
Total	317	208.1887			

Multiple Range Tests: Scheffé test with significance level .05

The difference between two means is significant if MEAN(J)-MEAN(I) >= .5486 * RANGE * SQRT(1/N(I) + 1/N(J)) with the following value(s) for RANGE: 3.48

(*) Indicates significant differences which are shown in the lower triangle

```
                          G   G   G
                          r   r   r
                          p   p   p
                          3   2   1
Mean          CLASS
1.7500        Grp 3
2.0496        Grp 2       *
2.7059        Grp 1       *   *
```

Group	Count	Standard Mean	Standard Deviation	Error	95 Pct Conf Int for Mean
Grp 1	106	2.7059	.7717	.1872	2.3091 TO 3.1027
Grp 2	106	2.0496	.8394	.0707	1.9099 TO 2.1894
Grp 3	106	1.7313	.7157	.0566	1.6195 TO 1.8430
Total	318	1.9245	.8104	.0454	1.8351 TO 2.0139

GROUP	MINIMUM	MAXIMUM
Grp 1	1.0000	4.0000
Grp 2	1.0000	4.0000
Grp 3	1.0000	4.0000
TOTAL	1.0000	4.0000

which differ significantly from each other at the .05 significance level are identified with an asterisk (*). These results reveal that Group 1 differs significantly from both Groups 2 and 3 and that Group 2 differs significantly from Group 3. Thus, each group differs significantly from each other group.

The final part of the computer output provides basic descriptive information for the independent variable, including the means, standard deviations, and minimum and maximum values for each of the three groups. These descriptive data reveal that Group 1 (laughing 25 times per day) had a mean life satisfaction score of $\overline{X}_{25} = 2.7059$, Group 2 (laughing 15 times per day) had a mean life satisfaction score of $\overline{X}_{15} = 2.0496$, and Group 3 (laughing 5 times per day) had a mean life satisfaction score of $\overline{X}_5 = 1.7313$.

Overall, people who laugh 25 times per day are significantly more satisfied with their lives than are people who laugh either 15 or 5 times per day, and people who laugh 15 times per day are significantly more satisfied with their lives than are people who laugh only 5 times per day. Thus, laughter causes increased life satisfaction.

Computer Problems

1. Conduct F-tests to examine the following hypotheses regarding differences among the three class structures (**CLASS**) and indicate whether the null hypothesis should be rejected or not rejected in each case. If a significant F is obtained, identify which groups differ significantly from which other groups based on the results of Scheffé's post-hoc test.
   a. Students in the cooperative classroom will rate the instructor higher in rapport (**RAPPORT**) than will students in either the competitive or individualistic classrooms.
   b. Students in the cooperative classroom will rate the instructor as more friendly (**FRIEND**) than will students in either the competitive or individualistic classrooms.
   c. Students in the competitive classroom will rate the class as more challenging (**CHALL**) than will students in either the cooperative or individualistic classrooms.
   d. Students in the individualistic classroom will indicate they put greater effort in the course (**EFFORT**) than will students in either the competitive or cooperative classrooms.
   e. Students in the cooperative classroom will rate e-mail more favorably (**FAVOR**) than will students in the competitive or individualistic classrooms.
2. Conduct F-tests to examine the following hypotheses regarding differences among the four student class levels (**CLSLVL**) and indicate whether the null hypothesis should be rejected or not rejected in each case. If a significant F is obtained, identify which groups differ significantly from which other groups based on the results of Scheffé's post-hoc test.
   a. Freshmen will indicate that the instructor had a higher level of knowledge (**KNOW**) than will the other three class levels.
   b. Juniors will rate the instructor as more outgoing (**OUTGOING**) than will sophomores.
   c. Seniors will be more likely to indicate having learned something valuable from the course (**VALUE**) than will the other three class levels.
   d. Juniors and seniors will indicate feeling more comfortable seeking help from the instructor (**SEEK**) than will the freshmen and sophomores.

Chapter 8 ❖ Multiple-Factor Analysis of Variance (ANOVA)

Introduction to Multiple-Factor ANOVA

Multiple-factor analysis of variance continues the set of tests, z, t, and F, used to explore mean differences among groups. Recall that the appropriate statistical is determined by identifying each of the following components: (1) the level of measurement of the dependent variable, (2) the number of independent variables, and (3) the number of levels for each independent variable. The z-, t-, and F-tests each involve one dependent variable measured at the interval- or ratio-level. The two-sample z- and t-tests are based on one independent variable with two levels, with the appropriate test determined by whether the population variance is known (z-test if known, t-test if estimated from sample). Sample means for two groups (i.e., two levels of one independent variable) are compared to determine if the groups represent the same population. The one-way F-test (single-factor ANOVA) also involves one independent variable but having three or more levels. Again, group means are compared to determine if the samples are part of the same population. Finally, the multi-way F-test (multiple-factor ANOVA) involves more than one independent variable. That is, group means are compared where groups are defined as a function of two or more independent variables. This type of problem is termed a factorial design and is critical for understanding how multiple-factor ANOVA is conducted.

Factorial Designs

A *factorial design* is a type of experimental design in which subjects are randomly assigned to groups defined by two or more independent variables or factors. Factorial designs are a popular methodological approach because most events that occur are not determined by only one cause. Rather, most events are the result of many variables. For example, the type of person one is as an adult is influenced by the individual's family, peers, schooling, church and social activities, and so forth. That is, the variability of adult lifestyles is a function of multiple factors. Thus, when studying a particular event, many researchers wish to examine several of the most important causal factors that they believe influence the event's outcome.

Consider, for instance, the single-factor ANOVA problem from the previous chapter. The researcher was interested in the effect of a particular type of study technique on students' exam performance. As presented, this problem involved one independent variable or factor, type of study technique, which had three levels or conditions: use of a study guide, attendance at an extra help session, and no study guide or extra help (control). If the researcher had a total of 60 subjects to allocate to the conditions in this study, she would randomly assign 20 students to each group:

Study Guide	Help Session	Control
$N_{SG} = 20$	$N_{HS} = 20$	$N_C = 20$

Although there is nothing technically wrong with this one-way design, an alternative approach is to view this as a study with two factors rather than one. That is, instead of involving a single independent variable (type of study technique), this problem could be conceptualized as consisting of two independent variables: presence of a study guide (yes, no) and presence of an extra help session (yes, no). These two factors can be crossed with each other to produce a factorial design in which each level of the first factor is combined with each level of the second factor:

```
                            Presence of
                            Study Guide
                         ........................
                           Yes        No
                        ┌──────────┬──────────┐
Presence of      : Yes  │    I     │    II    │
Help Session     :      ├──────────┼──────────┤
                 : No   │   III    │    IV    │
                        └──────────┴──────────┘
```

FIGURE 8.1: A 2 x 2 factorial design with two independent variables – presence of study guide and presence of help session

Each block is called a *cell* in the factorial design, and can also be referred to as a condition or group. Block III (bottom left), for instance, represents a group of students who received the study guide (Presence of Study Guide = Yes) but did not attend the help session (Presence of Help Session = No), analogous to the Study Guide group in the one-way layout. Similarly, those in Block II attended a help session but did not receive the study guide, analogous to the Help Session group in the one-way layout. Finally, students in Block IV neither received the study guide nor attended a help session, analogous to the Control group in the one-way layout. However, notice that the two-way layout of the factorial design actually has four not three groups. The fourth group of students, Block I, received both the study guide and attended the help session,

representing a combination of the two factors. This block allows the researcher to determine whether the two factors (study guide and help session) interact with one another in any way, such that perhaps the highest exam score occurs among students who both use the study guide and attend the help session (Block I) or among those who do neither (Block IV). The ability to test for this interaction is not possible with the one-way layout. No group received both the study guide and help session in the single-factor ANOVA design. Thus, one important benefit of a factorial design over a single-factor layout is the ability to test for interactions of independent variables.

A second benefit of the factorial design comes in the form of increased power. Recall that power refers to the ability to detect significant differences among groups. One way to increase power that was discussed with respect to the t-test in Chapter 6 was to increase the size of the sample. The more subjects per group, the more ability or power one has to detect a significant difference among the groups. With the 60 available subjects, the one-way layout yielded 20 students who received the study guide and 20 students who went to the help session. If these same 60 subjects are randomly assigned to conditions in the factorial design, with an equal number of subjects in each condition, the following distribution of subjects is obtained, where N equals number of subjects:

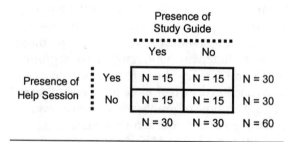

FIGURE 8.2: Random assignment of a total of N = 60 subjects to conditions of a 2 x 2 factorial design

With the factorial design, notice that a total of 30 students received the study guide, not 20. Fifteen students received the study guide and attended a help session and an additional 15 students received the study guide but did not attend a help session. Thus, regardless of what help session status students had, a total of 30 students received the study guide. Similarly, the number of students who attended a help session, regardless of whether or not they received a study guide, also was 30. With 10 additional students receiving a study guide and 10 additional students attending a help session, the factorial design is more powerful than the one-way layout with the same total number of subjects. In sum, a factorial design provides increased power over a conventional one-way (single-factor) layout due to an increased number of subjects across levels of the independent variables.

For ease of reference, factorial designs are referred to in terms of the number of independent variables and the number of levels of each independent variable. For instance, the current problem is an example of a 2 x 2 factorial design. The *number* of numbers indicates how many independent variables there are. Since this problem has two factors, presence of study guide and presence of help session, there are two numbers given. The *value* of each number indicates the number of levels of each independent variable. Since both factors have two levels (Yes, No), the value of each number is 2. The number of conditions or groups there are can be derived easily by simply multiplying the levels of each independent variable. In this problem, there are a total of 2 x 2 = 4 conditions.

A 2 x 2 is the simplest form of a factorial design. Other factorial designs may have more than two factors and/or more than two levels for each independent variable. For instance, a researcher is interested in whether there is a difference in mean heart rate among younger (< 35), middle-aged (35-45), and older (> 45) males and females who jog, swim, ride bicycle, or play tennis for one hour per day. The dependent measure is heart rate, which is ratio-level data. This study involves three independent variables: IV #1 = age group (<35, 35-45, >45); IV #2 = gender (male, female); IV #3 = exercise activity (jogging, swimming, biking, tennis). This is a 3 x 2 x 4 factorial design with 24 groups. There are three numbers designating the factorial design because there are three independent variables. The first number equals 3 because there are three levels to the first independent variable, age group. The second number equals 2 because there are two levels to the second independent variable, gender. Finally, the third number equals 4 because there are four levels to the third inde-

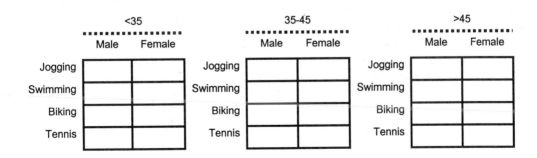

FIGURE 8.3: A 3 x 2 x 4 factorial design with three independent variables – age group, gender, and exercise activity

pendent variable, exercise activity. A pictorial layout of this factorial design (Figure 8.3) illustrates each of the 24 groups.

Main and Interaction Effects

With a one-way or single-factor ANOVA, there was only one F-test conducted to determine if there was any difference among the levels of the single independent variable. However, with a factorial design, there are multiple independent variables which can be examined for differences. For instance, with the 2 x 2 factorial design above there are actually three F-test tests to be conducted. The first F-test determines if students who used the study guide scored significantly different than students who did not use the study guide. Such a statistical procedure tests for a main effect of that independent variable. A *main effect* is an effect or difference across levels for a single independent variable. In this example, the first F-test assesses if there is a main effect for presence of study guide. The second statistical test assesses if students who attended the help session scored differently than students who did not attend the help session. Again, since only one independent variable is involved, this statistical test determines if there is a main effect for presence of help session. Finally, the third F-test assesses whether there is a difference in mean exam score for students as a function of both study guide and help session. This statistical test examines whether an interaction exists between the two independent variables. An *interaction effect* is an effect or difference across levels of two or more independent variables. In this example, the third F-test assesses if there is an interaction effect between presence of study guide and presence of help session. Each of the three F-tests described above is included as part of a single statistical procedure known as multiple-factor ANOVA,

which controls the Type I error of conducting many tests.

With the 3 x 2 x 4 example with age group, gender, and exercise activity, there are actually seven different F-tests conducted as part of the multiple-factor ANOVA. With three independent variables, there are three possible main effects to be tested: a main effect for age group, a main effect for gender, and a main effect for exercise activity. There also are four possible interaction effects. First, there is a possible two-way interaction between age group and gender. Second, there is a possible two-way interaction between age group and exercise activity. Third, there is a possible two-way interaction between gender and exercise activity. Thus, there are three possible two-way interaction effects to be tested via separate F-tests. Finally, there is a possible three-way interaction among all three factors in the study, age group, gender, and exercise activity.

The null and alternative hypotheses used to test for main effects are the same as those described for the single-factor ANOVA problem. For instance, the researcher may hypothesize that there will be a difference in exam scores between those who receive the study guide and those who do not, that is, that there will be a main effect for presence of study guide. The corresponding null and alternative hypotheses for the test of this main effect are:

$$H_0: \mu_{SG} = \mu_{No\ SG}$$
$$H_a: \mu_{SG} \neq \mu_{No\ SG}$$

If the researcher had hypothesized that those who obtained the study guide would score higher than those who did not use the study guide, the null and research hypotheses could be phrased as directional hypotheses, H_0: $\mu_{SG} \leq \mu_{No\ SG}$ and H_a: $\mu_{SG} > \mu_{No\ SG}$, although the F-test is conducted exactly the same way for both nondirectional and directional hypotheses. The null and research hypotheses for the test of the main effect for presence of help session are the same as those for presence of study guide:

$$H_0: \mu_{HS} = \mu_{No\ HS}$$
$$H_a: \mu_{HS} \neq \mu_{No\ HS}$$

To help conceptualize a main effect, consider the following cell and marginal means obtained from the 60 students participating in this study:

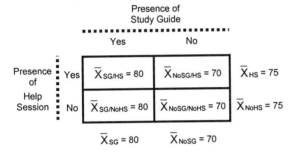

FIGURE 8.4: Main effect for presence of study guide, no main effect for presence of help session, no interaction effect

The group that received a study guide and attended a help session had a mean score of 80, indicated by the cell mean $\overline{X}_{SG/HS} = 80$. Similarly, the group that received the study guide but did not attend the help session had a mean $\overline{X}_{SG/NoHS} = 80$. Because there were an equal number of subjects in each of the two conditions that received a study guide, N = 15 per group, the two cell means can be averaged to form the marginal mean of $\overline{X}_{SG} = 80$ for all students who received the study guide (N = 30). Alternatively, the 30 individual students' scores can be averaged to obtain this same mean. The marginal mean for students who did not use the study guide, regardless of whether they attended a help session, was $\overline{X}_{NoSG} = 70$. For the purpose of these conceptual illustrations, we will assume that any difference in means is a significant difference. Later in this chapter we will discuss exactly how main and interaction effects are tested for sig-

nificance. Since those who received the study guide scored significantly different ($\overline{X}_{SG} = 80$) than did those who did not receive the study guide ($\overline{X}_{NoSG} = 70$), there is a main effect for presence of study guide. Students who used the study guide scored higher than did those who did not use the study guide. Notice that the main effect is for the independent variable, presence of study guide, not for the levels of the variable (study guide vs. no study guide). Additionally, note that the test for the main effect is across levels of the other independent variable, presence of help session. Thus, to test for main effects, only the marginal means are of interest.

To determine if there is a main effect for presence of help session, the second independent variable, the same procedure is conducted. With equal sample sizes in each condition, the marginal means are determined by simply averaging the cell means for each level of the independent variable. Thus, for instance, the marginal mean for those who attended a help session $\overline{X}_{HS} = 75$ is the average score of those who attended the help session and received a study guide $\overline{X}_{SG/HS} = 80$ and those who attended a help session but did not receive a study guide $\overline{X}_{NoSG/HS} = 70$. Examining the marginal means for the two levels of this second independent variable reveals no main effect for presence of help session since those who attended the help session scored the same ($\overline{X}_{HS} = 75$) as did those who did not attend the help session ($\overline{X}_{NoHS} = 75$).

In addition to examination of the marginal means, main effects also can be identified from a graphical depiction of the cell means. With a simple 2 x 2 factorial design, the levels of one factor are plotted on the x-axis and the levels of the second factor are plotted inside the graph. Which factor is plotted on the x-axis is arbitrary, and both graphs yield the same results. For the present example, Figure 8.5 depicts the two equivalent alternative graphical depictions of the mean results.

There are two general rules for identifying main effects from these graphical depictions: (1) if the lines inside the graph are not parallel to the x-axis, there is a main effect for the factor plotted on the x-axis; (2) if the lines inside the graph do not coincide or overlap, there is a main effect for the factor plotted inside the graph. Applying these rules to the left graph in Figure 8.5, there is a main effect for presence of study guide and no main effect for presence of help session. First, because the lines inside the graph are not parallel to the x-axis, there is a main effect for presence of study guide. Second, because the lines overlap (the lines appear separated in the graph only to highlight that there are two lines), there is no main effect for presence of help session. Similarly, when the same rules are applied to the right graph in Figure 8.5 identical results are obtained. First, because the lines inside the graph are parallel to the x-axis, there is no main effect for presence of help session. Second, because the lines inside the graph do not overlap, there is a main effect for presence of study guide.

Testing for an interaction effect between the two factors requires that each cell mean be examined, since an interaction indicates that the difference in means across levels of the

second factor at one level of the first factor is not the same as the difference in means across levels of the second factor at the second level of the first factor. This idea should become clearer through an example. The null and research hypotheses involved in testing for the two-way interaction can be stated one of two ways, depending upon which independent variable is designated as the first factor and which is designated as the second. Assuming the first factor is presence of help session and the second factor is presence of study guide, the null and research hypotheses are:

H_0: $\mu_{SG/HS} - \mu_{No\ SG/HS} = \mu_{SG/No\ HS} - \mu_{No\ SG/No\ HS}$
H_a: $\mu_{SG/HS} - \mu_{No\ SG/HS} \neq \mu_{SG/No\ HS} - \mu_{No\ SG/No\ HS}$

Testing the null hypothesis involves examining whether the difference between using the study guide or not for those who attended the help session is the same as the difference between using the study guide or not for those who did not attend the help session. If this difference is the same, there is no interaction since the combination of the two factors does not differentially influence subjects. For those who attended a help session (the top row cell means in Figure 8.4), the difference between means for those who used a study guide vs. those who did not is as follows:

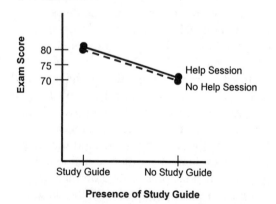

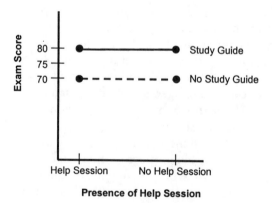

FIGURE 8.5: Main effect for presence of study guide, no main effect for presence of help session, no interaction effect

$$\overline{X}_{SG/HS} - \overline{X}_{NoSG/HS} = 80 - 70 = 10$$

By this same method, for those who did not attend a help session (the bottom row cell means in Figure 8.4), the difference between means for those who used a study guide vs. those who did not is as follows:

$$\overline{X}_{SG/NoHS} - \overline{X}_{NoSG/NoHS} = 80 - 70 = 10$$

Since these two differences are identical (10 = 10), there is no interaction effect.

The results are identical if the first factor is designated as presence of study guide and the second factor is presence of help session, with the following null and research hypotheses:

H_0: $\mu_{SG/HS}$ - $\mu_{SG/No\,HS}$ = $\mu_{No\,SG/HS}$ - $\mu_{No\,SG/No\,HS}$

H_a: $\mu_{SG/HS}$ - $\mu_{SG/No\,HS}$ ≠ $\mu_{No\,SG/HS}$ - $\mu_{No\,SG/No\,HS}$

Here, testing the null hypothesis involves examining whether the difference between attending the help session or not for those who used the study guide is the same as the difference between attending the help session or not for those who did not use the study guide. In this case, the means from the first column in Figure 8.4 are subtracted, $\overline{X}_{SG/HS} - \overline{X}_{SG/NoHS} = 80 - 80 = 0$, and compared with the difference in means from the second column $\overline{X}_{NoSG/HS} - \overline{X}_{NoSG/NoHS} = 70 - 70 = 0$. Since these two differences are identical (0 = 0), there is no interaction effect. Whether cell means are subtracted across rows or across columns, the results are identical: there is no interaction effect.

The rule for identifying interactions graphically is very simple: if the two lines inside the graph are not parallel to each other, there is an interaction. Referring to the left graph in Figure 8.5, the two lines are parallel to one another (in fact, they are exactly on top of one another); thus there is no interaction effect. The same result can be observed in the right graph: the two lines are parallel to one another, indi-

cating no interaction effect.

As another example, consider if the following cell means were obtained instead for the four groups in this study:

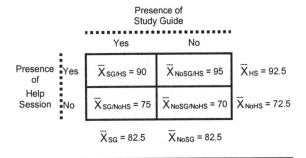

FIGURE 8.6: No main effect for presence of study guide, main effect for presence of help session, interaction effect

Again, given an equal sample size in each group, the marginal means for each factor are computed as the average of the corresponding cell means for each level of the factor. The two versions of these data are depicted graphically in Figure 8.7. These results indicate no main effect for presence of study guide, a main effect for presence of help session, and an interaction effect. When an interaction is present, main effects tend to be easiest to observe via the marginal means. As can be seen in Figure 8.6, those who used the study guide scored the same on average ($\overline{X}_{SG} = 82.5$) as did those who did not use the study guide ($\overline{X}_{NoSG} = 82.5$): there is no main effect for presence of study guide. In contrast, those who attended the help session scored higher on average ($\overline{X}_{HS} = 92.5$) than did those who did not attend the help session ($\overline{X}_{No\,HS} = 72.5$). In the graphs in Figure 8.7, the main effects can be visualized by averaging. For instance, in the left graph, the average for those who used a study guide, across the help session and no help session groups, would be at a point falling halfway between the two lines in the graph at the mark for study guide. The point representing the average for those who did not use the study guide would fall at exactly the same distance along the y-axis, between the help session and no help session lines at the mark for no study guide group. This would indicate the absence of a main effect for presence of study guide. In contrast to the less visually obvious main effects in this example, Figure 8.7 clearly depicts the interaction effect. In both the left and right graphs, the two lines inside the diagrams are not parallel to each other: there is an interaction between presence of study guide and presence of help session. This same interaction effect can be derived through the cell means, e.g., the differ ences $\overline{X}_{SG/HS} - \overline{X}_{NoSG/HS} = 90 - 95 = -5$ and $\overline{X}_{SG/NoHS} - \overline{X}_{NoSG/NoHS} = 75 - 70 = +5$ are not equal.

Conducting a Multiple-Factor Analysis of Variance

Now that we have described the underlying conceptual basis of main and interaction effects, we turn to the statistics of determining whether significant group differences exist. With the conceptual examples discussed in the section above, any difference in means was assumed to be a significant difference. Of course, this is not a valid assumption, and to deter-

mine if any observed differences in means truly are indicative of a true difference in the underlying populations, rather than simply sampling error, a test of significance must be conducted. The details behind the required statistical test, the F-test, already were discussed extensively in the previous chapter. However, we will review the basic components and apply them to the extended analysis of variance problem involving two or more independent variables.

In the simplest multiple-factor ANOVA problem, involving a 2 x 2 factorial design, there are two possible main effects, one for each factor, and one possible interaction effect. In the 2 x 2 example described above, there are three possible significant effects: a main effect for presence of study guide, a main effect for presence of help session, and an interaction effect between presence of study guide and presence of help session. The final results of the analysis of variance can yield significance of none or any combination of these effects (e.g., two main effects and an interaction, one main effect and an interaction, two main effects and no interaction, an interaction and no main effects, one main effect only, no effects at all, etc.).

A researcher conducts the study guide and

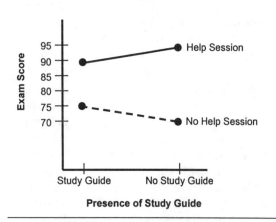

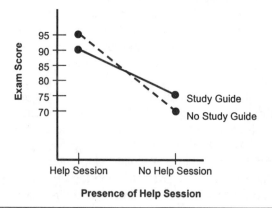

FIGURE 8.7: No main effect for presence of study guide, main effect for presence of help session, interaction effect

help session experiment outlined above utilizing a total of 60 participants, with an equal number of subjects randomly assigned to each condition in the study. The following mean exam scores were obtained:

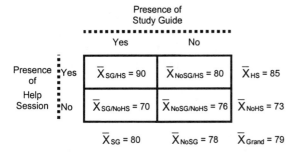

FIGURE 8.8: Marginal and cell means for a 2 x 2 factorial

Conducting a multiple-factor ANOVA involves creating the same type of ANOVA summary table described for the single factor analysis of variance, with the sums of squares, degrees of freedom, mean squares, and calculated F-value. However, because multiple statistical tests are conducted with the multiple-factor ANOVA problem (e.g., two tests for main effects and one test for an interaction), the ANOVA summary table is extended to include each of the components, SS, MS, df, and F, for a separate statistical test for each effect.

Recall from Chapter 7 that total variability in scores is represented by the sum of squares total and is calculated as the difference between each individual score and the grand mean for the entire set of scores:

$$SS_{Total} = \sum (X - \overline{X}_{Grand})^2$$

In the current multiple-factor ANOVA problem, sum of squares total is computed by taking each of the 60 individual exam scores, comparing them to the grand mean $\overline{X}_{Grand} = 79$, squaring these differences, and summing them across all 60 subjects. Without providing the

details of this calculation, the sum of squares total value computed for the present problem is $SS_{Total} = 11180$.

As described in the previous chapter, total variability can be subdivided into two sources: variability between groups and variability within groups. Variability between groups is the difference between each group mean and the grand mean weighted by the number of subjects per group:

$$SS_{Between} = \sum n_k (\overline{X}_k - \overline{X}_{Grand})^2$$

With the single-factor ANOVA problem, there is only one source of between-groups variability since there is only one independent variable and one effect being assessed. However, with a multiple-factor analysis of variance problem there are multiple sources of between-groups variability, one for each effect being tested. Thus, for instance, one source of between-groups variability is presence of study guide, factor J. Applying the general sum of squares between formula above to this factor, the sum of squares value for the study guide source of between-groups variability is calculated as:

$$SS_{StudyGuide(j)} = \sum n_j (\overline{X}_j - \overline{X}_{Grand})^2 = 30(80-79)^2 + 30(78-79)^2 = 60$$

A second source of between-groups variability in this problem is presence of help session, factor K. Again, applying the general sum of squares between formula to this factor yields the following computation of the sum of squares for the help session source of between-groups variability:

$$SS_{HelpSession(k)} = \sum n_k (\overline{X}_k - \overline{X}_{Grand})^2 = 30(85-79)^2 + 30(73-79)^2 = 2160$$

Clearly, there is tremendous variability between groups for presence of help session, but not for presence of study guide.

The final source of variability is variability

between groups for the interaction of the two factors, presence of study guide and presence of help session. Conceptually, calculation of the sum of squares (between) for the interaction effect is the same as for the main effects: subtract the grand mean ($\overline{X}_{Grand} = 79$) from the (adjusted) group means ($\overset{*}{X}_{jk}$), which are the individual cell means, square these differences, and weight by the number of subjects per group ($n_{jk} = 15$):

$$SS_{\substack{Study\ Guide\ (j) \\ x\ Help\ Session\ (k)}} = \sum n_{jk}(\overset{*}{X}_{jk} - \overline{X}_{Grand})^2$$

The complexity of computing the sum of squares for the interaction term is that the individual cell means ($\overline{X}_{jk}$) reported in Figure 8.8 are not used in the computation. Rather, cell means that are adjusted for variability due to the main effects of the separate factors ($\overset{*}{X}_{jk}$) are utilized in the formula. Without detailing these calculations, the adjusted cell means are computed by nullifying or removing the effects in each individual score that are due to or can be explained by the separate main effects for study guide and help session, since variability due to these two sources already is accounted for in the sums of squares for the separate factors. In this problem, the sum of squares for the interaction source of between-groups variability is computed to be $SS_{SGxHS} = 740$.

The within-groups sum of squares is calculated in the same way as was described with the single-factor analysis of variance:

$$SS_{Within} = \sum(X - \overline{X}_k)^2$$

The difference between each individual score and its own group mean is computed, squared, and summed across all subjects in the study. This calculation yields a measure of individual or error variability not explained by the particular group the participant is in. With the multiple-factor analysis of variance problem,

sum of squares within-groups is more commonly referred to as *sum of squares error*. The calculation involves defining a group in terms of the levels of all factors. Thus, an individual exam score is designated as X_{ijk}, meaning individual (I) within a particular study guide (J) and help session (K) group. This individual score is compared with the mean of that person's study guide/help session group $\overline{X}_{jk}$. Sum of squares error, then, is calculated as:

$$SS_{Error} = \sum(X_{ijk} - \overline{X}_{jk})^2$$

Because this calculation involves 60 subjects, we will not perform the entire computation here, but it proceeds by taking the 15 subjects in the study guide/help session group and comparing their exam scores to the mean of that group ($\overline{X}_{SG/HS} = 90$), taking the 15 subjects in the no study guide/help session group and comparing their exam scores to the mean of that group ($\overline{X}_{NoSG/HS} = 80$), and so forth for each of the four groups in the study. In this problem, sum of squares error is calculated as $SS_{Error} = 8220$.

The following partial ANOVA summary table provides the sums of squares for this problem, with each of the three between-groups sources of variability, one for each effect tested in the analysis, broken out separately:

Partial ANOVA Summary Table

Source	SS	df	MS	F
Study Guide	60			
Help Session	2160			
Study Guide x Help Session	740			
Error	8220			
Total	11180			

The results of this multiple-factor analysis of variance will yield three separate F-tests, one for each effect. Completion of the remainder of the ANOVA summary table proceeds exactly as with the single-factor ANOVA.

First, degrees of freedom are calculated for each source of variability. Degrees of freedom for each main effect are simply the number of groups or levels of that factor minus one:

$$df_{SG} = J - 1 = 2 - 1 = 1$$
$$df_{HS} = K - 1 = 2 - 1 = 1$$

Degrees of freedom for the interaction effect is the product of the degrees of freedom for the separate factors that constitute the interaction:

$$df_{SGxHS} = (J - 1)x(K - 1) = (2 - 1)x(2 - 1) = (1)x(1) = 1$$

Degrees of freedom for the error term is calculated as the number of subjects in the study minus the product of the number of levels of each independent variable:

$$df_{Error} = N - JK = 60 - (2)x(2) = 60 - 4 = 56$$

And, of course, degrees of freedom for the entire study are the number of participants minus one, equal to the sum of the degrees of freedom associated with all main and interaction effects and the error term:

$$df_{Total} = N - 1 = 60 - 1 = 59$$
$$df_{Total} = 1 + 1 + 1 + 56 = 59$$

Calculation of the mean square values was described extensively in Chapter 7:

$$MS = \frac{SS}{df}$$

The mean squares for this problem are calculated as follows:

$$MS_{SG} = \frac{SS_{SG}}{df_{SG}} = \frac{60}{1} = 60$$

$$MS_{HS} = \frac{SS_{HS}}{df_{HS}} = \frac{2160}{1} = 2160$$

$$MS_{SGxHS} = \frac{SS_{SGxHS}}{df_{SGxHS}} = \frac{740}{1} = 740$$

$$MS_{Error} = \frac{SS_{Error}}{df_{Error}} = \frac{8220}{56} = 146.79$$

Finally, the F-values are calculated as described in the previous chapter:

$$F = \frac{MS_{Between}}{MS_{Within}}$$

With the multiple-factor ANOVA problem, the mean square between value is really the mean square between corresponding to each main and interaction effect (MS_{Effect}) and the mean square within value is called the mean square error (MS_{Error}). Thus, the exact same equation can be stated more generally for the multiple-factor ANOVA problem as:

$$F = \frac{MS_{Effect}}{MS_{Error}}$$

There will be as many F-values computed and F-tests conducted as there are effects being tested. Therefore, in the present problem, there will be a total of three F-values since the researcher is testing for two main effects and one interaction effect, calculated as follows:

$$F_{SG} = \frac{MS_{SG}}{MS_{Error}} = \frac{60}{146.79} = 0.41$$

$$F_{HS} = \frac{MS_{HS}}{MS_{Error}} = \frac{2160}{146.79} = 14.72$$

$$F_{\text{SGxHS}} = \frac{MS_{\text{SGxHS}}}{MS_{\text{Error}}} = \frac{740}{146.79} = 5.04$$

The completed ANOVA table now looks like the following:

Source	SS	df	MS	F
Study Guide	60	1	60	0.41
Help Session	2160	1	2160	14.72
Study Guide x Help Session	740	1	740	5.04
Error	8220	56	146.79	
Total	11180			

The next step in conducting the F-test is to compare each calculated F-value to the appropriate critical value to determine whether to reject the null hypothesis associated with the test of that effect. Any calculated F that is greater than or equal to its associated critical value indicates that the null hypothesis should be rejected for that test and there is a significant effect. The critical value for each test is based on the degrees of freedom associated with that effect, which may differ for each test, and the error degrees of freedom, which will be identical for each test. In this problem, the degrees of freedom are the same for the test of each effect, 1 and 56. The critical F-values obtained from the F-table are $F_{(1,56).05} = 4.02$ and $F_{(1,56).01} = 7.12$.

TABLE 8.1: Two-Way ANOVA Summary Table

Source of Variation (Source)	Sum of Squares (SS)	Degrees of Freedom (df)	Mean Square (MS)	Calculated F (F)
Factor J	$\sum n_j \left(\bar{X}_j - \bar{X}_{\text{Grand}} \right)^2$	(J-1)*	$\frac{SS_J}{df_J}$	$F_J = \frac{MS_J}{MS_{\text{Error}}}$
Factor K	$\sum n_k \left(\bar{X}_k - \bar{X}_{\text{Grand}} \right)^2$	(K-1)**	$\frac{SS_K}{df_K}$	$F_K = \frac{MS_K}{MS_{\text{Error}}}$
J x K	$\sum n_{jk} \left(\bar{X}^*_{jk} - \bar{X}_{\text{Grand}} \right)^2$	(J-1)x(K-1)	$\frac{SS_{JxK}}{df_{JxK}}$	$F_{JxK} = \frac{MS_{JxK}}{MS_{\text{Error}}}$
Error	$\sum \left(X_{ijk} - \bar{X}_{jk} \right)^2$	N – JK***	$\frac{SS_{\text{Error}}}{df_{\text{Error}}}$	
Total	$\sum \left(X_{ijk} - \bar{X}_{\text{Grand}} \right)^2$	N - 1		

* Where J = number of levels for Factor J

** Where K = number of levels for Factor K

*** Where N = number of subjects

Three separate statistical tests are conducted for this problem. First, there is no main effect for presence of study guide, since the calculated F of 0.41 is not greater than or equal to the critical F of 4.02 at the .05 level. Using a study guide does not cause students to obtain different exam scores versus not using a study guide. Second, there is a main effect for presence of help session, since the calculated F of 14.72 is larger than the critical F of 7.12 at the .01 level. The null hypothesis is rejected at $p < .01$; attending a help session causes students to obtain higher exam scores than does not attending a help session. Finally, there is a significant interaction effect, since the calculated F of 5.04 is larger than the critical F of 4.02 at the .05 level. The null hypothesis is rejected at $p < .05$; there is some difference in final exam scores as a function of the students' particular study guide/help session group. However, because more than two groups are involved in this effect, a post-hoc test such as the Scheffé is required to determine exactly where those differences are.

Table 8.1 provides a summary of the formulas used for completing a two-way (multiple-factor) ANOVA table.

An Example of Multiple-Factor ANOVA

A researcher hypothesizes that students who take vitamins will perform better on exams than will students who do not take vitamins. He also hypothesizes that the more students exercise the higher they will perform on exams. The researcher solicits 60 university students to participate in his study. He randomly assigns an equal number of subjects to either take vitamins daily for a month prior to an exam or to not take vitamins. He also randomly assigns these same 60 subjects to one of three exercise conditions, 20 per group, for the same one month: no daily exercise, exercise ½

hour per day, exercise 1 hour per day. The assignment of subjects to this 2 x 3 factorial design, involving 6 conditions, is depicted in the following diagram:

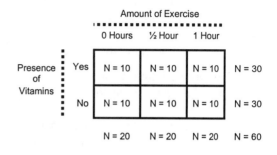

FIGURE 8.9: Random assignment of a total of N = 60 subjects to conditions of a 2 x 3 factorial design

This study involves two independent variables: presence of vitamins and amount of exercise. The first factor, presence of vitamins, has two levels (yes, no) and the second factor, amount of exercise, has three levels (0 hours/day, ½ hour/day, 1 hour/day). The dependent variable is exam score, which is measured at the ratio-level. With one dependent variable measured at the interval- or ratio-level data and more than one independent variable, the appropriate analytical procedure is a multiple-factor ANOVA. The following group means are obtained in this study:

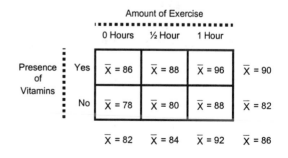

FIGURE 8.10: Cell and marginal means obtained from 2 x 3 factorial design

QUESTION: There actually are three questions to answer with this problem, one for each effect being tested. Since there are two factors (independent variables), there are two possible main effects: one for presence of vitamins and one for amount of exercise. There also is one possible two-way interaction effect between presence of vitamins and amount of exercise.

Q #1: Does taking vitamins cause students to score higher on exams than not taking vitamins?

Q #2: Does daily exercise cause students to score higher on exams than not exercising?

Q #3: Does some particular combination of vitamin intake and amount of exercise cause students to score higher on exams?

ANSWER:

Step 1: Identify the hypotheses for this study.

There are three null hypotheses tested in this study, corresponding with the two main effects and the interaction effect. The corresponding alternative hypotheses are based on the researcher's predictions. For the test of the main effect for presence of vitamins, the null and alternative hypotheses are:

$$H_0: \mu_{Vit} \leq \mu_{No\ Vit}$$
$$H_a: \mu_{Vit} > \mu_{No\ Vit}$$

For the test of the main effect for amount of exercise, the null and alternative hypotheses are:

$$H_0: \mu_{0\ Hours} \geq \mu_{1/2\ Hour} \geq \mu_{1\ Hour}$$
$$H_a: \mu_{0\ Hours} < \mu_{1/2\ Hour} < \mu_{1\ Hour}$$

Finally, the null and alternative hypotheses for the test of the interaction effect are:

$$H_0: \mu_{Vit/1\ Hour} - \mu_{No\ Vit/1\ Hour} =$$
$$\mu_{Vit/1/2\ Hour} - \mu_{No\ Vit/1/2\ Hour} =$$
$$\mu_{Vit/0\ Hours} - \mu_{No\ Vit/0\ Hours}$$

$$H_a: \mu_{Vit/1\ Hour} - \mu_{No\ Vit/1\ Hour} \neq$$
$$\mu_{Vit/1/2\ Hour} - \mu_{No\ Vit/1/2\ Hour} \neq$$
$$\mu_{Vit/0\ Hours} - \mu_{No\ Vit/0\ Hours}$$

Although the hypotheses for tests of the two main effects are directional (based on the research hypotheses provided by the investigator), recall that the F-test is conducted identically for both directional and nondirectional hypotheses.

Step 2: Begin the ANOVA table and compute the sums of squares.

The sums of squares for the tests of the two main effects are computed easily. The sum of squares for the presence of vitamins factor is:

$$SS_{Vitamins(j)} = \sum n_j(\overline{X}_j - \overline{X}_{Grand})^2 = 30(90-86)^2 + 30(82-86)^2 = 960$$

The sum of squares for the amount of exercise factor is:

$$SS_{Exercise(k)} = \sum n_k(\overline{X}_k - \overline{X}_{Grand})^2 = 20(82-86)^2 + 20(84-86)^2 + 20(92-86)^2 = 1120$$

Because of the rather lengthy computations involved in obtaining the sum of squares for the interaction and error terms with a multiple-factor ANOVA problem, the calculated values are simply provided in the following partial ANOVA table:

Source	SS	df	MS	F
Vitamins	960			
Exercise	1120			
Vitamins x Exercise	350			
Error	7160			
Total	9590			

Step 3: Calculate the degrees of freedom.

For each main effect, the term for degrees of freedom is simply the number of levels of the factor minus one. For each interaction effect, the degrees of freedom term is the product of the degrees of freedom for each factor involved in the interaction. Thus, the degrees of freedom for each of the three effects being tested are:

$$df_{Vit} = J - 1 = 2 - 1 = 1$$

$$df_{Ex} = K - 1 = 3 - 1 = 2$$

$$df_{VitxEx} = (J - 1) \times (K - 1) = (2 - 1) \times (3 - 1) = (1) \times (2) = 2$$

Degrees of freedom for the error term is the number of subjects in the study minus the total number of groups or conditions:

$$df_{Error} = N - (J) \times (K) = 60 - (3) \times (2) = 60 - 6 = 54$$

Finally, the sum of all the between and error degrees of freedom equals the total degrees of freedom in the study, the number of subjects minus one:

$$df_{Total} = N - 1 = 60 - 1 = 59$$
$$df_{Total} = 1 + 2 + 2 + 54 = 59$$

Step 4: Compute the values for the mean square.

Each mean square value is calculated as the sum of squares divided by its corresponding degrees of freedom. The four mean square values for this problem are computed as follows:

$$MS_{Vit} = \frac{SS_{Vit}}{df_{Vit}} = \frac{960}{1} = 960$$

$$MS_{Ex} = \frac{SS_{Ex}}{df_{Ex}} = \frac{1120}{2} = 560$$

$$MS_{VitxEx} = \frac{SS_{VitxEx}}{df_{VitxEx}} = \frac{350}{2} = 175$$

$$MS_{Error} = \frac{SS_{Error}}{df_{Error}} = \frac{7160}{54} = 132.59$$

Step 5: Compute the F-values.

Using the general formula for the F statistic, F-values are computed for each of the three tests being conducted in this problem as follows:

$$F_{Vit} = \frac{MS_{Vit}}{MS_{Error}} = \frac{960}{132.59} = 7.24$$

$$F_{Ex} = \frac{MS_{Ex}}{MS_{Error}} = \frac{560}{132.59} = 4.22$$

$$F_{VitxEx} = \frac{MS_{VitxEx}}{MS_{Error}} = \frac{175}{132.59} = 1.32$$

The completed ANOVA table, with degrees of freedom, mean squares, and F-values added, is the following:

Source	SS	df	MS	F
Vitamins	960	1	960	7.24
Exercise	1120	2	560	4.22
Vitamins x Exercise	350	2	175	1.32
Error	7160	54	132.59	
Total	9590	59		

Step 6: Conduct each F-test.

Each F-test is conducted with critical values using the degrees of freedom corresponding to the effect being tested. In this problem, the main effect for presence of vitamins is tested with 1 and 54 degrees of freedom, with the following critical F-values: $F_{(1,54).05} = 4.02$ and $F_{(1,54).01} = 7.12$. Since the calculated F of 7.24 is larger than the critical F of 7.12 at the .01 level, the null hypothesis is rejected at $p < .01$. As hypothesized, using vitamins causes students to score better on exams than does not using vitamins.

Both the exercise main effect and the inter-action effect are tested with 2 and 54 degrees of freedom, with the following critical F-values: $F_{(2,54).05} = 3.17$ and $F_{(2,54).01} = 5.01$. For the exercise main effect, the calculated F of 4.22 is larger than the critical F of 3.17 at the .05 level; thus, the null hypothesis is rejected at $p < .05$. A post-hoc test is required at this point to determine which of the three exercise groups differ from one another; however, it appears that more exercise causes higher exam performance. Finally, for the interaction effect, since the calculated F of 1.32 is not greater than or equal to the critical F of 3.17 at the .05 level, the null hypothesis is not rejected. Amount of exercise does not result in differential performance for those who take vitamins vs. those who do not.

Step 7: State final conclusion both statistically and in words.

Statistically, the final conclusion is to reject H_0 at $p < .01$ for the test of the main effect of presence of vitamins, reject H_0 at $p < .05$ for the test of the main effect of amount of exercise, and do not reject H_0 for the test of the interaction effect of presence of vitamins and amount of exercise. That is, there is a main effect for presence of vitamins, a main effect for amount of exercise, and no interaction effect. In words, the researcher can conclude that taking vitamins improves exam performance vs. not taking vitamins, and exercising improves exam performance vs. not exercising. However, amount of exercise does not have a differential impact on exam performance as a function of taking vitamins or not.

To help visualize these results, refer back to the conceptual background provided earlier in this chapter to understand main and interaction effects. Consider the following diagram depicting each of the six cell means from Figure 8.10:

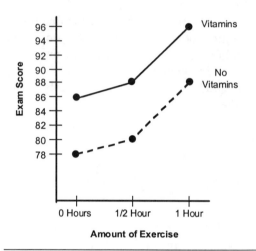

FIGURE 8.11: Main effect for presence of vitamins, main effect for amount of exercise, no interaction effect

The two lines inside the graph in Figure 8.11 are not parallel to the x-axis; thus, there is a main effect for the factor graphed on the x-axis, amount of exercise. The two lines inside the graph are separated from one another; thus, there is a main effect for the factor inside the graph, presence of vitamins. Finally, because the lines inside the graph are parallel to one another, there is no interaction effect. Conceptually, these results are identical to those obtained statistically with the multiple-factor ANOVA.

Summary

Multiple-factor analysis of variance is an extension of single-factor ANOVA involving more than two factors. Both single- and multiple-factor ANOVA are conducted similarly using an F-test. A study involving two or more factors is called a factorial design. Factorial designs are designated by the number of factors and number of levels of each factor. A main effect is an effect for one independent variable alone, whereas an interaction effect is an effect resulting from the combination of levels of two or more factors. As part of the same analysis of variance procedure, separate F-tests are conducted for each main and interaction effect involved in the factorial design.

Key Terms

- cell
- factorial design
- interaction effect
- main effect
- sum of squares error

Problems

1. For each of the following, indicate the appropriate statistical test to:
   a. examine group differences involving one independent variable and two groups only.
   b. examine group differences involving more than one independent variable.
   c. examine group differences involving one independent variable and three or more groups.
2. For each of the following factorial designs, indicate the number of factors (independent variables):
   a. 2 x 3
   b. 3 x 6 x 8 x 3 x 2
   c. 3 x 4
   d. 6 x 2 x 2
   e. 3 x 2 x 3
   f. 4 x 3 x 2 x 5
3. For each of the following factorial designs, indicate the number of levels for the factor specified:

a. 3 x 2 x 4	2nd factor
b. 2 x 6 x 9 x 3 x 4	3rd factor
c. 3 x 5 x 4 x 4	1st factor
d. 2 x 3	2nd factor
e. 5 x 6 x 3	4th factor
f. 3 x 2	2nd factor

4. For each of the following factorial designs,

indicate the total number of experimental conditions (groups or cells) in the study:
   a. 4 x 3
   b. 2 x 2 x 2
   c. 2 x 3 x 4
5. For each of the following designs, indicate the total number of subjects who participated in the study:
   a. 3 x 2 x 3   N = 5 subjects per condition
   b. 4 x 3   N = 16 subjects per condition
   c. 3 x 3 x 3   N = 20 subjects per condition
6. Examining group differences for a single factor involves testing for a(n) (*main* or *interaction*) effect?
7. Examining group differences for the combination of two or more factors involves testing for a(n) (*main* or *interaction*) effect?
8. A corporation wishes to determine whether a face-to-face conference or a teleconference is viewed as more satisfactory by their national versus international firms and by their management staff versus regular employees. Satisfaction is measured on a Likert-type scale from 1 - 7, with 1 indicating the least satisfaction and 7 indicating the most satisfaction.
   a. What type of factorial design is this?
   b. How many possible main effects are there?
   c. How many possible interaction effects are there?
9. Sixty children from kindergarten, 60 children from 3rd grade, and 60 children from 5th grade are randomly assigned within grade to view a 30 minute violent program, with either 0, 5, or 10 acts of violence per minute. Following this, within grade, children are again randomly assigned to do one of the following activities for 10 minutes: read a short book, play on a swingset, watch a cartoon on TV, or sit alone in a room. The experimenter then has each child play on the playground with his or her classmates and observes

how aggressive the child is in terms of the number of hits/kicks the child delivers to playmates.

a. What is/are the independent variable(s)?

b. What is/are the dependent variable(s)?

c. What type of factorial design is this?

d. What type of statistical analysis should be used to assess group differences?

e. How many children watched 5 acts of violence?

f. How many 5th graders sat alone in a room after viewing the 30 minute program?

g. If the analysis revealed that the most aggressive children were those who viewed 10 acts of violence and then sat alone in a room, what type of effect would this be (*main* or *interaction*) and what factor(s) is/are involved?

h. If 5th graders were more aggressive than either kindergartners or 3rd graders, what type of effect would this be (*main* or *interaction*) and what factor(s) is/are involved?

10. A researcher is interested in the effects of caffeine and amount of sleep on people's memory. He obtains a total of 100 subjects and randomly assigns an equal number to conditions in his study. The researcher designs a study where subjects are randomly assigned to either sleep 4 hours per night or 8 hours per night for one week prior to the memory task. He also randomly assigns subjects to either drink 5 cups of coffee or 5 cups of water in the three hours immediately prior to the memory task. The researcher then brings subjects into his lab and gives them 2 minutes to memorize a list of 25 words. At the end of the two minutes, subjects are asked to recall as many words as possible.

a. The researcher obtains the following mean number of words recalled for

subjects in each condition in his study:

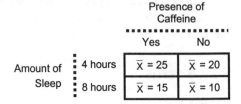

		Presence of Caffeine	
		Yes	No
Amount of Sleep	4 hours	$\bar{X} = 25$	$\bar{X} = 20$
	8 hours	$\bar{X} = 15$	$\bar{X} = 10$

Assume all differences in means are significant differences via an F-test. Identify all main and interaction effects.

b. Suppose instead the researcher obtained cell means as depicted in the following diagram:

		Presence of Caffeine	
		Yes	No
Amount of Sleep	4 hours	$\bar{X} = 20$	$\bar{X} = 10$
	8 hours	$\bar{X} = 10$	$\bar{X} = 20$

Assume all differences in means are significant differences via an F-test. Identify all main and interaction effects.

c. Suppose instead the researcher obtained cell means as depicted in the following graph:

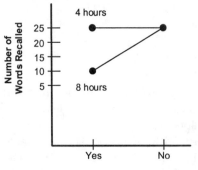

Assume all differences in means are significant differences via an F-test. Identify all main and interaction effects.

11. A researcher wishes to determine if married men are more or less likely to be depressed than single men after viewing a program about either divorce or marriage. Twenty-four married men and 36 single men volunteered for the study. Half of the married men are randomly assigned to watch a program about divorce and the other half of the married men are randomly assigned to watch a program about marriage. Similarly, the researcher randomly assigns half of the single men to watch a program about divorce and half to watch a program about marriage. Following viewing each man is asked to indicate how depressed he feels on a scale from 1, "not at all depressed," to 7, "extremely depressed". Data obtained from this study are as follows:

Source	SS	df	MS	F
Marital Status	8.2			
Program Type	7.5			
Marital x Program	14.7			
Error				
Total	142.4			

$\overline{X}_{Marr, Div} = 2.04$ $\overline{X}_{Marr, Marr} = 5.76$ $\overline{X}_{Sing, Div} = 5.00$
$\overline{X}_{Sing, Marr} = 4.89$

a. State the null and research hypotheses for both main effects and the interaction effect.
b. How many married men saw the program about marriage?
c. Complete the F-table and conduct all F-tests.
d. Are there any main effects or an interaction effect?
e. State your final decisions both statistically and in words.

Suppose, instead, that 36 married men and 36 single men had participated in this study and the ANOVA table looked as follows with the same sample means:

Source	SS	df	MS	F
Marital Status				
Program Type	12.6			
Marital x Program	9.8			
Error	204.0			
Total	237.2			

$\overline{X}_{Marr, Div} = 2.04$ $\overline{X}_{Marr, Marr} = 5.76$ $\overline{X}_{Sing, Div} = 5.00$
$\overline{X}_{Sing, Marr} = 4.89$

f. Complete the F-table and conduct all F-tests.
g. Are there any main effects or an interaction effect?
h. State your final decisions both statistically and in words.

12. A diet program wishes to determine whether there is a difference in men's and women's ability to exert self-control with respect to consuming nonnutritional food depending on how much exposure they have to it and whether they are warned of the negative consequences of eating it. Sixty male and sixty female subjects who are concerned with watching their weight are randomly assigned to spend 5, 10, or 15 minutes in a room with a table full of desserts. Each subject is told not to eat the food in the room. Half of the subjects are randomly assigned to receive an additional reminder about how bad consumption of the desserts would be while the other subjects receive no warning. They are then watched from a two-way mirror and the quantity of food the subject eats is

recorded. The following ANOVA table is obtained:

Source	SS	df	MS	F
Gender	40			
Exposure	30			
Warning	20			
Gend. x Expos.	60			
Gend. x Warn.	20			
Expos. x Warn.	20			
Gend. x Expos. x Warn.	80			
Error	648			
Total	918			

a. What type of factorial design is this?
b. How many potential main effects are there?
c. How many potential interaction effects are there?
d. Complete the F-table and conduct all F-tests.
e. Are there any main effects or interaction effects?
f. State your final decisions both statistically and in words.

Desire for Marriage and Life Satisfaction Among Unmarried Heterosexual Adults

Adapted from article by same title, Frazier, P., Arikian, N., Benson, S., Losoff, A., & Maurer, S. (1996). *Journal of Social and Personal Relationships, 13,* 225-239.

IN THIS study the researchers explored unmarried people's reasons for being single, their desire for marriage, and their satisfaction with their lives. In particular, these investigators were interested in unmarried adults over 30 years of age. A total of 251 people were recruited for the study from ads and a singles group. Among the information assessed in the study was the desire for marriage among never-married and divorced single men and women. Along these lines, the researchers hypothesized that:

> ... unmarried men would have more desire for marriage ... than would unmarried women ... [with] no main effects of marital history. However, ... there would be an interaction between sex and marital history in desire for marriage. Specifically, ... there would be a greater difference in desire for marriage between divorced men and women than between never-married men and women.

Participants completed a questionnaire that assessed singles' desire for marriage as well as other items. All questions asked participants to indicate their level of agreement with statements on a 7-point scale (1=strongly disagree to 7=strongly agree). Differences were examined for the two factors, sex and marital history, and for the interaction by conducting a two-way ANOVA on singles' level of desire for marriage.

> The overall mean on the scale assessing desire for marriage was right at the midpoint, reflecting only moderate desire for marriage (M=4.04 on a 7-point scale with higher scores indicating more desire for marriage). Results of a two-way ANOVA with desire for marriage as the dependent variable and sex and marital history as independent variables showed main effects of sex ($F[1, 212]=5.92, p < .03$) and marital history ($F[1, 212]=15.15, p < .001$) as well as a sex by marital history interaction ($F[1, 212]=6.95, p < .02$). Specifically,

(continued on page 170)

Desire for Marriage and Life Satisfaction Among Unmarried Heterosexual Adults (continued)

men reported more desire for marriage than did women and never-married individuals reported more desire for marriage than did divorced individuals. However, follow-up tests indicated that never-married women (M=4.33), never-married men (M=4.31) and divorced men (M=4.23) expressed approximately equal levels of desire for marriage, while divorced women had significantly less desire for marriage (M=3.52) than any other group, $p < .05$.

The results revealed that desire for marriage does differ as a function of both sex and marital history. The researchers concluded their findings contradict several popular assumptions held by the general public such as that everyone wants to be married, that men are afraid of commitment, and that women are desperate for marriage.

Sex and marital history differences (means)

	Total (N = 217)	Men (N = 83)	Women (N = 134)	Divorced (N = 111)	Never-Married (N = 106)
Desire for marriage	4.04	4.27	3.90	3.77	4.32

Note: Table adapted from original article (i.e., other dependent variables were not included)

Children's Reactions to Dreams Conveyed in Mass Media Programming

Adapted from article by same title, Wilson, B. (1991), *Communication Research, 18*, 283-305.

THE RESEARCHER examined children's cognitive and emotional responses to dreams depicted in mass media content. Children's emotional responses to arousing scenes often depend on their comprehension of specific events in the plot, such as whether they believe the character is dreaming or actually is experiencing the frightening event. Because the occurrence of dream sequences often is not made explicit in media programming, this study assessed children's ability to comprehend formal features (e.g., cuts, fades, flashbacks, dissolves) that signal a dream. One of the several hypotheses posed in this study was that:

> H: There will be no age differences in comprehension of the nature of dreams.

A total of 120 children from two grade levels (kindergarten and first vs. second through fourth) watched one of four versions of a frightening movie scene that were created by factorially varying the inclusion of a prologue and an epilogue. The film segment was taken from the 1986 remake of the movie *Invaders From Mars* and showed a boy who discovers a spaceship containing a number of giant beasts. In the prologue condition the boy is shown getting ready for bed and is seen before the main segment, whereas in the epilogue condition the boy is shown thrashing in bed with his parents reassuring him everything is fine and is seen after the main segment. Both the prologue and epilogue indicated that the story was just a dream without explicit reference. A 2 x 2 x 2 x 2 between-subjects factorial design was conducted. The independent variables were gender, grade level, presence vs. absence of a prologue, and presence vs. absence of an epilogue. The dependent variable was measured by a dream comprehension index which was the sum of children's correct responses to four closed-ended items about the nature of dreams (e.g., Are dreams real or not real?). The results were reported as follows:

> ... an analysis of variance on the index revealed a significant interaction between prologue and grade level $F(1, 103) = 3.95$, $p = .05$, $\eta^2 = .04$. Younger children who viewed the prologue scored significantly higher on the dream

(continued on page 172)

Children's Reactions to Dreams Conveyed in Mass Media Programming (continued)

index (M = 3.8) than did younger children who did not see the prologue (M = 3.4). In contrast, there was no difference in comprehension scores among older children in the two conditions (no prologue: M = 3.8; prologue: M = 3.8).

The analysis also revealed main effects that approached significance for prologue, $F(1, 103) = 3.48$, $p < .07$, $\eta^2 = .03$, and for grade level, $F(1, 103) = 3.68$, $p < .06$, $\eta^2 = .03$. However, both of these effects were due primarily to the significant interaction between these two factors. Children who viewed the prologue tended to score higher on dream comprehension (M = 3.8) than did those who did not see the prologue (M = 3.6), and older children tended to score higher (M = 3.8) than did younger children (M = 3.6).

The hypothesis was partially supported. While most children recognized dreams as internal, unrealistic events, some of the younger ones did not. It was found that prior knowledge of an upcoming dream can influence children's interpretations of and emotional reactions to dreamed events in a program.

Computer Section

Overview of Multiple-Factor ANOVA

Multiple-factor analysis of variance involves assessing whether there are significant differences in group means for multiple (more than one) independent variables or factors. This analysis is accomplished through a single procedure which produces separate F-tests to examine differences in group means for levels of each factor, termed main effects, and to examine differences in group means across levels of two or more factors considered jointly, termed interaction effects. Conducting a multiple-factor analysis of variance on the computer involves running an ANOVA command and specifying: (1) the dependent measure, and (2) the independent variables for which mean differences are to be compared. Additional specifications may include printouts of group means for tests of all main and interaction effects.

Example Output for Multiple-Factor ANOVA

A researcher wishes to investigate how a doctor's vocabulary, medical jargon (1) vs. normal speech (2), and interaction style, impersonal (1) vs. personal (2), influence patients' satisfaction with their doctor. The two independent variables produce a 2 x 2 factorial design and a total of four conditions. At a walk-in clinic, 292 people were randomly assigned to conditions in this study with 73 subjects per condition. Subjects in each group saw the same doctor during their visit; however, the doctor varied her interaction style and her vocabulary, depending upon the condition to which subjects were assigned. After completing the doctor's visit, each patient was asked to indicate on a scale from 1 to 4 how satisfied they were with the doctor. The results of a multiple-factor ANOVA as shown in Table 8.2 were obtained.

Interpretation of Multiple-Factor ANOVA Output

The first part of the output provides the means for each level of each independent variable in the analysis. Two sets of means are included: unweighted and weighted. Unweighted means are the true means obtained for each group whereas weighted means are the averages for each group taking into consideration differences in the number of subjects per group (i.e., the means are weighted by the number of subjects per cell). Unweighted and weighted means will be identical when the number of subjects in each condition is equal, as was true in this example. Most of the time, unweighted means are reported. If the number of subjects per condition is substantially different, researchers may wish to report weighted rather than unweighted means as a more accurate representation of the average scores in each group in the larger populations.

The next part of the output indicates that the multiple-factor ANOVA involved assessing differences in means on the dependent variable PATSAT (Patient Satisfaction with Doctor) for the two independent variables SPEECH (Vocabulary) and STYLE (Interaction Style).

The ANOVA table in the computer output should look very familiar to what was presented in the text. In this example, there are three F-tests conducted: for a main effect for SPEECH, for a main effect for STYLE, and for an interaction of SPEECH BY STYLE.

The degrees of freedom for the SPEECH factor are the number of groups minus one, $df_{Speech} = J - 1 = 2 - 1 = 1$; degrees of freedom for the STYLE factor are the number of groups minus one, $df_{Style} = K - 1 = 2 - 1 = 1$; degrees of

TABLE 8.2

A N A L Y S I S O F V A R I A N C E

PATSAT   PATIENT SATISFACTION WITH DOCTOR
by SPEECH   Vocabulary
   STYLE   Interaction Style

Combined Observed Means for SPEECH
Variable...PATSAT
SPEECH
1	WGT.	1.69071
	UNWGT.	1.69071
2	WGT.	1.92263
	UNWGT.	1.92263

Combined Observed Means for STYLE
Variable ... PATSAT
STYLE
1	WGT.	1.61098
	UNWGT.	1.61098
2	WGT.	2.00235
	UNWGT.	2.00235

A n a l y s i s o f V a r i a n c e – design 1

Tests of Significance for PATSAT using UNIQUE sums of squares

Source of Variation	Sum of Squares	DF	Mean Square	F	Sig of F
SPEECH	3.57	1	3.57	6.07	.014
STYLE	10.18	1	10.18	17.27	.000
SPEECH BY STYLE	.36	1	.36	.61	.436
WITHIN+RESIDUAL	169.65	288	.59		
(Model)	13.40	3	4.47	7.58	.000
(Total)	183.05	291	.63		

R-Squared = .073
Adjusted R-Squared = .064

Adjusted and Estimated Means
Variable...PATSAT   PATIENT SATISFACTION WITH DOCTOR

CELL	Obs. Mn	Adj. Mn	Est. Mn	Raw Resid.	Std. Resid.
1	1.458	1.458	1.458	.000	.000
2	1.923	1.923	1.923	.000	.000
3	1.764	1.764	1.764	.000	.000
4	2.082	2.082	2.082	.000	.000

Combined Adjusted Means for SPEECH
Variable .. PATSAT
SPEECH
| 1 | UNWGT. | 1.69071 |
| 2 | UNWGT. | 1.92263 |

Combined Adjusted Means for STYLE
Variable .. PATSAT
STYLE
| 1 | UNWGT. | 1.61098 |
| 2 | UNWGT. | 2.00235 |

freedom for the SPEECH BY STYLE interaction are the product of the degrees of freedom for each variable in the interaction, $(J - 1) \times (K - 1) = (2 - 1) \times (2 - 1) = (1) \times (1) = 1$; the error (within + residual) degrees of freedom is the total number of subjects minus the product of the number of levels of each variable, $df_{Error} = N - JK = 292 - (2) \times (2) = 288$; and the total degrees of freedom is the sum of the degrees of freedom associated with each effect or the total number of subjects in the study minus one, $df_{Total} = N - 1 = 292 - 1 = 291$. Each F-value is computed as the mean square for the effect divided by the mean square error, e.g., for the main effect for SPEECH:

$$F = \frac{3.57}{0.59} = 6.07$$

The results indicate that there is a main effect for SPEECH (p = .014), a main effect for STYLE (p = .000), and no interaction. Examination of the means for each independent variable from the first part of the sample output indicates that patients were more satisfied with the doctor when she used normal speech ($\overline{X} = 1.92$) than when she used medical jargon ($\overline{X} = 1.69$). Patients also were more satisfied with the doctor when her interaction style was personal ($\overline{X} = 2.00$) rather than impersonal ($\overline{X} = 1.61$).

In the last part of the output, the R-squared value represents the percentage of variance in the dependent variable that is explained by the independent variables (7.3%), and is applicable if this problem were viewed as a regression model (see Chapter 11). Finally, the output also includes information on the means in each of the four cells of this 2×2 factorial design. These means would be used to identify where differences exist in the case of a significant interaction effect, which was not obtained in this example.

Computer Problems

1. Conduct a multiple-factor ANOVA to examine each of the following hypotheses regarding differences due to class structure (**CLASS**) and instructor gender (**GENDER**). Be sure to indicate which effect, main or interaction, the researcher is hypothesizing. Indicate clearly the statistical decision for the test of each null hypothesis, including those the researcher did not hypothesize. If a significant F is obtained, identify which groups differ significantly from which other groups (when only two groups are involved) or if a post-hoc test is necessary to identify the specific significant differences.

    a. Students in the cooperative and individualistic classrooms will rate the course higher overall (**COURSE**) than will those in the competitive classroom. Students who have the female instructor will evaluate the course higher overall than will those who have the male instructor.

    b. Students in the competitive classroom will indicate having put more effort into the course (**EFFORT**) than will those in the individualistic and competitive classrooms. Students who have the male instructor will indicate putting more effort into the course than will those with the female instructor.

    c. Students in the cooperative classroom will rate the instructor higher overall (**INSTRUCT**) than will students in either the competitive or individualistic classrooms. Among those who have the male instructor, students in the competitive classroom will rate the instructor higher than will those in the cooperative or individualistic classrooms; in contrast, among those who have the female instructor, students in the cooperative classroom will rate the instructor higher than will those in the competitive or individualistic classrooms.

2. Conduct a multiple-factor ANOVA to examine each of the following hypotheses regarding differences due to instructor gender (**GENDER**) and learning location (**CONDIT**). Be sure to indicate which effect, main or interaction, the researcher is hypothesizing. Indicate clearly the statistical decision for the test of each null hypothesis, including those the researcher did not hypothesize. If a significant F is obtained, identify which groups differ significantly from which other groups (when only two groups are involved) or if a post-hoc test is necessary to identify the specific significant differences.

   a. Students in the live classroom will rate the instructor as more aware when students did not understand material (**AWARE**) than will those in the mediated classroom. Students who have the female instructor will indicate the instructor is more aware when students did not understand the material than will students who have the male instructor.

   b. Students in the mediated classroom will indicate using e-mail more to contact their classmates (**STUDENT1**) than will those in the live classroom. Students with the female instructor will be more likely to indicate using e-mail to contact their classmates than will those with the male instructor.

   c. Students with the female instructor in the live classroom or the male instructor in the mediated classroom will indi

cate having more interest in the subject matter as a result of taking the course (**MORELIKE**) than will those in the other two conditions.

3. Conduct a multiple-factor ANOVA to examine each of the following hypotheses regarding differences due to instructor gender (**GENDER**), class structure (**CLASS**), and learning location (**CONDIT**). Be sure to indicate which effect, main or interaction, the researcher is hypothesizing. Indicate clearly the statistical decision for the test of each null hypothesis, including those the researcher did not hypothesize. If a significant F is obtained, identify which groups differ significantly from which other groups (when only two groups are involved) or if a post-hoc test is necessary to identify the specific significant differences.

   a. Students with the female instructor in the cooperative classroom in a live setting will indicate the instructor had the highest level of rapport (**RAPPORT**) than will students in any other condition.

   b. Students with the male instructor in the competitive classroom in a mediated setting will indicate the course was more challenging (**CHALL**) than will students in any other condition.

   c. Students in the cooperative classroom will indicate having a higher understanding of the course material (**UNDERST**) than will students in the competitive or individualistic classrooms. Students with the female instructor in the live setting or the male instructor in the mediated setting will have the highest understanding of course material.

Chapter 9 ❖ Correlation

What is Simple Correlation?

Correlation is perhaps one of the easiest statistical concepts to master because most of us already are aware of the fundamental idea of a relationship between two variables. For example, based on experiences from school, a student might assume that there is a positive relationship between the amount of time students spend studying and their performance on exams. That is, the more time one spends studying for an exam, the better he or she should perform on an exam; likewise, the less time spent studying for an exam, the worse one should perform on the exam. Of course, not all students who study a lot perform well on exams or vice versa, but in general this relationship seems reasonable. Such a *positive* or *direct relationship* can be depicted visually in a line graph as an upward sloping line, where one variable is plotted on the x-axis (e.g., hours spent studying for a particular exam) and the other variable is plotted on the y-axis (e.g., score on the exam):

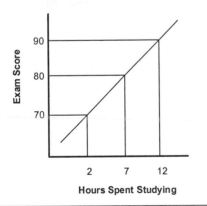

FIGURE 9.1: Upward sloping graph

Based on the relationship depicted in Figure 9.1, a student who studies 7 hours for a particular exam can expect to score an 80 on the exam. If the student increases the amount of time he or she studies to 12 hours, the corresponding exam score increases to 90. If the student decreases the amount of time he or she studies to 2 hours, the corresponding exam score decreases to 70.

Similarly, one also might assume that there is a *negative* or *inverse relationship* between the amount of time a student spends partying and his or her performance on an exam. That is, the more time one spends partying before an exam, the lower his or her exam score should be; similarly, the less time spent partying before an exam, the higher one's exam score should be. This type of relationship is depicted graphically as a downward sloping line:

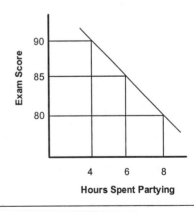

FIGURE 9.2: Downward sloping graph

A student who parties 6 hours the night before an exam can expect to score an 85. If the student increases the level of partying to 8 hours, he or she should only score an 80 on the exam. If the student reduces his or her party-ing to only 4 hours, the resultant exam score will be a 90.

The two examples described above illus-trate the concept of correlation. A *simple corre-lation* is the relationship between two variables in terms of how these variables are related to or associated with one another, in other words, how they covary. To represent the simple correlation between two variables measured at the interval- or ratio-level, a statistic called the *Pearson product-moment correlation* or the *Pearson r* is computed (the Pearson r is named after the statistician Karl Pearson, who developed this statistic). The value of Pearson r can range between -1.00 and +1.00 and has two major characteristics: (1) direction, and (2) magnitude.

Direction refers to whether the correlation is positive (direct) or negative (inverse), and is indicated by the sign (+ or -) of r. A positive relationship means that the variables vary together. That is, as X (hours spent studying) increases, Y (exam score) increases, and as X decreases, Y decreases. A negative relationship means that the variables vary inversely. In other words, as X (hours spent partying) increases, Y (exam score) decreases, and as X decreases, Y increases.

The *magnitude* of a correlation is the strength of the relationship between the two variables. The larger the value of r in absolute terms (ignoring the + or - sign), the stronger the relationship is between the two variables. Because most variables do not covary per-fectly, the magnitude is important for deter-mining the extent to which two variables do vary together. For example, educational research has shown that SAT scores and college GPA are somewhat positively related, that is, they have a positive correlation (r) that is greater than zero but less than one. This moderate, positive relationship suggests that, in general, a student who has a 1500 SAT score

probably will have a high college GPA whereas a student who has a 900 SAT score presumably will have a lower college GPA. Of course, sometimes students with low SAT scores have high college GPAs and vice versa, indicating that the relationship between these two variables is not perfect. Such a moderate, positive correlation can be depicted graphi-cally as follows:

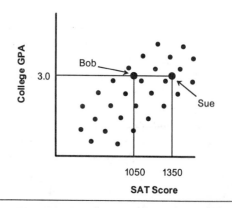

FIGURE 9.3: A moderate positive relationship

Each point in the graph represents the plot of an individual's SAT score and college GPA. The upward sloping direction of the points indicates that there is generally a positive rela-tionship between the two variables. Higher SAT scores tend to be associated with higher college GPAs. However, there also is substan-tial variation in this general relationship, which can be observed with the two students indicated by the arrows. Both of these students have a college GPA of 3.0. However, Sue had a fairly high SAT score (1350) whereas Bob had a relatively lower SAT score (1050). Clearly, then, the relationship between SAT score and college GPA is not perfect, since some students who have quite different SAT scores can still earn the same GPA in college.

If the relationship between two variables is perfect, then the correlation (r) equals either +1.00 or -1.00 (see Figure 9.4). With a perfect relationship, all of the individual data points

FIGURE 9.4: Perfect positive (left) and perfect negative (right) relationships

fall along a straight line. When the relationship between two variables is less than perfect, the correlation (r) is less than ±1.00 and not all of the points fall along a straight line. The closer together the points are, the stronger the correlation is and the closer the Pearson r value is to ±1.00. The more the data points are spread out from one another, the weaker the correlation is. For instance, in Figure 9.3, SAT score and college GPA are moderately, positively correlated with an r = +.60. The upward sloping direction of the data points clearly suggests that a positive relationship exists between these two variables. The fact that the data points are fairly tightly clustered indicates that this is a moderately strong relationship.

As another example, consider Figure 9.5, which indicates that there is a slight negative

relationship between size of high school one attended and college GPA (r = -.20). Although there is an overall downward trend in these data, there also is a great deal of variability, as indicated by the extensive spread in the data. Notice that the sign of the correlation (+ or -) is irrelevant for judging the strength or magnitude of the correlation: +.60 in the first example is a stronger correlation than is -.20 in the second example. This difference in magnitude can be seen in the two graphs; the points are clustered fairly tightly together for the correlation r = +.60 (Figure 9.3) whereas the points are distributed farther apart for the correlation r = -.20 (Figure 9.5).

Finally, consider the situation where there is no relationship between two variables, such as number of towels one owns and college GPA:

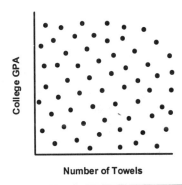

FIGURE 9.6: No relationship

There exists no upward or downward trend to these data, indicating that they do not covary together.

Computing a Simple Correlation: the Pearson r

In this section, we describe how the Pearson r is calculated. Data on both variables must be available for all subjects used in the calculation of Pearson r. For instance, calculating the correlation between height and weight for 10

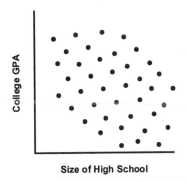

FIGURE 9.5: Slight negative relationship

subjects requires that all 10 subjects have both a measure for height and a measure for weight. If one of the variables is missing for a subject, that individual cannot be included in the calculation of Pearson r and the correlation would be based only on 9 subjects.

A researcher is interested in whether there is a relationship between the number of hours students study the day before an exam and their score on the exam. Data are collected from six students and reported below, along with the mean and standard deviation for each of the two variables:

Student	Hours Studying	Exam Score
Mary	5	88
Pat	2	76
Sean	8	94
Lisa	4	82
Missy	6	85
	$\overline{X}_{Std} = 5$	$\overline{X}_{Ex} = 85$
	$SD_{Std} = 2$	$SD_{Ex} = 6$

By ordering these data according to hours studying, it appears that there is a positive relationship between hours studying and exam score:

Student	Hours Studying	Exam Score
Pat	2	76
Lisa	4	82
Mary	5	88
Missy	6	85
Sean	8	94
	$\overline{X}_{Std} = 5$	$\overline{X}_{Ex} = 85$
	$SD_{Std} = 2$	$SD_{Ex} = 6$

Although it is not necessary to order the data in this way to compute Pearson r, this exercise provides an intuitive sense of whether there appears to be any relationship between the two variables. These data appear to be quite strongly, positively correlated: students who study generally have higher exams scores. However, this relationship is not perfect, since

Missy studied longer (6 hours) than did Mary (5 hours), but scored lower (85 vs. 88).

Pearson based his computation of the correlation statistic, r, on the concept of z-scores. Recall that a z-score is the translation of a raw score into a standardized score using the mean and standard deviation of the raw scores:

$$z = \frac{X - \overline{X}}{SD}$$

By expressing data as standardized scores (z) rather than raw scores (X), data measured in different units (e.g., hours vs. exam points) with different means and standard deviations can be directly compared. For this example, each individual student's number of hours studying and exam score is translated into a z-score using the above z-score formula (see Table 9.1). Translation of the raw scores into z-scores for the two variables reveals the similarity in the two sets of data. Pat scored one and a half standard deviation units below the mean in both studying time and exam score. Similarly, Lisa scored a half standard deviation unit below the mean on both variables. Mary and Missy scored at or just above the mean on both variables. Finally, Sean scored one and a half standard deviation units above the mean for both studying time and exam score. This tremendous similarity in z-scores indicates that, if a student scores above the mean on one variable, he or she probably scores above the mean on the other variable, and vice versa. In other words, these two variables strongly covary together positively. The closer the z-scores of each of the two variables are in value, the stronger the correlation. If the z-scores are the same sign for both variables (i.e., both positive or both negative), the correlation is positive. If the z-scores are opposite signs for the two variables (one positive, one negative), the correlation is negative.

The Pearson r is calculated by simply multiplying the two z-scores together to produce a measure of the covariability between the two variables, summing these products across all subjects, and then averaging this value by dividing by the total number of subjects (N)[1]:

$$r_{x_1 x_2} = \frac{\sum z_{x_1} z_{x_2}}{N}$$

For these data, multiplying the two z-scores together for each student yields the results shown in Table 9.2. The correlation for these data, then, is calculated as:

$$r_{(Std)(Ex)} = \frac{\sum z_{Std} z_{Ex}}{N} = \frac{4.75}{5} = .95$$

Because the sign of the correlation, r, is positive, the relationship between hours studying and exam score is positive. The fact that .95 is

TABLE 9.1

Student	Studying	Score	$z_{Std} = \dfrac{X_{Std} - \overline{X}_{Std}}{SD_{Std}}$	$z_{Ex} = \dfrac{X_{Ex} - \overline{X}_{Ex}}{SD_{Ex}}$
Pat	2	76	$z = \dfrac{2-5}{2} = -1.5$	$z = \dfrac{76-85}{6} = -1.5$
Lisa	4	82	$z = \dfrac{4-5}{2} = -0.5$	$z = \dfrac{82-85}{6} = -0.5$
Mary	5	88	$z = \dfrac{5-5}{2} = 0$	$z = \dfrac{88-85}{6} = 0.5$
Missy	6	85	$z = \dfrac{6-5}{2} = 0.5$	$z = \dfrac{85-85}{6} = 0$
Sean	8	94	$z = \dfrac{8-5}{2} = 1.5$	$z = \dfrac{94-85}{6} = 1.5$

$$\overline{X}_{Std} = 5 \qquad \overline{X}_{Ex} = 85$$
$$SD_{Std} = 2 \qquad SD_{Ex} = 6$$

TABLE 9.2

Student	Studying	Score	z_{Std}	z_{Ex}	$z_{Std} z_{Ex}$
Pat	2	76	-1.5	-1.5	(-1.5)(-1.5) = 2.25
Lisa	4	82	-0.5	-0.5	(-0.5)(-0.5) = 0.25
Mary	5	88	0	0.5	(0)(0.5) = 0
Missy	6	85	0.5	0	(0.5)(0) = 0
Sean	8	94	1.5	1.5	(1.5)(1.5) = 2.25
					Sum = 4.75

$$\overline{X}_{Std} = 5 \qquad \overline{X}_{Ex} = 85$$
$$SD_{Std} = 2 \qquad SD_{Ex} = 6$$

very close to 1.00 indicates that there is a very strong correlation between these two variables.[2]

Testing a Correlation for Statistical Significance

If a non-zero Pearson r is calculated for a sample of data, the question arises as to is whether this correlation is significant. That is, is the correlation found in this sample indicative of a true relationship between the two variables in the larger population? Or is the computed r-value different from zero in the sample purely due to chance or random factors, when in fact there really is no relationship between the two variables in the population? For instance, suppose that a researcher randomly samples 10 days in a year and computes a correlation of r = -.15 between the number of pig's feet eaten per day in Kentucky and the number of inches of rainfall in Washington on the same day. This correlation suggests that there is a slight, inverse relationship between these two variables: the more pig's feet eaten on a given day in Kentucky, the lower the rainfall is in Washington. Although it is not impossible that these two variables are somehow truly related, it is more likely that in the larger population (all days) that there really is no relationship whatsoever between these two variables, that is, that $\rho = 0$, where the Greek letter ρ (rho) represents the correlation in the larger population. In this case, the fact that a non-zero correlation was obtained in the sample is purely due to random or chance factors and is not indicative of a true relationship between pig's feet and rainfall in the larger population.

Just as a calculated t-value of 1.56 or a calculated F-value of 3.14 is not meaningful in and of itself, so too, a calculated r-value is not informative all by itself. In order to determine whether the observed correlation between variables in a sample of data is indicative of a

true correlation in the larger population, the calculated r-value must be compared with a critical r. Testing a calculated correlation for significance involves testing whether the null hypothesis is true. As suggested above, the null hypothesis is that there is no relationship or correlation between two variables in the population:

$$H_0: \ \rho = 0$$

In contrast, the alternative hypothesis or the hypothesis the researcher advances is that there is a non-zero relationship between the two variables in the larger population:

$$H_a: \ \rho \neq 0$$

This set of hypotheses is nondirectional since the researcher is not predicting whether the correlation will be positive or negative. Directional predictions also can be advanced. If the correlation in the population is predicted to be positive, the corresponding null and alternative hypotheses are:

$$H_0: \ \rho \leq 0$$
$$H_a: \ \rho > 0$$

If the correlation in the population is predicted to be negative, the corresponding null and alternative hypotheses are:

$$H_0: \ \rho \geq 0$$
$$H_a: \ \rho < 0$$

Notice that the parameter ρ (rho) refers to the correlation in the population, which is always referenced in the null and alternative hypotheses, whereas the statistic r represents the correlation in a sample.

Determining whether to reject the null hypothesis involves comparison of the calculated r-value with a critical r based on a distribution of correlations computed for the size sample used. Recall from Chapter 4 that the distribution of differences used for a two-sample z-test or t-test was a theoretical distribution of differences between two sample means. Two random samples of a particular size were drawn, a mean computed for each sample, and a difference between the two sample means calculated. This process was repeated indefinitely and the differences were all plotted, yielding the sampling distribution of differences. Due to sampling error (i.e., random chance in how samples were drawn), the difference between sample means was sometimes larger or smaller than zero. But, on average, the difference in means between any two samples drawn from the same population was always zero ($\mu = 0$). To conduct a two-sample z-test or t-test, a calculated value was compared with the appropriate distribution of differences to determine if the difference in sample means was so large that it fell in the outermost 5% of the distribution of differences. If the standardized difference, the z-score or t-score, was this large, the conclusion was that these two groups actually represent different populations, since very few differences are as large as the one observed from samples that actually represent the same population.

The process for testing a calculated correlation in a sample is very similar to the method described above for a z-test or t-test. Consider drawing a random sample of some size (N) from a larger population and computing a correlation between two totally unrelated variables for this sample. Those sampled are replaced into the population and another random sample of the same size (N) is drawn with the above procedure repeated to produce another correlation. This process is repeated indefinitely yielding an indefinite number of correlations between the unrelated variables. By chance, some calculated correlations will be positive and some will be negative, but because the two variables truly have no relationship with one another, most of the correlations computed will be zero. A plot of all of these correlations produces a sampling

distribution of correlations shaped approximately like a normal distribution, with a correlation of zero (the mean) as the most frequently occurring score (the mode). This sampling distribution of correlations is referred to as an *r-distribution*.

The r-test is conducted by comparing a calculated correlation between two variables in a sample with the r-values from the r-distribution. If the calculated correlation is so large that it falls in the outermost 5% of the r-distribution, then the null hypothesis is rejected and the conclusion is that there is a significant correlation between these two variables in the larger population. Since less than 5% of all sample correlations fall in the outermost part of the r-distribution when there actually is no relationship between the two variables, the Type I error is .05. The r-test also can be conducted with more stringent rejection criteria, such as .01.

Because the r-distribution includes both positive and negative correlations and has a mean correlation of zero, both nondirectional and directional hypotheses can be tested. That is, as with the t-test, both one-tailed and two-tailed tests of the correlation coefficient can be conducted. If a nondirectional research hypothesis is advanced (i.e., H_a: $\rho \neq 0$), then a two-tailed test is computed. The 5% error is distributed in both the lower and upper tails of the r-distribution, with 2.5% error in each tail. In contrast, if a directional research hypothesis is predicted (i.e., H_a: $\rho > 0$ or H_a: $\rho < 0$), then a one-tailed test is performed. The 5% error is concentrated in either the upper tail (H_a: $\rho > 0$) or the lower tail (H_a: $\rho < 0$) of the r-distribution for hypothesis testing. As described for the t-test, a one-tailed test is more powerful than a two-tailed test because the critical value needed to reject H_0 is smaller. However, a one-tailed test does not allow examination of a correlation in the opposite than predicted direction.

Just as there were a series of t-distributions based on the sample sizes involved, so too are there a series of r-distributions based on the sample size used to compute the correlation. As with all of the statistical tests we have covered, the series of r-distributions are referred to in terms of degrees of freedom (number of scores that are free to vary) rather than sample size. With two sets of scores, both from the same sample, one degree of freedom is lost from each set of scores. Thus, the degrees of freedom for referring to the appropriate r-distribution for the r-test are:

$$df = N - 2$$

Suppose 10 subjects (N) are selected and each person's height and weight is measured. A Pearson correlation (r) is then computed between height and weight for these 10 people. To test the null hypothesis that there is no relationship between height and weight in the larger population, the calculated r-value must be compared with a critical r from the theoretical r-distribution derived with a sample of size 10, or $df = N - 2 = 10 - 2 = 8$. For the problem concerning whether there is a relationship between hours studying and exam score, there were $N = 5$ subjects and $df = N - 2 = 5 - 2 = 3$.

The critical values needed to reject H_0 follow a very similar pattern to the critical values for the t- and F-distributions as a function of degrees of freedom. The larger the degrees of freedom, the more the sample represents the population and the more the r-distribution approaches a normal distribution. The smaller the degrees of freedom, the less the sample represents the population and the r-distribution is more platykurtic. Thus, with small samples, the critical value which must be exceeded is larger, making it more difficult to reject H_0. The critical values for different degrees of freedom and rejection levels (.05 and .01) for one- and two-tailed tests are compiled in an *r-table* (Appendix A). For

instance, for a two-tailed test, the critical values with 8 degrees of freedom at the .05 and .01 significance levels are, $r_{(8).05} = \pm.6319$ and $r_{(8).01} = \pm.7646$, respectively. Similarly, for a one-tailed test, the critical values with 8 degrees of freedom at the .05 and .01 significance levels are $r_{(8).05} = +.5495$ or $-.5495$ and $r_{(8).01} = +.7155$ or $-.7155$ depending on the direction hypothesized.

For the hours of studying and exam score problem, the calculated correlation between these two variables based on a sample of size $N = 5$ was $r = +.95$. The two-tailed critical value needed to reject the null hypothesis that there actually is no relationship between hours studying and exam performance in the population is $r_{(3).05} = .8783$. Since the calculated $r = .95$ is larger in absolute terms than the critical $r = \pm.8783$, the null hypothesis is rejected at the $p < .05$ level. The conclusion is that there is a significant relationship between hours studying and exam score with a Type I error or chance of being wrong of less than .05. To see if the Type I error can be reduced even further, the r-test is conducted at the .01 level with a critical value of $r_{(3).01} = .9587$. Since the calculated $r = .95$ is not larger than the critical $r = \pm.9587$, H_0 cannot be rejected at the more stringent probability level. The final conclusion is to reject H_0 at the $p < .05$ level. There is a significant relationship between hours studying and exam score, with less than a 5% chance that this decision is incorrect and there really is no relationship between these two variables.

If this had been a directional hypothesis positing that the correlation between hours studying and exam score would be positive (H_a: $\rho > 0$; H_0: $\rho \leq 0$), the statistical decision would be to reject H_0 at $p < .01$ based on a one-tailed critical value of $r_{(3).01} = +.9343$. Recall that when conducting a one-tailed test, the observed sample value must fall in the direction hypothesized (positive or negative). For instance, if the researcher predicts a positive correlation but observes a very large negative correlation, the null hypothesis cannot be rejected because a one-tailed test only allows examination of a correlation in the direction predicted.

Correlation Does Not Equal Causation

At this point we want to emphasize what is probably the most important aspect to interpreting a significant correlation and one of the most common mistakes students make when describing a correlation. *Correlation does not equal causation.* Obtaining a significant correlation means simply that there is a relationship between two variables; it does *not* mean that one variable causes the other variable. For instance, one may find that there is a significant negative relationship between hours of TV viewing and performance in school such that students who watch a lot of TV perform poorly in school and students who watch very little TV perform quite well in school. However, the existence of this negative correlation does not allow one to draw the conclusion that watching a lot of TV causes students to perform poorly in school. Although this may, in fact, be the case, significant correlation in and of itself is not adequate to allow a researcher to draw this conclusion.

When two variables are found to be significantly related, there exist three possibilities as to why this relationship exist. First, Variable X causes Variable Y: watching a lot of TV causes students to perform poorly in school. Second, Variable Y causes Variable X: performing poorly in school causes students to watch a lot of TV. Finally, a *third variable*, Z, causes both X and Y: lack of time spent interacting with parents causes students to both watch more TV and perform poorly in school.

Amount of Variance Explained

Although the magnitude of the correlation coefficient, r, provides a sense of the strength of the relationship between two variables, there exists a more precise method for determining how much knowledge of the variability in one variable is explained by variability in the other variable. A correlation of -1.00 or +1.00 means that one variable (e.g., height) perfectly explains all of the variation in the other variable (e.g., weight). With a perfect correlation between the variables, 100% of the variability in one variable is explained by the other variable. This complete knowledge means that by knowing a person's height one can predict exactly what his or her weight will be because 100% of the variability in people's weight is attributable to variations in their height. The value denoting the variance two variables share with each other is termed the *coefficient of determination* and is equal to the square of the correlation coefficient: r^2. If the correlation between height and weight is r = +.70, then r^2 = .49, which means that 49% of the variability in people's weight can be explained by differences in their heights, and the other 51% of the variability in weight is explained by other factors, such as diet, heredity, and exercise.

Consider the relationship between the number of inches of rainfall in Iowa per year and the number of new successful TV shows on the FOX network per year. The correlation between Iowa rainfall and successful FOX shows is r = 0 with a coefficient of determination of r^2 = 0. Variability in the number of inches of rainfall in Iowa does not explain any of the variability in the number of successful TV shows on the FOX network from one year to the next. The fact that these two variables are completely unrelated can be depicted visually in a Venn diagram such as the following:

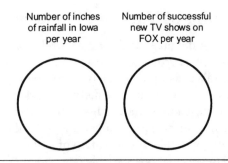

FIGURE 9.7: Coefficient of determination $r^2 = 0$

In a *Venn diagram* each variable is represented by a circle, with the amount of variance the variables share with one another denoted by the degree to which the circles overlap. Since the two circles in Figure 9.7 do not overlap at all, the two variables share no variance, $r^2 = 0$.

Suppose instead that the correlation between number of inches of Iowa rainfall and number of new successful FOX TV shows per year is $r = +.30$ with a coefficient of determination of $r^2 = .09$ as depicted in the following diagram:

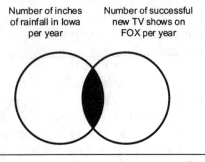

FIGURE 9.8: Coefficient of determination $r^2 = .09$

The slight amount of overlap of the two circles in the Venn diagram in Figure 9.8 indicates that the two variables share some variance in common. Nine percent of the variability in the number of successful TV shows on FOX per year can be explained by the number of inches of rainfall received in Iowa per year, and vice

versa.

Finally, suppose the correlation between Iowa rainfall and successful FOX shows is $r = -.80$ with a coefficient of determination of $r^2 = .64$:

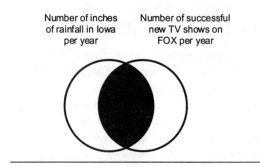

FIGURE 9.9: Coefficient of determination $r^2 = .64$

Fully 64% of the variability in one variable can be explained by variability in the other variable, as illustrated by the large overlapping area in the two circles in Figure 9.9. The most extreme situation is two completely overlapping circles, with a correlation $r = \pm1.00$ and $r^2 = 1.00$, or 100% of the variability accounted for.

An Example of Correlation

A researcher believes that the more television students watch, the worse they perform at school. She randomly samples 52 students at a university and asks them to indicate how many hours per day they watch television. She then goes to the Registrar's Office and obtains the grade point average (GPA) for these 52 students.

QUESTION: Is there a significant negative relationship between amount of television students watch and their college GPA?

ANSWER:

Step 1: What are the hypotheses for this

study?

The researcher is predicting that there is a negative relationship or correlation between how much TV college students watch and how well they perform in school. The hypotheses for this study are:

$$H_0: \quad \rho \geq 0$$
$$H_a: \quad \rho < 0$$

Step 2: Compute the value of the correlation.

Since calculating the Pearson r is a rather lengthy and laborious process for a sample size of N = 52, we will not show the detailed computations here. However, deriving the Pearson r for this problem involves calculating 52 z-scores for the number of hours of TV watched per day for each student and 52 z-scores for the GPA for each student. The two z-scores are multiplied for each student, summed across all 52 students, and divided by the total number of students:

$$r_{(TV)(GPA)} = \frac{\sum z_{TV} z_{GPA}}{N}$$

The correlation calculated for this problem is r = -0.33.

Step 3: Calculate the degrees of freedom.

With one degree of freedom lost for each of the two sets of scores, the degrees of freedom for this problem are: df = N - 2 = 52 - 2 = 50.

Step 4: Look up the critical value at the .05 level.

Using the r-table, the critical value for a one-tailed r-test with 50 degrees of freedom at the .05 significance level is $r_{(50).05} = .2306$.

Step 5: Compare the calculated r to the critical r at the .05 level.

Because this is a directional test, the calculated correlation first must be examined to insure that the value falls in the hypothesized direction. The observed sample correlation is negative, consistent with the researcher's prediction; thus, the calculated value can be compared with the one-tailed critical value. Since the calculated r = -0.33 is larger (in absolute terms) than the critical r = .2306, the null hypothesis is rejected at the $p < .05$ significance level. There is a significant negative relationship between television viewing and college GPA, with a Type I error of less than .05.

Step 6: Look up the critical value at the .01 level.

Using the r-table, the critical value for a one-tailed r-test with 50 degrees of freedom at the .01 significance level is $r_{(50).01} = .3218$.

Step 7: Compare the calculated r to the critical r at the .01 level.

Since the calculated r = -0.33 is larger (in absolute terms) than the critical r = .3218 at the .01 level, the null hypothesis is rejected at the $p < .01$ significance level. The researcher can conclude that there is a significant negative relationship between amount of television viewed and college GPA with a Type I error of less than .01.

Step 8: State the final conclusion both statistically and in words.

Statistically, the researcher's final decision is to reject H_0 at the $p < .01$ level. There is a significant negative relationship between number of hours of TV viewed per day and college GPA among university students, with less than a 1% chance that there actually is no relationship at all (or a positive relationship) between these variables.

Summary

Simple correlation refers to the degree to which two variables vary together and is represented by a statistic called the Pearson product-moment correlation or the Pearson r. The magnitude of a correlation refers to the strength of the relationship between two variables and the direction indicates whether the two variables have a positive, direct relationship or a negative, inverse relationship. A Pearson correlation is tested for significance based on a series of distributions called the r-distributions. A calculated r must equal or exceed the critical r-value obtained from the r-table in order to reject the null hypothesis. Both one- and two-tailed hypothesis tests can be conducted for correlation depending on whether the researcher advances a directional or nondirectional prediction. The amount of variance in one variable which is attributable to the other variable is the coefficient of determination, r^2. A Venn diagram can be used to depict the amount of variance shared among variables.

Key Terms

- coefficient of determination (r^2)
- direction
- magnitude
- negative, inverse relationship
- Pearson product-moment correlation or Pearson r (r or ρ)
- positive, direct relationship
- r-distributions
- r-table
- simple correlation
- third variable
- Venn diagram

Problems

1. To examine the relationship or association between two variables which statistical test is conducted?
2. The following questions refer to characteristics of a simple correlation:

a. What is the range of values that a correlation coefficient can possibly assume?
b. What does the sign of a correlation coefficient indicate?
c. What can be inferred about the relationship between two variables when there is a positive correlation: as one variable increases, the other variable (*increases* or *decreases*)?
d. What can be inferred about the relationship between two variables when there is a negative correlation: as one variable increases, the other variable (*increases* or *decreases*)?
e. What does the magnitude of a correlation coefficient reveal?
3. For each of the correlations depicted below, indicate the approximate magnitude of the correlation (*none, low, moderate, high,* or *perfect*) and the direction of the correlation (*positive, negative,* or *none*)?

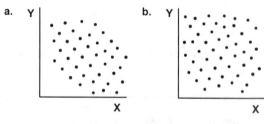

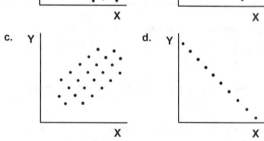

4. What is a simple correlation and how is it symbolized?
5. For each of the following pairs, indicate which is the stronger correlation:
a. r = +0.56   or   r = +0.78
b. r = -0.13   or   r = -0.02

c. $r = +0.86$ or $r = -1.00$
d. $r = -0.92$ or $r = +0.42$
e. $r = -0.21$ or $r = 0.00$
f. $r = -1.00$ or $r = +1.00$

6. A researcher hypothesizes that perceptions of a person's attractiveness will be positively related to perceptions of the person's intelligence. To test this hypothesis, the researcher shows five subjects a photograph of an unfamiliar person and asks them to rate the person on a 1-9 scale in terms of attractiveness (1=unattractive, 9=attractive) and also to rate the person on a 1-9 scale in terms of intelligence (1=unintelligent, 9=intelligent). The following data are obtained for this study:

Subject	Attractiveness Rating	Intelligence Rating
Bill	8	6
Tim	5	6
Sue	4	5
Ann	6	5
Kelly	2	3

a. Calculate the Pearson r for these data.
b. State the null and research hypotheses.
c. Conduct a test of the correlation coefficient.
d. State your decision both statistically and in words.

7. A researcher wishes to assess the relationship between computer consultants' deteriorating vision and the amount of time they spend in front of a computer screen. Thirty consultants' weekly amount of time spent typing on a computer and their vision are measured. The data reveal that the correlation between these two variables is $r = -0.43$.
a. What is the magnitude and direction of this correlation?
b. State the null and research hypotheses.
c. Conduct a test of the correlation coeffi-

cient.
d. State your decision both statistically and in words.

8. A researcher is interested in whether there is a relationship between the amount of eye contact a person has during a conversation and how much he or she talks. The researcher observes 42 subjects engaged in a five-minute conversation with a confederate and measures the number of seconds each subject maintains eye contact with the confederate and also how many seconds the subject talks during the conversation. The correlation between eye contact and talkativeness is calculated as $r = -0.24$.
a. What is the magnitude and direction of this correlation?
b. State the null and research hypotheses.
c. Conduct a test of the correlation coefficient.
d. State your decision both statistically and in words.

9. A researcher suspects that there is a positive relationship between number of days of rainfall per year and the number of absentee days from work. Ten people are randomly selected from cities across the country and the number of days of rainfall in each person's city last year is measured along with the number of days each person was absent from work during the previous year. A correlation of $r = +0.78$ is obtained.
a. What is the magnitude and direction of this correlation?
b. State the null and research hypotheses.
c. Conduct a test of the correlation coefficient.
d. State your decision both statistically and in words.

10. What statistic indicates the percentage of variance two variables share? How is this symbolized?

11. For each of the following correlations,

calculate the percentage of variance in one variable that is accounted for by the other variable:

a. $r = +0.84$
b. $r = -0.13$
c. $r = -1.00$
d. $r = +0.22$
e. $r = 0.00$
f. $r = +0.92$
g. $r = -0.57$

12. Find r^2 for each correlation below and explain what the shaded section of each Venn diagram represents.

a.
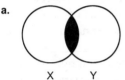

X   Y

r = 0.4

b.
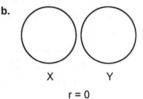

X   Y

r = 0

c.

r = +1.00

d.

r = -0.9

Notes

1 Alternatively, the correlation formula can be computed as

$$r_{x_1 x_2} = \frac{\sum z_{x_1} z_{x_2}}{N - 1}$$

if the z-scores were calculated using the unbiased estimator of the population standard deviation, s_x, which uses N - 1 in the denominator instead of N:

$$z = \frac{X - \overline{X}}{s_x}$$

2 A somewhat faster computational formula for computing the correlation between two variables (X_1 and X_2), particularly when there are many scores involved, is the following:

$$r_{x_1 x_2} = \frac{N(\sum X_1 X_2) - (\sum X_1)(\sum X_2)}{\sqrt{[N \sum X_1^2 - (\sum X_1)^2][N \sum X_2^2 - (\sum X_2)^2]}}$$

Predictors, Elicitors, and Concomitants of Social Blushing

Adapted from article by same title, Leary, M., & Meadows, S. (1991). *Personality Processes and Individual Differences, 60,* 254-262.

THIS STUDY focused on people's behavioral tendency to blush. Given that little research has been devoted to this topic, the researchers investigated a central and rudimentary question: Why do people blush? They argue that blushing is an involuntary remedial display that "occurs when people perceive that their standing in an important social group or relationship may be in jeopardy." Thus, they offer the following hypothesis:

> blushing propensity is associated with the importance people place on their relationships with others.

A total of 220 undergraduate students participated in the study. All participants completed a series of measures that consisted of (1) a Blushing Propensity scale which examined the degree to which people blush in 14 everyday social settings, (2) personality inventories, and (3) a questionnaire dealing with the experience of blushing. The items for each measure were rated on a 5-point scale (1=never; 5=always). Researchers conducted a Pearson product-moment correlation between blushing propensity and the other measures. The results indicated that:

> ... blushing propensity correlated most highly with measures that tapped aspects of people's social concerns: embarrassability ($r = .54, p < .01$), interaction anxiousness ($r = .51, p < .01$), fear of negative evaluation ($r = .48, p < .01$), and physique anxiety ($r = .36, p < .01$).... Also as predicted, those who blushed frequently expressed a greater need for being included by others (inclusion, $r = .17, p < .05$) and indicated that they were more likely to regulate their own behavior by attending to others' actions (attention to social comparisons information, $r = .32, p < .01$).

In general, the results demonstrated that people's reported blushing correlated most strongly with measures that reflect their concerns with how they are regarded by others: the more anxious and concerned people are, the more they blush.

The Relationship Between Time to Completion and Achievement on Multiple-Choice Exams

Adapted from article by same title, Herman, W. (1997). *Journal of Research and Development in Education, 30,* 113-117.

THIS RESEARCH involved examining the relationship between the time needed to complete multiple-choice examinations in the college classroom and student exam performance. Previous studies consistently have shown little relationship between exam performance and time to completion. However, the objective of this study was to explore personal tempo (the time needed to complete the examination) in test taking as an explanation for a lack of relationship between these two variables. A total of 130 students participated in the study. The length of time it took students to finish a 100 item multiple-choice test for both a midterm and final exam were recorded and compared to the final grade each student received in the class. As expected:

> The resultant correlation coefficients were low and not statistically significant ($p >$ .05). Although the range of coefficients extended from +.27 to -.30, the coefficients of determination for these values suggest that .04% and 9% of variance in examination performance could be explained by differences in time to completion variables.

Correlations between time to completion and achievement

Class	N	r Midterm Exam	N	r Final Exam
Psy 101	40	-.26	38	-.11
Psy 240	21	-.30	22	-.21
Edu 312	36	.14	35	.27
Psy 240	32	.03	32	-.02

The above findings corroborate previous studies refuting the belief that students who are among the first or last to finish an exam will either receive especially high or low scores. Rather, this researcher argues that teachers and students "should become more aware of personal tempo as a consistent variable that is unrelated to examination performance in the classroom and strive to change ineffective test taking behaviors while maintaining successful strategies" (p. 117).

Computer Section

Overview of Simple Correlation

Conducting a statistical test of simple correlation involves assessing whether there is a significant relationship or association between two variables. On the computer, a correlation command is utilized and the two variables which should be correlated with each other are specified. Additionally, most programs allow the researcher to specify whether the correlation should be tested using one- or two-tailed critical values.

Example Output for Simple Correlation

A number of medical organizations have expressed concern that emergency room doctors' long shifts (e.g., 72 hours) may be related to how frequently they make mistakes with patients. To determine whether there is any justification for this concern, a researcher gathered information for 500 doctors at several county hospital emergency rooms. In particular, he examined the association between the average number of mistakes made by the doctor per hour and the duration of the doctor's shift. Since this was primarily an exploratory investigation, the researcher tested his hypothesis utilizing a two-tailed test. The correlational data are displayed in Table 9.3.

Interpretation of Simple Correlation Output

This correlation is between the two variables MISTAKE (average number of mistakes the doctor makes per hour) and TIME (the total duration of the doctor's shift). A total of 500 doctors' mistakes were available and 497 shift times were obtained. Thus, the correlation between MISTAKE and TIME was computed based on the 497 doctors for which both scores were available. This correlation was calculated as $r = +0.6223$ and was significant at $p = .006$ (two-tailed). Thus, the longer doctors' shifts were the more mistakes they made per hour on average. However, caution must be exercised to *not* conclude based on these data that longer emergency room shifts *cause* more mistakes. These findings have demonstrated only that there is a relationship between these two variables, not the underlying causal nature of this relationship.

Computer Problems

1. Conduct r-tests to examine the following hypotheses regarding the relationship between students' self-reported performance in the course (OUTCOME) and a variety of other student ratings. Indicate whether the null hypothesis should be rejected or not rejected in each case and whether a one- or two-tailed hypothesis test was conducted.

   a. There will be a positive relationship between students' perceptions of how well they performed in the course and their overall rating of the instructor

---

TABLE 9.3: Correlation Coefficients

	MISTAKE	TIME
MISTAKE	1.0000	.6223
	(500)	(497)
	P= .	P= .006
TIME	.6223	1.0000
	(497)	(497)
	P = .006	P = .

(Coefficient/(Cases)/2-tailed Significance)

" . " is printed if a coefficient cannot be computed

(INSTRUCT).

b. There will be a positive relationship between students' perceptions of how well they performed in the course and their perceptions of how much effort they put into the course (EFFORT).

c. There will be a relationship between students' perceptions of how well they performed in the course and their perceptions of how knowledgeable the instructor was (KNOW).

d. There will be a relationship between students' perceptions of how well they performed in the course and their perceptions of how qualified the instructor was (QUAL).

e. There will be a relationship between students' perceptions of how well they performed in the course and their perceptions of how fun it was to use e-mail (FUN).

2. Conduct r-tests to examine the following hypotheses regarding the relationship between the students' overall rating of the course (COURSE) and a variety of other student ratings. Indicate whether the null hypothesis should be rejected or not rejected in each case and whether a one- or two-tailed hypothesis test was conducted.

a. There will be a relationship between students' overall evaluation of the course and how intellectually challenging (CHALL) they perceive the class.

b. There will be a relationship between students' overall evaluation of the course and the instructor's enthusiasm (ENTHUS) for the subject.

c. There will be a positive relationship between students' overall evaluation of the course and the instructor's perceived expertise (EXPERT).

d. There will be a positive relationship between students' overall evaluation of the course and students expressed interest in the course subject matter (LIKECLAS).

e. There will be a negative relationship between students' overall evaluation of the course and the helpfulness of e-mail (HINDER).

Chapter 10 ❖ Bivariate Linear Regression

From Correlation to Regression

In science, a major objective is to predict the value of one variable based on values of one or more other variables. For instance, college admissions departments attempt to use a students' SAT score and high school GPA to predict how well they will perform at the university level. A very basic form of prediction is obtained through a statistical procedure called bivariate linear regression, which is based on the concept of simple correlation covered in the previous chapter. *Bivariate linear regression* involves specifying a straight-line or linear relationship between two variables such that one variable can be used to predict the second variable.

The move from simple correlation to bivariate linear regression is very straightforward. In fact, linear regression is just another way to view a simple correlation between variables. If two variables (bivariate) are significantly related (Pearson r is significant), then one variable is a significant predictor of the other variable, and vice versa. If the value of one variable, called the *predictor variable*, is known, then information obtained from this variable can be used to predict the value of the other variable, called the *criterion variable*, better than chance. The predictor variable is analogous to an independent variable from analysis of variance, and the criterion variable is analogous to a dependent variable.

The ability to predict one variable from a second variable is based on the linear relationship between the two variables. Figure 10.1 depicts a moderate, positive correlation between SAT score (X) and college GPA (Y),

where each data point represents an individual's SAT-GPA combination. Notice that the data points generally are clustered relatively close together and move in an upward-sloping direction – the higher one's SAT score, the better his or her college GPA. A linear relationship is specified for these data by drawing a line through all of the points that best fits the data. When the points are clustered near the line, the correlation is strong. When the points are more spread out from the line, the correlation is weaker. This line is called the *line of best fit* or the *regression line* and is drawn in such a way that across all data points, the sum of the average squared distance between each point and the line (sum of squares) is as small as possible, a concept termed *least squares*.

With bivariate linear regression, the regression line is specified using the basic formula for a line covered in most high school algebra classes. A line depicts the relationship between two variables, X (plotted on the x-axis) and Y

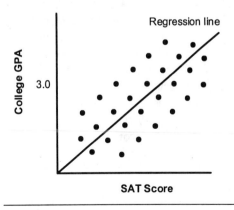

FIGURE 10.1: Moderate, positive correlation

(plotted on the y-axis), and is defined by the equation:

$$\hat{Y} = bX + a$$

This equation indicates that Y is a function of X, where X is the predictor variable and Y is the criterion variable. Commonly, the symbol $\hat{Y}$ (Y-hat) is used to indicate the predicted value of the criterion variable, and Y is used to indicate the actual, observed value of the criterion variable. The function or relationship between X and Y is defined by two features: a slope and a constant. The *slope* of a line refers to the degree to which the line is slanted upward (a positive slope) or downward (a negative slope) and is designated by the statistic "b" called the *bivariate regression coefficient*. The slope indicates how many units Y increases for every one unit increase in X. For instance, a slope of b = 2 means that as X increases by 1 unit, Y increases by 2 units. A slope of b = -0.5 means that as X increases by 1 unit, Y decreases by one half unit. The *constant* indicates where the line crosses or intercepts the y-axis; hence, the constant is also referred to as the *intercept* and is designated by the symbol "a." The regression equation can be used to predict values of Y based on different values of X.

Consider the following regression equation where a student's SAT score (X) is used to predict his or her college GPA (Y): $\hat{Y}$ = .0021X + 0.5. This linear relationship is depicted in Figure 10.2. The bivariate regression coefficient is b = .0021, meaning that for every one point increase in SAT score, college GPA goes up by .0021. The intercept a = +0.5 indicates that the regression line crosses the y-axis at a college GPA of 0.5. Using this regression equation, a student with an SAT score of 1000 is predicted to have a college GPA of 2.6: $\hat{Y}$ = .0021X + 0.5 = .0021(1000) + 0.5 = 2.1 + .5 = 2.6. Similarly, a student with a 1420 SAT score is predicted to have a GPA of approximately 3.5: $\hat{Y}$ = .0021X + 0.5 = .0021(1420) + 0.5 = 3.0 + 0.5 = 3.482.

Deriving the Regression Equation

Clearly, the regression equation is very useful for predicting values of one variable based on values of a second variable. The regression equation is derived based on data collected from a sample. The regression coefficient, b, is calculated from the correlation between the two variables r_{xy} and the two sample standard deviations, SD_y and SD_x:[1]

$$b = r_{xy} \frac{SD_y}{SD_x}$$

Although the regression coefficient is a function of the correlation, different slopes can exist for the same correlation as a function of the standard deviations for the two variables. For example, both of the graphs in Figure 10.3 illustrate perfect positive correlations (since all of the data points fall exactly on a straight line), with r = +1.00. However, the graph on the left has a line with a much steeper slope (b = +0.50) than does the line in the graph on the right (b = +0.33). This difference is due to

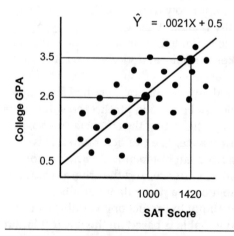

FIGURE 10.2: Bivariate linear regression equation $\hat{Y}$ = .0021X + 0.5 to predict college GPA from SAT score

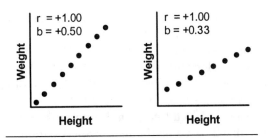

FIGURE 10.3: Perfect positive correlations with steeper slope b = +0.50 (left) and flatter slope b = +0.33 (right)

the fact that the ratio of the two standard deviations is 1 to 2 in the left graph (e.g., SD_y = 5, SD_x = 10) whereas the ratio of the two standard deviations is 1 to 3 in the second graph (e.g., SD_y = 2, SD_x = 6).

The intercept, a, is calculated from the regression coefficient, b, and the sample means for the two variables, $\overline{X}$ and $\overline{Y}$:

$$a = \overline{Y} - b\overline{X}$$

With an intercept and a slope, a regression equation can be constructed and used for prediction. Consider the following data for hours studying and exam score presented in Chapter 9:

Student	Hours Studying (X)	Exam Score (Y)
Pat	2	76
Lisa	4	82
Mary	5	88
Missy	6	85
Sean	8	94
	$\overline{X}_{Std}$ = 5	$\overline{Y}_{Ex}$ = 85
	SD_{Std} = 2	SD_{Ex} = 6

The correlation obtained for these data was $r_{(Std)(Ex)}$ = +0.95. The regression equation to predict exam score from number of hours studying is derived as follows:

$$b = r_{(Std)(Ex)} \frac{SD_{Ex}}{SD_{Std}} = (+0.95)\left(\frac{6}{2}\right) = 2.85$$

$$a = \overline{Y} - b\overline{X} = 85 - (2.85)(5) = 70.75$$

$$\hat{Y} = bX + a = 2.85X + 70.75$$

This regression equation indicates that for every one additional hour a student studies before an exam, his or her exam score goes up by nearly three points (2.85). A student who does not study at all is predicted to have an exam score equal to 70.75, the intercept. Using this regression equation, exam scores can be predicted for students who study various numbers of hours. For instance, if a student studies for 3 hours before an exam, then his or her exam score is predicted to be: $\hat{Y}$ = 2.85X + 70.75 = 2.85(3) + 70.75 = 79.30, as illustrated in the following graph:

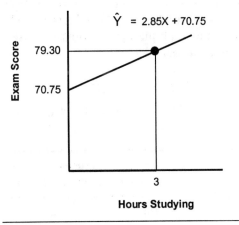

FIGURE 10.4: Bivariate linear regression equation $\hat{Y} = 2.85X + 70.75$ to predict exam score from hours studying

Prediction and Error

Bivariate linear regression involves predicting one variable (Y) from a second variable (X) based on a regression equation. Unless there is a perfect correlation between the two variables, with all observed data points falling exactly on the regression line, there will be some error between the actual value of Y observed in the sample and the value predicted from the regression equation ($\hat{Y}$). That is, all predicted values, by definition, fall along the regression line defined by a regression equation. If the correlation between X and Y is perfect, then all observed values also fall on this regression line. If the correlation between X and Y is less than perfect, then some observed values will not fall exactly on the regression line. This difference between actual and predicted values is error in prediction.

The *standard error of the estimate (SEE)* is used to obtain a measure of the magnitude of error involved in predicting Y from X in a particular regression equation. The standard error of the estimate is similar to the standard deviation, which is an average measure of the variability in a set of data. Recall from Chapter 3 that the population standard deviation estimated from a sample, s_x (the unbiased estimator), is calculated as:

$$s_x = \sqrt{\frac{\sum(X-\overline{X})^2}{N-1}} = \sqrt{\frac{SS_x}{N-1}} = \sqrt{\frac{SS_x}{df}}$$

Similar to the standard deviation, the standard error of the estimate is a standard or average measure of the variability of the actual, observed values from values predicted by the regression line. In other words, the SEE provides a sense of how far the actual observed scores in a set of data differ from the scores that are predicted based on the regression equation. The standard error of the estimate based on predicting Y from X, $s_{y \bullet x}$, is calculated as follows:

$$s_{y \bullet x} = \sqrt{\frac{\sum(Y-\hat{Y})^2}{N-2}} = \sqrt{\frac{SS_{Res}}{N-2}} = \sqrt{\frac{SS_{Res}}{df}}$$

This calculation of the standard error of the estimate involves the *sum of squares residual (SS$_{Res}$)*, which is the sum of the squared differences between each individual's actual observed score (Y) and the score predicted by the regression equation ($\hat{Y}$), and the degrees of freedom for bivariate linear regression and correlation, df = N - 2.

For the hours studying and exam score problem, calculating the standard error of the estimate first requires that a predicted score be computed for each student based on the regression equation, as shown below:

Student	Hours Studying (X)	Exam Score (Y)	Predicted Exam Score ($\hat{Y}$)
Pat	2	76	$\hat{Y}$ = 2.85(2) + 70.75 = 76.45
Lisa	4	82	$\hat{Y}$ = 2.85(4) + 70.75 = 82.15
Mary	5	88	$\hat{Y}$ = 2.85(5) + 70.75 = 85.00
Missy	6	85	$\hat{Y}$ = 2.85(6) + 70.75 = 87.85
Sean	8	94	$\hat{Y}$ = 2.85(8) + 70.75 = 93.55
	$\overline{X}_{Std}$ = 5	$\overline{Y}_{Ex}$ = 85	
	SD_{Std} = 2	SD_{Ex} = 6	

These predicted values are then compared with the actual observed values to produce the sum of squares residual (see Table 10.1). The standard error of the estimate for this problem is then computed as follows:

$$s_{y \cdot x} = \sqrt{\frac{\sum (Y - \hat{Y})^2}{N - 2}} = \sqrt{\frac{17.55}{5 - 2}} = \sqrt{\frac{17.55}{3}} = \sqrt{5.85} = 2.419$$

This measure indicates that, on average, a predicted exam score varies about 2 to 3 points from the actual exam score.

One important point about the standard error of the estimate is that it has an inverse relationship with the correlation between X and Y. Although the correlation r_{xy} is not used directly to compute the SEE, the two values are closely related. If the correlation between the two variables is perfect, r = +1.00 or r = -1.00, then the difference between the actual Y-value (Y) and the predicted Y-value ($\hat{Y}$) will always be zero and the standard error of the estimate will equal zero. The lower the correlation, the more any individual data point deviates from the regression line. The farther an actual Y-value is from the value predicted by the regression line, the greater will be the dif-ference or residual between actual and predicted Y-values, and the higher will be the standard error of the estimate. Thus, the standard error of the estimate provides a measure of how accurate prediction is from the regression equation. The higher the correlation, the smaller the standard error of the estimate and the more accurate the prediction.

Significance of the Regression Equation

Although the standard error of the estimate provides a useful measure of the accuracy of prediction from a regression equation, it does not directly reveal whether the regression equation predicts better than chance. That is, if the standard error of the estimate for the exam score problem was 30 points, the regression equation would be very poor in predicting exam scores, and simply guessing someone's score probably would be about as accurate as using the regression equation. To determine if the regression equation predicts better than chance, it must be assessed for significance. There are three different ways to assess a bivariate regression equation for significance,

TABLE 10.1

Student	Hours Studying (X)	Exam Score (Y)	Predicted Score ($\hat{Y}$)	Y - $\hat{Y}$	$(Y - \hat{Y})^2$
Pat	2	76	76.45	76-76.45 = -0.45	$(-0.45)^2$ = 0.2025
Lisa	4	82	82.15	82-82.15 = -0.15	$(-0.15)^2$ = 0.0225
Mary	5	88	85.00	88-85 = 3.00	3^2 = 9.0000
Missy	6	85	87.85	85-87.85 = -2.85	$(-2.85)^2$ = 8.1225
Sean	8	94	93.55	94-93.55 = 0.45	$(0.45)^2$ = 0.2025
	$\overline{X}_{Std} = 5$	$\overline{Y}_{Ex} = 85$			Σ = 17.5500
	$SD_{Std} = 2$	$SD_{Ex} = 6$			

and we will discuss all three approaches. The first method is perhaps the simplest and one which was already described in the previous chapter. The second and third methods, while somewhat more involved computationally, are important to understand because they will prove crucial for significance testing with multiple regression in Chapter 11.

The most straightforward method for assessing whether a bivariate linear regression equation predicts better than chance is to determine whether the correlation between the two variables is significant. If the correlation is significant, then the bivariate linear regression equation is significant. Because the two variables are determined to be significantly related via correlation, then by definition, one variable can be used to predict the other variable better than chance. For the exam score problem we have been discussing, the correlation between hours studying and exam score observed in the sample of 5 subjects was $r = +0.95$. As described in Chapter 9, the two-tailed critical value at the .05 level is $r_{(3).05} = .8783$ and the correlation is significant. Since the simple correlation is significant, the bivariate regression equation is significant; this regression equation predicts exam score from hours studying better than chance.

A second method for assessing the regression equation for significance is to conduct a t-test to assess the bivariate regression coefficient, b, for significance. A t-test of the bivariate regression coefficient tests the null hypothesis that the slope of the regression line in the population is equal to zero, that is, that there is no relationship between the two variables. Recall from Chapter 6 that a two-sample t-test involved the ratio of the difference between means to the standard error of the difference:

$$t = \frac{\overline{X}_1 - \overline{X}_2}{s_{diff}}$$

Similarly, the t-test for the bivariate regression coefficient compares the regression coefficient, b, with its standard error, s_b:

$$t = \frac{b}{s_b}$$

The standard error of the bivariate regression coefficient is a function of the standard error of the estimate ($s_{y \bullet x}$) and the variability in the predictor variable.[2] The calculated t-value is compared to the critical t-value obtained using the same degrees of freedom as the correlation:

$$df = N - 2$$

In the problem above with hours studying and exam score, the calculated regression coefficient is $b = 2.85$ and the standard error of the regression coefficient is $s_b = 0.54$.[3] The calculated t-value is:

$$t = \frac{b}{s_b} = \frac{2.85}{0.54} = 5.28$$

To determine whether this calculated t-value is significant, it is compared to a two-tailed critical t-value with $N - 2 = 5 - 2 = 3$ degrees of freedom. The critical t-value (two-tailed) at the .05 level is $t_{(3).05} = 3.182$ and the critical t-value at the .01 level is $t_{(3).01} = 5.841$. Since the calculated value of 5.28 is larger than 3.182 but not larger than 5.841, the correct statistical decision is to reject H_0 at the $p < .05$ level and conclude that the regression equation is significant. Notice that this statistical conclusion is identical to the result obtained when the correlation was assessed for significance.

Finally, the third method for assessing the significance of the regression equation is to conduct an F-test. Recall from Chapter 7 that total variability measured how each individual score (X) differed from the grand mean ($\overline{X}_{Grand}$) for a dependent variable. Total variability consisted of two sources of variability: between groups and within groups. Variability between groups identified differences due to the independent variable and was calculated as the difference between each group mean and the grand mean. Variability within groups identified the residual or error in individual scores that was not explained by differences due to the independent variable and was calculated as the difference between each individual score and its own group mean. Conducting the F-test, then, involved comparing the averages for these two sources of variability in a ratio of the variability due to the independent variable (mean square between) to the variability due to individual differences or error (mean square within).

Calculating the F-test for regression involves these exact same concepts. Total variability is defined identically to analysis of variance: how does each individual score differ from the grand mean of all scores. Since the criterion variable Y is analogous to the dependent measure, variability is defined in terms of the variable being predicted (e.g., exam score). Sum of squares total is the sum of the squared differences between each individual score and the grand mean of all scores:

$$SS_{Total} = \sum (Y - \overline{Y})^2$$

For the exam score problem, sum of squares total is calculated as shown in Table 10.2.

The total sum of squares, $SS_{Total} = 180$, is partitioned into two parts: sum of squares regression and sum of squares residual. *Sum of squares regression* (SS_{Reg}) is analogous to $SS_{Between}$ and is the part of the total variability that is attributable to the regression equation (i.e., the predictor variable). *Sum of squares residual* (SS_{Res}) is equivalent to SS_{Within} and is the portion of total variability that is not due to the regression equation (i.e., error). To clarify each of these components, recall that the regression equation defines a relationship between an independent (predictor) variable and a dependent (criterion) variable. Any variability that can be explained by the regression equation, SS_{Reg}, is attributable to differences in the predictor variable. Variability that cannot be explained by the regression equation, SS_{Res}, is not attributable to the predictor variable and is error or residual variability. A helpful way to understand the two components that comprise total variability is via Figure 10.5. Figure 10.5 depicts the regression line for the hours

TABLE 10.2

Student	Hours Studying (X)	Exam Score (Y)	$Y - \overline{Y}$	$(Y - \overline{Y})^2$
Pat	2	76	76-85 = -9	$(-9)^2$ = 81
Lisa	4	82	82-85 = -3	$(-3)^2$ = 9
Mary	5	88	88-85 = 3	3^2 = 9
Missy	6	85	85-85 = 0	0^2 = 0
Sean	8	94	94-85 = 9	9^2 = 81
	$\overline{X}_{Std} = 5$	$\overline{Y}_{Ex} = 85$		Σ = 180
	$SD_{Std} = 2$	$SD_{Ex} = 6$		

studying and exam score problem derived earlier in this chapter. Additionally, a horizontal line is drawn at the mean for exam score, $\overline{Y} = 85$. Total variability, variability due to regression, and variability due to error (residual) are illustrated for the first student, Pat. Pat, who studied for 2 hours, scored a 76 on the exam; this is the observed value, Y. The difference between the grand mean ($\overline{Y}$) and Pat's actual, observed score (Y) illustrates total variability (SS_{Total}): $Y - \overline{Y} = 76 - 85 = -9$. This 9-point difference can be broken down into two parts: how much of the variability can be explained by the regression line, and how

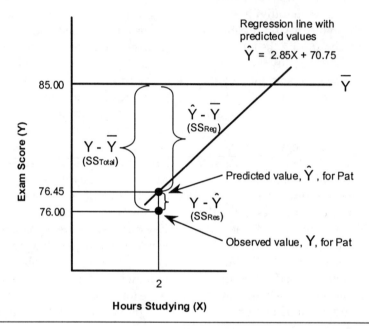

FIGURE 10.5: Breakdown of sum of squares for bivariate linear regression

TABLE 10.3

Student	Hours Studying (X)	Exam Score (Y)	Predicted Score ($\hat{Y}$)	$\hat{Y} - \overline{Y}$	$(\hat{Y} - \overline{Y})^2$
Pat	2	76	76.45	76.45-85 = -8.55	$(-8.55)^2 = 73.1025$
Lisa	4	82	82.15	82.15-85 = -2.85	$(-2.85)^2 = 8.1225$
Mary	5	88	85.00	85-85 = 0	$0^2 = 0$
Missy	6	85	87.85	87.85-85 = 2.85	$2.85^2 = 8.1225$
Sean	8	94	93.55	93.55-85 = 8.55	$8.55^2 = 73.1025$
	$\overline{X}_{Std} = 5$	$\overline{Y}_{Ex} = 85$			$\Sigma = 162.45$
	$SD_{Std} = 2$	$SD_{Ex} = 6$			

much variability is not attributable to the regression line (i.e., residual). Based on the regression equation derived from this sample of students, Pat is predicted to have scored a 76.45, $\hat{Y}$. The difference between this predicted value and the grand mean indicates how much of the total variability can be explained by the regression equation (SS_{Reg}): $\hat{Y} - \overline{Y} = 76.45 - 85 = -8.55$. The remaining part of the total variability cannot be explained by the predictor variable, number of hours studying, and is variability due to other factors. This error or residual variability is the difference between the score predicted by the regression equation and the actual, observed score (SS_{Res}): $Y - \hat{Y} = 76 - 76.45 = -0.45$. Notice that the sum of variability due to regression (-8.55) and variability due to error (-0.45) equals the total variability in Pat's score (-9).

As illustrated in Figure 10.5, sum of squares regression is calculated as the sum of the squared differences between the score predicted by the regression equation and the mean of the set of scores:

$$SS_{Reg} = \sum (\hat{Y} - \overline{Y})^2$$

For the exam score problem, SS_{Reg} is computed as shown in Table 10.3. A calculated value of $SS_{Reg} = 162.45$ indicates that a large portion of the total variability, $SS_{Total} = 180$, can be explained by the independent variable hours studying via the regression equation.

Sum of squares residual is computed as the difference between the observed score and the predicted score:

$$SS_{Res} = \sum (Y - \hat{Y})^2$$

The calculation of SS_{Res} was conducted earlier in this chapter when we discussed the computation of the standard error of the estimate and arrived at a value of $SS_{Res} = 17.55$. As a check that our calculations are correct, notice

that sum of squares regression plus sum of squares residual equals sum of squares total:

$$SS_{Total} = SS_{Reg} + SS_{Res} = 162.45 + 17.55 = 180$$

With the sums of squares computed, the only pieces of information required before the ANOVA table can be constructed and an F-value computed is the degrees of freedom. Recall that the total degrees of freedom for a set of data is always $df_{Total} = N - 1$. *Degrees of freedom regression (df_{Reg})* equals the number of predictor variables involved in the regression equation:

$$df_{Reg} = k$$

With bivariate linear regression, there is always one predictor variable so $df_{Reg} = k = 1$. *Degrees of freedom residual (df_{Res})* equals the total number of scores minus the number of predictor variables minus one:

$$df_{Res} = N - k - 1$$

With bivariate linear regression, $df_{Res} = N - k - 1 = N - 1 - 1 = N - 2$. Although the degrees of freedom are simplified for bivariate linear regression, we present the general formulas which will be revisited with multiple regression in the following chapter.

The ANOVA table can now be constructed in the method described extensively in Chapters 7 and 8 with analysis of variance. The F-test is conducted the same way for a regression problem as described previously:

Source	SS	df	MS	F
Regression	162.45	1	162.45	27.77
Residual	17.55	3	5.85	
Total	180.00	4		

From the F-table, the critical F-values obtained

for this problem are $F_{(1,3).05} = 10.13$ and $F_{(1,3).01} = 34.12$. Since the calculated F-value of 27.77 is larger than the critical value at the .05 level (10.13) but not larger than the critical value at the .01 level (34.12), the statistical decision is to reject H_0 at the $p < .05$ level and conclude that the regression equation does predict better than chance. Notice that this result is identical to the statistical conclusions obtained from the r-test and t-test methods for assessing the regression equation for significance.

In sum, the r-test is the simplest method for assessing the significance of a bivariate linear regression equation, and probably the preferred method in this simple case. As will be described in Chapter 11, the F-test is used to assess the overall significance of a regression equation, which may include multiple predictor variables, and the t-test is used to test the significance of a specific predictor variable. The importance of the t-test and F-test for assessing the significance of a regression equation will become clear in the next chapter.

An Example of Bivariate Linear Regression

Suppose a researcher is interested in predicting sedentary females' weights based on their heights. He obtains a sample of six women who do not exercise and measures their height and weight, yielding the following data:

Height	Weight
69	150
67	135
64	108
66	138
62	113
65	125
$\overline{X} = 65.5$	$\overline{Y} = 128.167$
$SD_x = 2.217$	$SD_y = 14.531$

The researcher calculates the correlation between the two variables as r = +.913.

QUESTION: Is height a significant predictor of sedentary females' weight?

ANSWER:

Step 1: Produce the regression equation.

The slope or regression coefficient, b, and the constant or intercept, a, are calculated for this problem as follows:[4]

$$b = r_{xy}\frac{SD_y}{SD_x} = (+0.913)\left(\frac{14.531}{2.217}\right) = 5.983$$

$$a = \overline{Y} - b\overline{X} = 128.167 - (5.983)(65.5) = -263.723$$

The regression equation is then produced:

$$\hat{Y} = bX + a = 5.983X - 263.723$$

Step 2: Assess the regression equation for significance.

Testing the regression equation for significance can be accomplished by (1) testing the correlation coefficient, r, for significance with an r-test, (2) testing the regression coefficient, b, for significance via a t-test, or (3) assessing the regression equation for significance by an F-test. For brevity, we will conduct the simplest test for bivariate linear regression: a test of the correlation coefficient.

The calculated correlation, r = +.913 is tested with N - 2 = 6 - 2 = 4 degrees of freedom. The two-tailed critical values are $r_{(4).05} = .8114$ and $r_{(4).01} = .9172$. Since the calculated r = .913 is larger than .8114 but not larger than .9172, the null hypothesis is rejected at the $p < .05$ level.

Step 3: State the final conclusion both statistically and in words.

Since the simple correlation between the two variables is significant, the regression equation is significant. Sedentary females' height is a significant predictor of their weight.

Summary

Bivariate linear regression involves predicting a criterion variable from a single predictor variable. A regression equation is developed for a regression line, which is the line which best fits the data based on minimizing the squared distance between each observed data point and the line, a concept termed least squares. The regression line has a slope (bivariate regression coefficient), which indicates how many units Y increases or decreases for every one unit increase in X, and a constant (intercept), which is where the regression line crosses the y-axis.

The accuracy of the regression line can be assessed via the standard error of the estimate, which is an average measure of the deviation between the actual, observed values of the criterion variable and those values predicted by the regression equation. To determine whether the regression equation predicts better than chance, one of three different significance tests can be conducted: an r-test to assess the correlation coefficient for significance, a t-test to assess the regression coefficient for significance, or an F-test to assess the regression equation for significance.

Key Terms

- bivariate linear regression
- bivariate regression coefficient (slope)
- constant (intercept)
- criterion variable
- degrees of freedom regression
- degrees of freedom residual
- least squares
- predictor variable
- regression line (line of best fit)
- standard error of the estimate (SEE or $S_{y•x}$)
- sum of squares regression (SS_{Reg})
- sum of squares residual (SS_{Res})

Problems

1. What is the purpose of bivariate linear regression?

2. What are two names for the line drawn through pairs of data points on a graph which minimizes the squared distance between each point and the line?

3. What is the concept of minimizing the squared distances between each individual data point and the regression line called?

4. What is the general equation for a regression line for bivariate linear regression?

5. What is the symbol for the slope of a line and what does it mean?

6. What is the symbol for the constant of a line and what does it mean?

7. For each of the following regression equations and X-values, give the best prediction of the Y-value:
   a. $\hat{Y} = +0.84X + 9$, $X = 3$
   b. $\hat{Y} = 32X + 5$, $X = 8$
   c. $\hat{Y} = 10X + 0.2$, $X = 5.3$
   d. $\hat{Y} = 0.33X + 0.55$, $X = 1$

8. What information does the standard error of the estimate (SEE) provide?

9. Is the relationship between the correlation coefficient (r) and the standard error of the estimate (SEE) positive or negative?

10. If the correlation between X and Y is high, will the SEE be small or large?

11. For each of the following pairs of correlations, indicate which one would have the lower standard error of the estimate (i.e., which would yield the most accurate prediction):
    a. r = +0.34 or r = -0.21
    b. r = 0.00 or r = -1.00
    c. r = +0.56 or r = +0.67
    d. r = -0.49 or r = + 0.32
    e. r = -0.98 or r = -0.56

12. Indicate for each of the following instances of linear regression whether the regression equation is significant (that is, whether it

predicts significantly better than chance):

a. A researcher samples 30 individuals and finds the correlation between the number of cigarettes smoked per day and the number of hours of sleep per day is r = -0.28. Can the researcher predict better than chance how much a person will sleep per day based on knowing how many cigarettes s/he smokes?

b. Twenty-two subjects participated in a study of how much time workers spend chatting with their colleagues during the day and how many cups of coffee they drink. The correlation was r = + 0.47. Could a manager predict better than chance how much time an employee will spend gossiping with co-workers based on knowing how many cups of coffee s/he drinks per day?

13. Consider Problem #6 in Chapter 9 regarding the relationship between ratings of a person's attractiveness and their intelligence. Suppose this same researcher is interested in determining whether how attractive a person is rated can be used to predict how intelligent the person will be perceived.

a. Produce the regression equation.

b. If a person is rated a 3 in attractiveness on a 9-point scale, how intelligent s/he is predicted to be on a 9-point scale?

c. Determine if prediction is better than chance by conducting an r-test.

d. Determine if prediction is better than chance by conducting a t-test.

e. Determine if prediction is better than chance by conducting an F-test.

Notes

1   Alternatively, the unbiased standard deviations, s_x and s_y, can be used:

$$b = r_{xy} \frac{s_y}{s_x}$$

Since the calculation of the standard deviations differ by whether N or N - 1 is used in the computation, both formulas yield identical results provided both the biased or unbiased estimators are used.

2   The standard error of the regression coefficient (s_b) is calculated as:

$$s_b = \sqrt{\frac{s_{y \cdot x}^2}{SS_x}}$$

3   For this problem, the standard error of the regression coefficient is calculated using the standard error of the estimate computed in the text, $s_{y \cdot x} = 2.419$, and the sum of squares for the predictor (X) variable:

$$SS_x = \Sigma (X - \overline{X})^2$$

$$= (2-5)^2 + (4-5)^2 + (5-5)^2 + (6-5)^2 + (8-5)^2 = 20$$

Using these values, the standard error of the bivariate regression coefficient (s_b) is calculated as:

$$s_b = \sqrt{\frac{s_{y \cdot x}^2}{SS_x}} = \sqrt{\frac{2.419^2}{20}} = \sqrt{\frac{5.852}{20}} = 0.54$$

4   The slope and constant are calculated based on the exact means and standard deviations of the predictor and criterion variables, although we only report these descriptive statistics to three decimal places in the text.

💻 Computer Section

Overview of Bivariate Linear Regression

Bivariate linear regression involves determining whether values of a predictor variable, X, predict values of a criterion variable, Y, better than chance. Prediction is based on a regression equation, $\hat{Y} = bX + a$, where "$\hat{Y}$" is the predicted or criterion variable, "X" is the predictor variable, "a" is the constant or intercept, and "b" is the bivariate regression coefficient or slope of the regression line. To conduct a bivariate regression analysis on the computer,

a regression command is issued indicating: (1) the independent or predictor variable, X, and (2) the dependent or criterion variable, Y. Assessing bivariate linear regression for significance can be accomplished by testing the simple correlation for significance (r-test), by testing the bivariate regression coefficient for significance (t-test), or by testing the overall regression equation for significance (F-test).

Example Output for Bivariate Linear Regression

An insurance company wants to determine whether breadth of coverage predicts customers' satisfaction with their insurance plans. The

---

TABLE 10.4

REGRESSION

Equation Number 1   Dependent Variable ... SATIS (SATISFACTION)

Block Number 1.   Method: Enter COVERAGE

Variable(s) Entered on Step Number
1. COVERAGE

Multiple R	.88541
R Square	.78395
Adjusted R Square	.78323
Standard Error	.81147

Analysis of Variance

	DF	Sum of Squares	Mean Square
Regression	1	712.02273	712.02273
Residual	298	196.22727	.65848

F = 1081.31133   Signif F = .0000

Variables in the Equation

Variable	B	SE B	Beta	T	Sig T
COVERAGE	.536364	.016311	.885410	32.883	.0000
(Constant)	1.400000	.101208		13.833	.0000

End Block Number 1   All requested variables entered.

company samples 300 current customers and identifies how narrow or broad each customer's insurance coverage is on a scale from 1 to 10, with 10 indicating the broadest coverage. The company also asks customers to complete a questionnaire that assesses how satisfied they are with their current insurance plan on a scale from 1 to 7. The regression output shown in Table 10.4 is obtained.

Interpretation of Bivariate Linear Regression Output

Breadth of coverage of a customer's current insurance plan (COVERAGE) is the independent variable used to predict customer satisfaction with their insurance plan (SATIS). The first part of the regression output provides overall information about the analysis, including the correlation among variables and the amount of variance in the criterion variable that is accounted for by the predictor variable. For bivariate linear regression, multiple R, which will be described in the following chapter on multiple regression, is identical to the simple correlation r between the two variables. Similarly, the R squared value is analogous to the coefficient of determination for simple correlation with two variables, r^2. For this problem, the simple correlation between breadth of coverage and customer satisfaction is .88541. More than 78% of the variability in satisfaction is explained by breadth of policy coverage.

The next part of the output provides the results of the F-test used to test the regression equation for significance. With $k = 1$ predictor variable and $N = 300$ subjects, $df_{Reg} = k = 1$ and $df_{Res} = N - k - 1 = 300 - 1 - 1 = 298$. With a calculated F-value of:

$$F = \frac{MS_{Reg}}{MS_{Res}} = \frac{712.02273}{.65848} = 1081.31133$$

the regression equation is highly significant at

$p = .0000$ (critical $F_{(1,298).01} \approx 6.73$).

The last part of the regression output provides information about the predictor variable and the intercept of the regression equation. The slope and constant for this regression equation are $b = 0.536364$ and $a = 1.4$. The regression coefficient is tested for significance via a t-test:

$$t = \frac{b}{s_b} = \frac{.536364}{.016311} = 32.883$$

The calculated t-value tested with $df = N - 2 = 300 - 2 = 298$ is also highly significant at $p = .0000$ (critical $t_{(298).01} \approx 2.60$), consistent with the significant F-value obtained in the ANOVA table (notice that $F = t^2$). The following regression equation is obtained for this study and is highly significant:

$$\hat{Y} = 0.536364X + 1.4$$

The final conclusion is that customers' breadth of insurance coverage is a highly significant, positive predictor of their satisfaction with their policy. A customer who has a broader insurance policy is expected to be more satisfied with his or her insurance plan than is a customer with a more narrow insurance policy. Breadth of coverage explains more than 78% (R^2) of a customer's satisfaction with their policy.

Computer Problems

Conduct a bivariate linear regression to examine each of the following hypotheses. Indicate whether each regression equation is significant and whether the bivariate regression coefficient is significant. If significant, identify the percentage of variance in the criterion variable that is accounted for by the predictor variable.

1. Students' rating of the instructor's demon-

strated enthusiasm for the material (**ENTHUS**) will be a significant positive predictor of their overall rating of the instructor (**INSTRUCT**).

2. Students' rating of the instructor's expertise (**EXPERT**) will be a significant positive predictor of their overall rating of the course (**COURSE**).

3. Students' rating of how challenging the course is (**CHALL**) will be a significant negative predictor of how well they think they did in the course (**OUTCOME**).

4. Students' rating of how well they think they can apply course material (**APPLY**) will be a significant positive predictor of how well they think they understand the material (**UNDERST**).

5. Students' rating of how much they are a person who likes to learn (**LEARN**) will be a significant positive predictor of how much effort they put into the course (**EFFORT**).

6. Students' rating of how fun they found e-mail (**FUN**) will be a significant positive predictor of how often they contacted their instructor (**TEACH1**).

Chapter 11 ❖ Multiple Regression

Beyond Simple Correlation and Bivariate Linear Regression

Simple correlation and bivariate linear regression focus on the relationship between two variables and prediction of one variable from the second variable. However, most occurrences in the real world are not related to or predicted by only one other variable. In fact, many variables tend to be related to each other in fairly complex ways. In this section we introduce correlation involving more than two variables and then describe multiple regression which concerns predicting a criterion variable from two or more predictor variables.

First, we will reexamine the simple correlation r_{xy} between two variables, height and weight, via a Venn diagram which depicts the amount of variance in weight that is attributable to or explained by variations in height and vice versa:

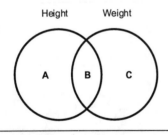

Height   Weight

FIGURE 11.1: Venn diagram depicting the proportion of variance shared between height and weight

The total variability (100%) in weight is represented by area B + C and the total variability in height is represented by area A + B. Recall that

the coefficient of determination for the simple correlation, r^2, is the amount of variability in one variable that is accounted for by the other variable. The amount of the total variability in weight that can be explained by height is represented by area B, which is expressed in the following proportion:

$$r^2_{(Weight)(Height)} = \frac{B}{B + C}$$

Area B is the amount of variability in weight that is explained by height out of the total variability in weight, area B + C. Similarly, the amount of the total variability in height that can be explained by weight is:

$$r^2_{(Height)(Weight)} = \frac{B}{A + B}$$

Because areas A + B and B + C are both 100%, the two proportions are identical. However, to be clear whether the situation is variability in weight that is explained by height $r^2_{(Weight)(Height)}$ or variability in height that is explained by weight $r^2_{(Height)(Weight)}$ separate and distinct notation is used.

Consider now a situation with a third variable, fat grams, as depicted in Figure 11.2. The overlapping circles represent the interrelationships of these three variables, with the sum of the areas within each circle representing the total variability for each variable. For instance, the total variability in fat grams is represented by area B + C + E + F and equals 100% of the variability in fat grams. Again, the variability in each variable that is explained by variability in a second variable, the coefficient of determination r^2, can be expressed as a simple proportion of areas from the Venn diagram. For

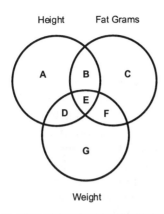

Height   Fat Grams

Weight

FIGURE 11.2: Venn diagram depicting the shared variance among height, fat grams, and weight

instance, for the simple correlation between height and weight, the total variability in weight (D + E + F + G) that can be explained by knowledge of the variability in height (D + E) is:

$$r^2_{(Weight)(Height)} = \frac{D+E}{D+E+F+G}$$

As another illustration, the variability in height that can be explained by variability in fat grams is:

$$r^2_{(Height)(Fat\ Grams)} = \frac{B+E}{A+B+D+E}$$

Because most variables in the real world are not related to just one other variable but rather to several other variables, it is frequently useful to determine how much information about a criterion variable is contained in multiple predictor variables. The *multiple correlation* assesses the relationship between one variable and two or more other variables and is represented by the *multiple R*. The multiple R is symbolized $R_{y \cdot x_1 x_2}$, the multiple correlation of a criterion variable, Y, with (•) multiple predictor variables, X_1, X_2, etc. The square of the multiple correlation, *R squared (R²)*, rep-

resents the amount of variance in one variable (e.g., Y) that is explained by the variability in two or more other variables (e.g., X_1 and X_2). For example, referring to Figure 11.2, the amount of the total variance in weight, D + E + F + G, that can be explained by variance in both height and fat grams combined is:

$$R^2_{(Weight) \bullet (Height)(Fat\ Grams)} = \frac{D+E+F}{D+E+F+G}$$

In this case, knowledge of both someone's height and intake of fat grams provides more information about that person's weight (D + E + F) than does knowledge of the person's height alone (D + E). Calculation of multiple R and R squared involves the combination of the correlations between the criterion variable and each predictor variable (e.g., areas D + E for the relationship of weight with height and areas E + F for the relationship of weight with fat grams) after removal of any shared variance among predictor variables.[1] That is, area E is removed from the sum of the areas contributed by each predictor variable, (D + E) + (E + F) - E, to prevent double-counting since both height and fat grams contribute area E.

Because the R² value is typically calculated from a sample of data and used to infer the relationship among variables in a larger population, this calculated value is a slight overestimation of the true relationship that exists, particularly if the multiple R is based on small samples or a large number of predictor variables. If generalizing the proportion of variance in a criterion variable that is explained by multiple predictor variables is of primary interest, a somewhat more conservative *adjusted R²* value is frequently reported. Calculation of the adjusted R² takes into account both the size of the sample and the number of predictor variables in order to produce a more accurate estimate of the amount of variance explained in the population.[2]

The multiple correlation provides information regarding the overall relationship of a criterion variable with a set of predictor variables but does not give any indication of the unique contribution that a particular predictor variable makes to a criterion variable. The simple correlation also does not give information on the unique relationship a predictor has with a criterion variable because the simple correlation between a predictor variable and the criterion variable does not remove any relationship shared with other predictor variables. For instance, the coefficient of determination for the simple correlation of weight with height in Figure 11.2 is:

$$r^2_{(Weight)(Height)} = \frac{D + E}{D + E + F + G}$$

Notice that area E is not unique to the predictor variable height but is shared with fat grams. To obtain a sense of the unique relationship between a criterion variable and a single predictor variable, two types of correlation can be assessed: partial correlation and semipartial correlation.

Partial correlation is the unique relationship between two variables removing or partialling out the effects of any third variables from both the criterion and predictor variables. The partial correlation is symbolized $r_{yx_1 \cdot x_2}$, the partial correlation of a criterion variable, Y, with a predictor variable, X_1, partialling out or removing the effects of (•) any third variables, predictor variable X_2, etc., from both variables Y and X_1. In other words, the relationship that Y and X_1 share with any third variables (e.g., X_2) is completely removed before the relationship between Y and X_1 is assessed. In terms of variance explained, the square of the partial correlation $r^2_{yx_1 \cdot x_2}$ represents the variability in X that is explained by Y out of the total variance in X which is unexplained by all other predictor variables. Consider the partial correlation between weight and height, partialling out fat grams. Since the partial correlation isolates the

relationship between two variables, any third variables are completely removed from both variables. In Figure 11.2, the circle representing total variability in fat grams, area B + C + E+ F is completely removed. Since fat grams can explain area E + F of the total variability in weight, this area is completely removed. Now, only area D + G remains as unexplained variability in weight. Of this unexplained variance, the amount that can be explained by variability in height is area D. Thus, the square of the partial correlation between weight and height partialling out fat grams is:

$$r^2_{(Weight)(Height) \cdot (Fat\ Grams)} = \frac{D}{D + G}$$

Similarly, the square of the partial correlation of fat grams with height partialling out weight is:

$$r^2_{(Fat\ Grams)(Height) \cdot (Weight)} = \frac{B}{B + C}$$

The partial correlation is useful for assessing whether a predictor variable explains a significant portion of the variance unexplained by any other predictor variables.

A second measure of the unique relationship between two variables is the semipartial or part correlation. The *semipartial (part) correlation* is the unique relationship between two variables removing or partialling out the effects of any third variables from the predictor variable only. The semipartial correlation is symbolized $r_{y(x_1 \cdot x_2)}$, the semipartial correlation of a criterion variable, Y, with a predictor variable, X_1, partialling out or removing the effects of (•) any third variables, predictor variable X_2, etc., from predictor variable X_1 (as noted by the use of the parentheses). In other words, the relationship that X_1 shares with any third variables (e.g., X_2) is completely removed before the relationship between Y and X_1 is assessed. In terms of variance explained, the square of the semipartial correlation $r^2_{y(x_1 \cdot x_2)}$ represents the proportion of the total variability in Y explained by X_1 alone and not by any other predictor variables. Consider the semipartial correlation between weight and height, partialling out fat grams. In Figure 11.2, the circle representing total variability in fat grams is removed from height, area B + E, but not from weight. Since fat grams can explain area E of the total variability in weight, this area is removed from height; height uniquely contributes only area D to explaining variability in weight. Since the square of the semipartial correlation involves the total variability in the criterion variable, area D + E + F + G for weight, the square of the semipartial correlation between weight and height, partialling out fat grams is:

$$r^2_{\text{Weight(Height}\bullet\text{Fat Grams)}} = \frac{D}{D+E+F+G}$$

Similarly, the square of the semipartial correlation of fat grams with height partialling out weight is:

$$r^2_{\text{Fat Grams(Height}\bullet\text{Weight)}} = \frac{B}{B+C+E+F}$$

The semipartial correlation is important for determining how much of the total variability in a criterion variable is explained by a particular predictor variable above and beyond the variability which is already explained by other predictor variables. Both the partial and semipartial correlations involve the unique contribution of the predictor variable, as indicated by the same area in the numerator of the coefficient of determination. The two correlations differ in terms of the base variance in the denominator of the coefficient. The partial correlation expresses the unique variance explained by a predictor variable out of the *unexplained variance* in the criterion variable whereas the semipartial correlation expresses the unique variance explained by a predictor

variable out of the *total variance* in the criterion variable. The multiple, partial, and semipartial correlations are fundamental concepts for understanding prediction involving multiple predictor variables, a statistical procedure known as multiple regression.

Multiple Regression

Multiple regression is a straightforward extension of bivariate linear regression described in Chapter 10 and involves predicting a criterion variable from two or more predictor variables. Recall that for bivariate linear regression, the general form of the regression equation is:

$$\hat{Y} = bX + a$$

With the two variable situation, X is the predictor variable, Y is the criterion variable, b is the regression coefficient for X indicating how many units Y increases for each one-unit increase in X, and a is the constant. With multiple regression, this basic regression equation is simply extended to include more than one predictor variable. With two predictor variables, X_1 and X_2, the multiple regression equation becomes:

$$\hat{Y} = b_1X_1 + b_2X_2 + a$$

Each predictor variable has its own slope, b_1, b_2, etc., which indicates how much Y changes for each one unit change in X_1, X_2, etc., when the effects of all other predictor variables are held constant. Thus, b is somewhat analogous in principle to the partial correlation coefficient and is called the *partial regression coefficient* since it specifies the relationship between a predictor variable and the criterion variable, partialling out or holding constant the effects of all other predictor variables. Calculation of each partial regression coefficient is similar to the computation for b discussed in Chapter 10, which involves the standard deviations of the criterion variable and predictor variable and the simple correlation between the two variables, as well as removal of shared variability with other predictor variables through the correlations of both variables with other predictor variables.[3] Similarly, the constant is calculated as a function of the mean of the criterion variable and the means and partial regression coefficients of each predictor variable.[4]

Based on values of all predictor variables, the multiple regression equation or *regression model* can be used to predict the corresponding value of the criterion variable. For instance, a researcher is trying to predict the number of hours per day people watch TV (Y) based on three predictor variables: number of hobbies (X_1), self-rating on a 1-7 social preference scale where 1 = "prefer to be with others" and 7 = "prefer to be alone" (X_2), and number of hours of reading (X_3). Based on data from a sample of 20 participants, the researcher obtains the following multiple regression equation:

$$\hat{Y} = -0.8X_1 + 0.3X_2 - 0.5X_3 + 6$$

Based on this model, the researcher can predict how many hours of TV a person will watch per day as a function of the values of the predictor variables. For instance, a person who has 3 hobbies, self rates themselves a 2 on a 7-point social preference scale, and reads 0.5 hours daily is predicted to watch almost 4 hours of TV per day:

$$\hat{Y} = -0.8(3) + 0.3(2) - 0.5(0.5) + 6 = -2.4 + 0.6 - 0.25 + 6 = 3.95$$

Testing the Significance of a Multiple Regression Equation

As discussed in Chapter 10, simply obtaining a regression equation is not indicative of whether the model is significant, that is whether the predictor variable(s) explains a significant amount of the variance in the crite-

rion variable. With a bivariate linear regression model, an easy way to assess the significance of the regression equation is to determine whether the simple correlation between the predictor variable and the criterion variable is significant. If the correlation is significant, the predictor variable explains a significant amount of variance in the criterion variable. With multiple regression, however, there is not one simple correlation that can be assessed for significance to determine whether the model predicts better than chance. The method for assessing a multiple regression equation for significance involves the other two significance tests described in Chapter 10, the F-test and the t-test. The F-test is used to determine whether the overall regression model is significant. That is, does the combination of all predictor variables included in the regression equation predict the criterion variable better than chance. The t-test is then used to assess whether each predictor variable is significant or if only certain predictor variables contribute significantly to explaining variance in the criterion variable.

First, an F-test is conducted to determine the overall significance of a multiple regression equation, that is, to assess whether there is a linear relationship among the set of predictor variables and the dependent variable. Recall that the F-test for regression is equivalent to the F-test for analysis of variance. The total variability in scores, SS_{Total}, consists of variability in the dependent or criterion variable that is due to the independent or predictor variables ($SS_{Between}$ or $SS_{Regression}$) and individual variability or error (SS_{Within} or $SS_{Residual}$). The F-test for bivariate linear and multiple regression is conducted exactly the same way. Sum of squares total is the sum of squared differences between each individual score on the criterion variable and the mean of the criterion variable: $SS_{Total} = \sum (Y - \overline{Y})^2$. Sum of squares regression is the sum of squared differences between each score predicted based on the regression model and the mean of the criterion variable: $SS_{Reg} = \sum(\hat{Y} - \bar{Y})^2$. Finally, sum of squares residual is the sum of squared differences between each observed score and the score predicted by the regression equation: $SS_{Res} = \sum(Y - \hat{Y})^2$. Based on these sources of variability and the corresponding degrees of freedom, $df_{Reg} = k$ and $df_{Res} = N - k - 1$, an ANOVA table is constructed and the F-test is conducted exactly as discussed in detail in the previous chapter. If the calculated F is significant, then the regression model is able to predict the criterion variable better than chance.

If the F-test is significant, then the combination of predictor variables explains a significant amount of variance in the criterion variable. As discussed earlier in the chapter, the square of the multiple correlation, R^2, indicates the percentage of variance in the criterion variable that is explained by the predictor variables in the sample. It is important to note, too, that this same variance measure can be obtained from the F-test results. Since SS_{Reg} provides a measure of the portion of variability in the criterion variable that is explained by the predictor variables (i.e., the regression model) and SS_{Total} is a measure of the total variability in the criterion, then the ratio of these two measures indicates the portion of total variability that can be explained by the predictor variables, R^2:

$$R^2 = \frac{SS_{Reg}}{SS_{Total}}$$

After a significant regression model is obtained, it is often informative to determine which specific predictor variables contribute significantly to prediction. Recall from Chapter 10 that the t-test is used to assess the bivariate regression coefficient (b) for significance, that is, to determine if the predictor variable explains a significant portion of the variability in the criterion variable. Because there was only one predictor variable with bivariate linear regression, testing the slope for significance was equivalent to testing the entire regression model. However, with multiple regression, obtaining a significant regression model does not necessarily mean that each individual predictor variable explains a significant portion of the variance in the criterion variable. A significant F-test only indicates that the combination of predictor variables included in the regression equation predict the criterion variable significantly better than chance. As described in Chapter 10, each partial regression coefficient and its standard error can be examined via a t-test to determine which particular predictors contribute significantly to prediction:

$$t = \frac{b}{s_b}$$

The calculated t-value then can be tested for significance using the residual degrees of freedom from the F-test, $df = N - k - 1$. A significant t-value indicates that there is a very small chance (e.g., 5% or less, 1% or less) that b is equal to zero. Rather, it is more likely that the partial regression coefficient is non-zero and the predictor variable explains a significant portion of the variance in the criterion variable.

In addition to the results of the t-tests for each predictor variable, a very useful statistic that directly compares the importance of each predictor variable to the regression model is the *standardized regression coefficient, Beta* (β). Because predictor variables may not all be measured in the same units (e.g., number of hobbies, rating on a 1-7 Likert scale, hours of reading) the partial regression coefficients (b) calculated for each of the predictor variables cannot be directly compared to determine which variables are the best predictors. If all predictor variables were measured in the same units (i.e., on the same scale), then the partial regression coefficients could be compared. In order to compare predictor variables measured in different units, the partial regression coefficients are standardized, much like a z-score is a standardization of a raw score allowing z-scores to be directly compared for different variables. Because each partial regression coefficient is a function of both the predictor (X) and criterion (Y) variables, standardization involves the standard deviations for both variables:

$$\beta = b\left(\frac{s_x}{s_y}\right)$$

Along with the significance of the t-test for each predictor variable, the Beta coefficients provide a useful measure of the relative contribution of each predictor variable to explaining variability in the criterion variable.

Types of Multiple Regression

Because multiple regression considers multiple independent or predictor variables, the question arises as to what order each independent variable should be entered into the regression equation. There are three usual methods to conducting multiple regression: standard, hierarchical, and statistical.

Standard multiple regression is perhaps the simplest approach and involves entering all predictor variables into the regression equation simultaneously. The contribution of each predictor variable is assessed in terms of its *unique* contribution to the criterion variable. Thus, even though a predictor variable may be highly correlated with the criterion variable, if it also is highly related to other predictor variables, its unique contribution to the regression equation may be low since it is redundant with other predictors.

Consider the implications of conducting a standard multiple regression in the following

example. A researcher is interested in predicting children's hours of weekly TV viewing based on the child's age and the number of hours of non-TV time the child spends with his/her family each week. Age and family time are the two predictor variables and hours of TV viewing is the criterion variable. It is not unrealistic to expect the two predictor variables to be related (correlated) in some way. For instance, as children get older they may spend fewer hours with their family. The researcher obtains a sample of 100 children and calculates the correlations among the three variables. The following Venn diagram depicts these relationships in terms of the variance accounted for by each variable:

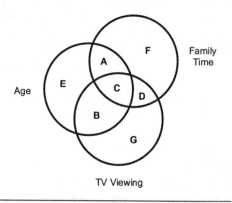

FIGURE 11.3: Prediction of TV viewing from age and family time

With standard multiple regression, both predictor variables are entered into the regression equation simultaneously. The variability attributed to each of the independent variables (age and family time) is only the area which each predictor variable uniquely contributes. Thus, age uniquely contributes area B to prediction of TV viewing, since no other predictor variable shares this area. Similarly, family time uniquely contributes area D to prediction of TV viewing. Since area B is quite large, the multiple regression would likely indicate that age is a highly significant predictor of TV viewing. In contrast, the regression results may indicate that family time, which contributes the relatively smaller area D, is a marginally significant or nonsignificant predictor of TV viewing. Interestingly, though, notice that family time actually shares quite a bit of variance (area C + D) with TV viewing, but the standard multiple regression would indicate that family time is relatively unimportant since it contributes relatively little that is unique to predicting TV viewing. Thus, when evaluating the results of a standard multiple regression analysis, it also is important to consider a predictor variable's simple correlation with the dependent measure, which would be quite high for family time and TV viewing. Notice, too, that the overlapping area C is considered in the computation of the R^2, the amount of variance in TV viewing accounted for when both predictor variables are considered together. However, this variance (area C) is not a unique contribution of any predictor variable, so it is not attributed to either one specifically.

Conducting a standard multiple regression is simply a matter of putting all predictor variables of interest into a regression equation and assessing the model for significance via the F-test. If the model is significant, each partial regression coefficient can be examined via a t-test to determine which predictor variables contribute a unique amount of variance to the criterion variable. Although very straightforward to analyze, the results of standard multiple regression may be somewhat difficult to interpret, particularly for nonsignificant predictors (e.g., family time in Figure 11.3), which are highly correlated with the criterion variable but also highly correlated with other predictor variables.

A second common multiple regression procedure is *hierarchical (sequential) multiple regression*. Hierarchical multiple regression involves entering the predictor variables into the re-

gression equation one at a time or in sets in an order specified by the researcher. The regression model is reassessed each time a new predictor variable(s) is added to determine if the addition results in a significant increase in the model's ability to predict the criterion variable. The contribution of each predictor variable is assessed in terms of what it adds to predictability at the time that it enters the regression equation. Thus, the same predictor variable may contribute either a lot or very little to explaining variance in the criterion variable depending upon when it enters the regression equation and how much variance it shares with other predictor variables. The order of entry of predictor variables should be guided by theoretical or logical considerations.

Consider again the example in Figure 11.3 utilizing a hierarchical multiple regression approach. Suppose the researcher decides that age is more important theoretically than family time, so he enters this variable into the regression equation first. Age will therefore contribute area B + C to predicting TV viewing. The regression model, which is a simple bivariate linear regression equation at this point, is significant; age is a significant predictor of TV viewing time. Family time is then added to the regression equation and the new model, with family time included, is reassessed for significance. Since area C already has been included previously in the model by the predictor variable age, this area cannot be duplicated when family time is entered into the equation. The unique contribution that family time makes to predictability when all other variables already in the equation are considered is area D only. Although the new regression model, with both predictor variables included, likely is still significant, the increase or change in R^2 between the first and second regression equations is probably not significant. That is, the additional variance contributed by family time, area D, is not sufficient to increase predictability of the model. Family time is not a significant predictor of TV viewing since it does not contribute much additional information about the criterion variable.

The results would be quite different if the researcher decided a priori that family time should be entered into the hierarchical regression equation before age. In this case, family time contributes area C + D, which likely would yield a significant bivariate linear regression model. Family time explains a significant portion of the variability in TV viewing time when it is entered first into the regression equation. Age is entered second into the regression equation and contributes area B only. Because area B is a large portion of variance, there is a good possibility that age will be identified as a significant predictor variable, despite the fact that it is not able to count the contribution of area C. Adding age to the regression model which includes only family time would result in a significant increase in the amount of variance in TV viewing explained by the predictor variables. Thus, both family time and age are significant predictors when family time is entered into the regression equation first.

Statistically, conducting a hierarchical multiple regression is very similar to the standard multiple regression approach just described with the additional step of assessing the change in the regression model at each step when new predictor variables are added to the equation. The F-test is used to determine whether a particular regression model is significant. Thus, for instance, with two predictor variables added one after the other, each of the two regression equations can be assessed for significance.

Although it is important to determine whether the overall regression equation is significant, with the sequential approach it also is of interest to determine whether the addition of predictor variables improves prediction.

That is, in the present example, both the first regression equation (with one predictor variable) and the second regression equation (with both predictor variables) may be significant. However, the addition of the second predictor variable to the model may not improve prediction above and beyond the predictive ability of the first regression equation. To determine whether the addition of a predictor variable(s) results in a significant increase in prediction, the change in R squared between the two models is tested for significance via a partial F-test. *R squared change* is the difference between the R^2 value obtained with the second regression equation (R_2^2) and the R^2 value obtained with the first regression equation (R_1^2):

$$R_{Change}^2 = R_2^2 - R_1^2$$

With the addition of one predictor variable to the model, R squared change is equal to the part correlation squared for the variable. For instance, in the family time, age, and TV viewing example, suppose family time is entered first into the regression model yielding a squared multiple correlation of $R_1^2 = .30$. Because this model contains only one predictor variable, the R squared value is equivalent to the coefficient of determination for the simple correlation between family time and TV viewing ($r^2 = .30$). Age is then added to the model yielding an R^2 value of $R_2^2 = .55$. R squared change is: $R_{Change}^2 = R_2^2 - R_1^2 = .55 - .30 = .25$. The addition of age to the model results in an additional 25% of the variance in viewing time explained. This is equivalent to the part correlation squared, that is, the portion of total variance in TV viewing time that is explained by age when family time is removed from age in Figure 11.3:

$$r_{TV\ Viewing(Age\bullet Family\ Time)}^2 = \frac{B}{B+C+D+G}$$

To determine if the addition of predictor variables to the model is significant, a *partial F-test* is conducted. This test is termed partial because it only assesses the additional part of the total variability in the criterion variable resulting from the addition of predictor variables to the regression model. The calculated F-value for the partial F-test is called *F change* since the change between the two models is being assessed. The value of F change is calculated as follows:

$$F_{Change} = \frac{\left(\dfrac{R_2^2 - R_1^2}{k_2 - k_1}\right)}{\left(\dfrac{1 - R_2^2}{N - k_2 - 1}\right)}$$

For the present problem involving 100 children (N), F change tests the difference between the second model with two predictor variables (k_2) and the first model with one predictor variable (k_1) for significance as follows:

$$F_{Change} = \frac{\left(\dfrac{R_2^2 - R_1^2}{k_2 - k_1}\right)}{\left(\dfrac{1 - R_2^2}{N - k_2 - 1}\right)} = \frac{\left(\dfrac{.55 - .30}{2 - 1}\right)}{\left(\dfrac{1 - .55}{100 - 2 - 1}\right)} = \frac{.25}{.00464} = 53.89$$

The calculated F value is then compared with a critical F-value with degrees of freedom of $df_1 = k_2 - k_1$ and $df_2 = N - k_2 - 1$, which notably are part of the calculation of the numerator and denominator respectively of F change. For the present problem, the degrees of freedom are calculated as follows: $df_1 = k_2 - k_1 = 2 - 1 = 1$; $df_2 = N - k_2 - 1 = 100 - 2 - 1 = 97$. Since the calculated F change value of 53.89 is larger than the critical F-value at the .01 level, $F_{(1,97).01} \approx 6.90$, the addition of age to the regression model results in a significant increase in prediction. Assuming both are significant, the second regression equation is a better predictor of TV viewing time than is the first regression equation.

The third approach to multiple regression is *statistical multiple regression* which is actually a class of techniques all similar in principle. Statistical multiple regression resembles hierarchical multiple regression in that predictor variables are entered (or removed) one at a time into (or from) the regression equation and the change in regression models is assessed for significance. However, with statistical multiple regression the order of entry or removal of predictor variables is based on statistical criteria rather than on theoretical considerations made by the researcher. With *forward selection* predictor variables are added to the regression model one at a time, with R^2 change assessed for significance at each step. The order of entry of predictor variables is determined by how much each one contributes to the criterion variable. The predictor variable which correlates most strongly with the criterion variable is added first, based on the idea that if this predictor variable does not explain a significant portion of variability in the criterion variable, then none of the other predictor variables alone will either. If the first predictor variable is significant, then the next strongest correlating predictor variable is added to the model and the partial F-test is conducted. Predictor variables continue to be added to the model until further additions no longer increase prediction significantly, that is, the partial F-test yields nonsignificant results.

Consider conducting the example illustrated in Figure 11.3 using statistical multiple regression with forward selection. Age has a higher correlation with TV viewing, sharing area B + C, than does family time, sharing area C + D. Because age has the highest simple correlation with TV viewing statistically, age is entered first into the regression equation, contributing area B + C to explaining the variance in TV viewing. If this bivariate regression model is significant, family time is entered second, since it still has area D in common with TV viewing and can contribute this amount. However, because this is such a small area, R² change likely is not significant, indicating that family time does not contribute significantly to predicting TV viewing. Thus, the regression model is complete with only age entered as a predictor variable.

In addition to forward selection, other variants of statistical multiple regression can be conducted. For instance, *backward selection* involves starting with a regression model with all predictor variables entered. Then, the predictor which correlates least strongly with the criterion variable is removed. Removal of predictor variables stops when prediction is significantly affected by the removal of a particular predictor variable. The final regression equation yields the most succinct model offering the best prediction with the fewest predictor variables.

Although not strictly considered multiple regression, we will mention here a related procedure known as discriminant analysis for situations in which the criterion variable is categorical. One of the requirements for conducting bivariate linear and multiple regression is that the criterion variable is continuous, that is, the data are in interval- or ratio-level form. All of the examples in this chapter and the previous one have involved predicting values for a continuous variable in terms of how much of something a person will have (e.g., how much a person will weigh, how many hours of TV a child will watch, what a student's college GPA will be). At times, however, a researcher may wish to predict which group a person will be in rather than how much of something a person will have. For example, a researcher may wish to predict whether a new freshman will graduate within 4 years or not. In such a case, the dependent measure is represented by nominal-level or categorical data and the regression involves predicting which of several groups a person

will be in. In this example, prediction is into one of two groups: graduation within 4 years or graduation in more than 4 years. As with multiple regression, there may be several predictor variables, such as high school GPA, SAT score, expected number of hours per week of non-school work, expected number of units taken per semester, etc., that may help determine which of the groups a person is likely to be in. In this type of situation, when the criterion variable is categorical rather than continuous, prediction to categories is made using a procedure called *discriminant analysis*, which is comparable to multiple regression for nominal-level data. Discriminant analysis is so named because it attempts to see how well the combination of predictor variables discriminates among groups represented by the criterion variable.

An Example of Multiple Regression

The researcher from Chapter 10 is interested in continuing his study of predicting sedentary females' weights. In particular, he is interested in knowing if women's height and their daily intake of fat grams are significant predictors of their weight. The researcher samples 10 sedentary females and measures their height, weight, and daily intake of fat grams, obtaining the following data:

Height	Fat Grams	Weight
69	55	150
67	65	135
64	60	108
66	45	138
62	50	113
65	70	125
68	60	180
64	45	140
63	70	110
67	50	165
$\overline{X}_1 = 65.5$	$\overline{X}_2 = 57$	$\overline{Y} = 136.4$
$s_{x_1} = 2.2730$	$s_{x_2} = 9.4868$	$s_y = 23.8104$

The researcher calculates the following simple correlations among the three variables: r_{yx_1} = .799, r_{yx_2} = -.287, $r_{x_1x_2}$ = .-.026. The partial regression coefficients and constant are calculated as: b_1 = 8.294, b_2 = -.669, a = -368.73.

QUESTION: Are height and fat grams significant predictors of sedentary females' weight?

ANSWER:

Step 1: Determine the type of multiple regression procedure to be conducted.

The researcher is interested in whether the combination of height and number of fat grams consumed provides significant prediction about a woman's weight, and if so, which predictor variables are significant. Because no order of entry is specified or of interest for this problem, a standard multiple regression is conducted.

Step 2: Derive the multiple regression equation.

Based on the partial regression coefficients and intercept calculated, the following regression equation is derived:

$$\hat{Y} = b_1X_1 + b_2X_2 + a = 8.294X_1 - .669X_2 - 368.73$$

Step 3: Test the regression model for significance.

To test the overall regression equation for significance, an F-test is conducted. For this problem, the F-test yields the following ANOVA table results:

Source	SS	df	MS	F
Regression	3616.02	2	1808.01	8.51
Residual	1486.38	7	212.34	
Total	5102.40	9		

With critical F-values of $F_{(2,7).05}$ = 4.74 and $F_{(2,7).01}$ = 9.55, the overall regression model is significant at $p < .05$ since the calculated F of 8.51 is larger than the critical F at the .05 level.

Step 4: Identify the significant predictor variables.

Based on the simple correlations, height is very strongly correlated with weight (.799) whereas fat grams is only somewhat correlated (-.287). Thus, we might expect height to be a significant predictor whereas fat grams may or may not be. Another useful method to conceptualize the relevant contribution of each predictor variables is through the standardized regression coefficients, β. The Beta coefficients for the two predictor variables are calculated as:

$$\beta_1 = b\left(\frac{s_{x_1}}{s_y}\right) = 8.294\left(\frac{2.2730}{23.8104}\right) = .792$$

$$\beta_2 = b\left(\frac{s_{x_2}}{s_y}\right) = -.669\left(\frac{9.4868}{23.8104}\right) = -.266$$

Consistent with our interpretation of the simple correlations, the Beta coefficients support the idea that height is a stronger predictor of weight than is fat grams.

To test more precisely whether the two variables are significant predictors of weight, t-tests are conducted. For height, the standard error of the regression coefficient is s_{b_1} = 2.13764 and for fat grams s_{b_2} = .51217. The following t-values are calculated for the two partial regression coefficients:

$$t = \frac{b_1}{s_{b_1}} = \frac{8.294}{2.13764} = 3.880$$

$$t = \frac{b_2}{s_{b_2}} = \frac{-.669}{.51217} = -1.305$$

Testing each of the partial regression coefficients for significance based on two-tailed critical values of $t_{(7).05} = 2.365$ and $t_{(7).01} = 3.499$ reveals that height is a significant predictor of weight at $p < .01$ whereas fat grams is not a significant predictor.

Step 5: Determine the proportion of variance accounted for by the model.

R squared, the proportion of variance in the criterion variable explained by the predictor variables included in the regression equation, is an important measure for interpreting the obtained results. A significant regression model can be obtained for a set of predictor variables that explains only 1 or 2% of the variance in a criterion variable, which may or may not be meaningful depending on the research question. In this problem, the proportion of variance explained by the model is:

$$R^2 = \frac{SS_{Reg}}{SS_{Total}} = \frac{3616.02}{5102.40} = .709$$

Thus, nearly 71% of the variance in sedentary females' weight can be explained by knowledge of their height and daily intake of fat grams.

Step 6: State the final conclusion both statistically and in words.

A standard multiple regression analysis with height and fat grams as predictors of weight yielded a significant model, although only height was a significant predictor variable. The model explained nearly 71% of the variability in weight.

In the computer section of this chapter, we present the results of this same problem using a hierarchical multiple regression approach instead of the standard multiple regression method presented here. A comparison of the hierarchical multiple regression results with those from the above standard multiple regression reveal two quite different conclusions.

Summary

The relationship of a criterion variable with two or more predictor variables is computed through the multiple correlation or multiple R. The amount of variance in the criterion variable that is accounted for by the combination of predictor variables is R squared. A more conservative measure of the actual variance accounted for in the population is found through adjusted R squared.

The unique relationship between a criterion and predictor variable, partialling out the effects of any other predictor variables from both the criterion and predictor variables, is the partial correlation. The semipartial or part correlation expresses the unique relationship between a criterion and predictor variable partialling out the effects of any third variables from the predictor variable of interest only.

Multiple regression involves prediction of a criterion variable from two or more predictor variables. The regression model or regression equation specifies the predicted value of the criterion variable based on a partial regression coefficient for each predictor variable and a constant. The multiple regression equation is tested for overall significance via an F-test, and each partial regression coefficient is tested for significance using a t-test to determine which predictor variables contribute significantly to prediction. The standardized regression coefficients (Betas) allow the direct comparison of predictor variables to assess which contribute more to prediction.

There are three major types of multiple regression. Standard multiple regression involves entering all predictor variables simultaneously into the regression model. Each predictor variable is assessed for significance based on what it uniquely contributes to prediction. Hierarchical or sequential multiple regression allows the researcher to specify the order of entry of predictor variables, with each predictor assessed for significance based on what it uniquely contributes to prediction at the time it enters the model. To determine if the addition of predictor variables adds to prediction at each step of a hierarchical regression, a partial F-test is conducted on the R square change between the two regression models (before and after the addition of predictor variables). Finally, with statistical multiple regression, predictor variables are entered or removed from the regression model based on statistical criteria. Two common types of statistical regression are forward selection, which involves the addition of predictor variables to the regression model, and backward selection, which is conducted by removing predictor variables from the model.

Key Terms

- adjusted R^2
- backward selection
- discriminant analysis
- F change
- forward selection
- hierarchical (sequential) multiple regression
- multiple correlation (multiple R)
- multiple regression
- partial correlation
- partial F-test
- partial regression coefficient (b)
- R squared (R^2)
- R squared change
- regression model
- semipartial (part) correlation
- standard multiple regression
- standardized regression coefficient, Beta (β)
- statistical multiple regression

Problems

1. What statistical measure of association assesses the relationship of a criterion variable with two or more predictor variables?

2. What statistical measure of association assesses the unique relationship of a criterion and predictor variable, removing the relationship both variables share with any third variables?

3. What statistical measure of association assesses the unique relationship of a criterion and predictor variable, removing the relationship the predictor variable shares with any third variables?

4. What is the symbol for the multiple correlation of variable Y with variables A, B, and C? What is the symbol for the coefficient of determination for the multiple correlation? What does this coefficient mean?

5. What is the symbol for the partial correlation of variables U and V partialling out the effect for variable Y? What is the symbol for the coefficient of determination for the partial correlation? What does this coefficient mean?

6. What is the symbol for the semipartial correlation of variables M and N partialling out the effect for variables O and P? What is the symbol for the coefficient of determination for the semipartial correlation? What does this coefficient mean?

7. What is the difference between R squared and adjusted R squared?

8. Refer to the following diagram:

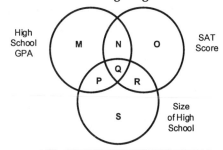

FIGURE 11.4: Venn diagram depicting interrelationships among high school GPA, SAT score, and size of high school

For each of the following, indicate the symbol for the coefficient of determination for the correlation (e.g., $r^2_{yx_1}$, $r^2_{yx_1 \cdot x_2}$, $R^2_{y \cdot x_1 x_2}$, etc.). Also indicate the ratio for the area depicting the amount of variance accounted for (e.g., $\frac{B+C}{A+B+C+D}$).

a. the multiple correlation of GPA with SAT score and size of high school.
b. the partial correlation of SAT score with size of high school, partialling out GPA.
c. the semipartial correlation of size of high school with GPA, partialling out SAT score.
d. the simple correlation of SAT score with GPA.
e. the multiple correlation of SAT score with size of high school and GPA.
f. the partial correlation of GPA with SAT score, partialling out size of high school.
g. the semipartial correlation of GPA with SAT score, partialling out size of high school.

9. For each of the following, indicate the appropriate statistical procedure:
a. a researcher wants to predict a continuous variable from one predictor variable.
b. a researcher wants to predict a continuous variable from two or more predictor variables.
c. a researcher wants to predict a categorical variable from one or more predictor variables.

10. In multiple regression, b refers to the _____ and Beta refers to the _____.
a. Which coefficient (b or Beta) is used to create the regression equation?
b. Which coefficient (b or Beta) is used to compare predictor variables directly?

11. With multiple regression, explain why partial regression coefficients are called "partial."

12. For each of the following, identify the correct multiple regression technique (standard, hierarchical, or statistical):
a. all predictor variables are entered into the regression equation simultaneously.
b. the predictor variable with the highest correlation with the criterion variable is entered into the regression equation first.
c. a researcher believes that a certain predictor variable is most important theoretically, and this variable is entered into the regression equation first.

13. A researcher wishes to predict marital satisfaction (HAPPY), measured on a 1 "not satisfied" to 10 "satisfied" scale, from two predictor variables: number of different topics the couple discusses per week (TOPICS) and number of arguments the couple has per week (ARGUE). The researcher randomly samples 200 married people and obtains the following data:

HAPPY:	$\bar{Y} = 6$	$s = 1.5$		
TOPICS:	$\bar{X} = 15$	$s = 2.5$	$b = +0.21$	$s_b = .093$
ARGUE:	$\bar{X} = 10$	$s = 2.0$	$b = -0.34$	$s_b = .110$
constant:	$a = 5$			
calculated F-value: $F = 4.8$				

a. Produce the multiple regression equation.
b. Consider a couple that discusses 8 different conversational topics per week and has 25 arguments per week. What is the predicted level of marital satisfaction based on the above regression model?
c. Consider a second couple that discusses 19 different topics per week and has 3 arguments per week. What is the predicted level of martial satisfaction

based on the above regression model?

d. Which couple (b or c) is predicted to have the highest level of marital satisfaction?

e. Is prediction from this regression model significantly better than chance?

f. Are the predictor variables significant? Calculate the Beta values for each of the predictor variables. Is one independent variable a better predictor (more significant) than another?

14. A researcher wishes to predict exam grades (GRADE), scored from 1 to 100, from three predictor variables: hours of studying per week (STUDY), hours of attendance at faculty office hours (OFFICE), and number of classes missed per semester (MISSED). The researcher randomly samples 44 college students and obtains the following data:

GRADE:	$\bar{Y} = 79$	s = 5.0		
STUDY:	$\bar{X} = 12$	s = 2.0	b= +0.79	s_b = .34
OFFICE:	$\bar{X} = 6$	s = 1.5	b = +0.58	s_b = .42
MISSED:	$\bar{X} = 8$	s = 3.0	b = -0.68	s_b = .22
constant:	a = 73			
calculated F-value:	F = 4.1			

a. Produce the multiple regression equation.

b. Consider a student who studies 15 hours per week for the class, attends 3 hours of office hours per week, and doesn't miss any classes during the semester. What is the predicted grade the student will achieve on the exam based on the above regression model?

c. Consider a student who studies 4 hours per week for the class, never attends office hours, and misses 16 classes during the semester. What is the predicted grade the student will achieve

on the exam based on the above regression model?

d. Which student (b or c) is predicted to have the highest exam grade?

e. Is prediction from this regression model significantly better than chance?

f. Are the predictor variables significant? Calculate the Beta values for each of the predictor variables. Is one independent variable a better predictor (more significant) than another?

15. A researcher is interested in whether number of hours of studying per week predicts college GPA. The researcher also is interested in whether number of extracurricular activities and number of roommates adds to prediction of college GPA, once number of hours of studying per week is taken into consideration. The researcher collects data from 35 university students and conducts a multiple regression entering number of hours of studying into the model first. He obtains an R squared of R^2 = .43. Next, the researcher enters number of extracurricular activities and number of roommates into the regression model. He obtains an R squared for this new model with all three predictor variables of R^2 = .57.

a. What type of multiple regression did the researcher conduct?

b. Calculate R squared change.

c. Is the regression model with only number of hours of studying entered significant?

d. Is the regression model with hours of studying, number of extracurricular activities, and number of roommates entered significant?

e. Is the addition of number of extracurricular activities and number of roommates to the regression model significant (i.e., conduct the partial F-test and determine if the results are significant).

Notes

1 The multiple correlation of a criterion variable, Y, with two predictor variables, X_1 and X_2, is:

$$R_{y \bullet x_1 x_2} = \sqrt{\frac{r^2_{yx_1} + r^2_{yx_2} - 2r_{yx_1} r_{yx_2} r_{x_1 x_2}}{1 - r^2_{x_1 x_2}}}$$

2 The adjusted R^2 is calculated as:

$$R^2_{Adj} = R^2 - \left(\frac{k(1 - R^2)}{N - k - 1} \right)$$

where N = the sample size and k = the number of predictor variables.

3 The partial regression coefficient, b_1, for the first predictor variable, X_1, in a two-predictor variable regression equation is calculated as:

$$b_1 = \left(\frac{S_y}{S_{x_1}} \right) \left(\frac{r_{yx_1} - r_{yx_2} r_{x_1 x_2}}{1 - r^2_{x_1 x_2}} \right)$$

4 The constant, a, in a two-predictor variable regression equation is calculated as:

$$a = \overline{Y} - b_1 \overline{X}_1 - b_2 \overline{X}_2$$

Predictors of Health Self-Appraisal: What's Involved in Feeling Healthy?

Adapted from article by same title, Andersen, M. & Lobel, M. (1995). *Basic and Applied Social Psychology, 16,* 121-136.

THE PURPOSE of this study was to investigate people's self-assessed health status. The researchers argue that understanding how people evaluate their health, especially when still healthy, may contribute to the medical profession's ability to promote healthy, preventive behaviors. A total of 455 undergraduates participated in a survey which included several standardized scales: the Pennebaker inventory of limbic languidness, a seriousness-of-illness rating scale, a neuroticism scale, a profile-mood-states scale, a self-evaluated health-status scale, an illness-vulnerability scale, and a vitality scale. In order to investigate the relation of each variable to self-assessed health status and account for overlap among the various predictors, the researchers conducted a hierarchical multiple regression analysis. Specifically, three models were tested: a medical model, a psychosocial model, and a biopsychosocial model. The results were reported in a table and in the article as follows:

The medical model included only the medical variables: symptoms and diseases. This model accounted for 24% of the variance in self-assessed health status. Both regression coefficients in the medical model were statistically significant (p < .01).

The psychosocial model included positive mood, negative mood, illness vulnerability, and vitality. This model explained 43% of the variance in self-assessed health, with each of the regression coefficients significant (p < .01).

The biopsychosocial model of self-assessed health status included symptoms, diseases, and the psychosocial variables. When this model was tested, the coefficient for symptoms was not significant (p > .05). The symptoms variable was therefore removed and the model retested. This revised version of the biopsychosocial model accounted for 45% of the variance in self-assessed health, with each regression coefficient statistically significant (p < .01).

(continued on page 228)

Predictors of Health Self-Appraisal: What's Involved in Feeling Healthy? (continued)

Hierarchical Regression Models of Self-Assessed Health Status
(adapted from original article)

Model/Step	Variable	Beta	F Value	R^2	r^2
Medical Model					
1	Symptoms	-.034	41.930*	.196	
2	Diseases	-.027	18.100*	.236	
Psychosocial Model					
1	Positive mood	.028	13.610*	.130	
2	Negative mood	-.022	31.170*	.196	
3	Illness vulnerability	-.154	100.580*	.365	
4	Vitality	.098	46.870*	.428	
Biopsychosocial Model**					
1	Diseases	-.042	39.970*	.187	.021*
2	Positive mood	.032	19.280*	.228	.024*
3	Negative mood	-.019	23.820*	.276	.006
4	Illness vulnerability	-.131	67.960*	.276	.062*
5	Vitality	.088	35.840*	.447	.055*

* $p < .01$

** The biopsychosocial model also included the psychosocial variables. Thus each of the variables unique contribution (semipartial correlations – r^2) were reported.

    While the biopsychosocial model explained the largest variance (45%), the psychosocial variables provided the greatest explanatory ability of perceived health. Note that the biopsychosocial model also included the psychosocial variables. By itself, biomedical concerns (i.e., diseases and symptoms) represented only a small portion of how laypeople defined health. The researchers thus concluded that lay concepts of health are not extensively defined by biomedical concerns for young people. Rather, young people's perceptions of their health are more influenced by mood, vitality, and sense of vulnerability to minor illnesses. The results of this study were limited to a sample that was young and in good health. However, it is during adolescence and college that many health-related habits are developed.

The Female Professional: Perceived Communication Proficiencies as Predictors of Organizational Advancement

Adapted from article by same title, Shockley-Zalabak, P., Staley, C., & Morley, D. (1988). *Human Relations, 41*, 553-567.

THE GOAL of this study was to explore perceived communication proficiency of female professionals as predictors of their organizational achievement levels. A total of 122 professionals (61 female employees and 61 of their supervisors) participated in the study. Both the female employees and their supervisors provided evaluations of the females' communication competencies. The predictor variables consisted of 15 communication skills: business writing, interviewing, group decision making, oral presentations, managing conflict, leadership/management techniques, interpersonal relationships, communication technology, listening, motivating people, handling grievances, giving directions, delegating authority, negotiating, and diagnosing organizational problems. All the independent variables were measured on a 7-point scale with 7 indicating exceptional work. The dependent variable was employee-achievement quotient and was determined by dividing the proportion of potential promotions obtained within the organization by the number of years the employee has been with her organization. The researchers conducted two stepwise multiple regressions on employee self and supervisor evaluations.

The first regression analysis indicated that supervisors' evaluations of seven employee communication skills were significant predictors of the employee's promotional achievements (R^2=.55, $F[7, 36]$ = 6.33, $p < .001$). Given the relatively small sample size and number of predictor variables, however, the adjusted R^2 of .46 is a more realistic estimate of the percentage of variance accounted for ... Using tables developed by Wilkinson (1979) to correct for this variable selection bias ... the overall regression equation [was found] to be significant well beyond the .01 level.

In terms of the Table results, the more highly evaluated an employee on writing and conflict management skills, the less likely she was to have received a high proportion of the promotions. Conversely, the more highly an employee was evaluated on leadership/management techniques and diagnosing organizational problems, the more likely she was to have experienced upward organizational mobility. Although listening, giving directions, and delegating authority also entered the equation they did not account for a significant percentage of the variance.

(continued on page 230)

The Female Professional: Perceived Communication Proficiencies as Predictors of Organizational Advancement (continued)

The second regression analysis used employee self-evaluations on the same communication skills to predict their promotional achievements. Although the observed R^2 of .14 appears to be significant ($F[3,55] = 3.05$, $p < .05$), it was not once the equation was adjusted to account for selection bias.

Stepwise Regression for Predicting Organizational Achievement (adapted from article)

Competency	Multiple R	R^2	R^2 Change	Beta	t-tests
Supervisors					
Managing conflict	.264	.070	.070	-.932	5.43**
Leadership	.478	.229	.159	.390	2.11*
Business writing	.597	.356	.127	-.683	-4.54**
Diagnosing problems	.681	.464	.108	.395	2.72*
Delegating authority	.716	.513	.049	.319	1.92
Giving directions	.734	.538	.026	.236	1.40
Listening	.743	.552	.014	.157	1.05
Self-Evaluation					
Leadership	.250	.063	.063	.332	2.32*
Negotiating skills	.348	.121	.058	-.308	-2.15*
Listening	.378	.143	.022	.161	1.18

* $p < .05$
** $p < .001$

Overall, the results of this study revealed that current supervisory evaluations of communication competencies accounted for approximately one half of the variance at which females advance in organizations. Female employees' own self-evaluations, however, were not predictive of promotional progress. In agreement with previous research, this study provides evidence for the importance of communication competencies in the organizational setting.

Computer Section

Overview of Multiple Regression

Multiple regression involves predicting a criterion variable from two or more predictor variables. There are several different approaches to multiple regression which vary in terms of the criteria used for entering predictor variables into the regression model. With standard multiple regression, all predictor variables are entered into the model simultaneously and the complete regression equation is tested for significance. With hierarchical and statistical multiple regression, predictor variables are entered in steps or blocks into the model, with the regression equation reassessed for significance at each step. Conducting multiple regression on the computer involves specifying: (1) the criterion and predictor variables, and (2) the type of multiple regression procedure to be conducted.

Example Output for Multiple Regression

In the example problem described in the text, a standard multiple regression was conducted using height and fat grams to predict weight using a sample of 10 sedentary females. Instead, suppose the researcher is interested in whether fat grams contributes significantly to predicting weight once height is taken into account. In this case, the researcher conducts a hierarchical multiple regression, entering height on the first step and fat grams on the second step. Using the same data set given in the text of this chapter, the multiple regression output shown in Table 11.1 is obtained from this hierarchical multiple regression analysis.

Interpretation of Multiple Regression Output

The first part of the multiple regression output provides basic descriptive information (the mean and standard deviation) for the criterion variable (WEIGHT) and the two predictor variables (HEIGHT and FATGRAMS) as well as the simple correlations between the variables. A quick examination of these correlations suggests that height is probably a significant predictor of weight ($r = .799$, $p = .003$) whereas fat grams may not be a significant predictor ($r = -.287$, $p = .211$).

This hierarchical multiple regression analysis is conducted in two steps or blocks. In the first block, height is entered as a predictor variable and the regression model is tested for significance. Because this first block involves a regression model with only one predictor variable, it is equivalent to a bivariate linear regression. As such, the multiple R = .79861 is equal to the simple correlation between weight and height r = .799. Since the simple correlation is significant, the regression model is significant. The calculated F = 14.08610, which is tested with $df_{Reg} = k = 1$ and $df_{Res} = N - k - 1 = 10 - 1 - 1 = 8$, is significant at $p = .0056$. The t-test of the regression coefficient yields identical results to the F-test:

$$t = \frac{b}{s_b} = \frac{8.365591}{2.228955} = 3.753$$

This calculated t-value tested with 8 degrees of freedom is significant at $p = .0056$. In sum, height is a significant predictor, explaining $R^2 = .63778$ or nearly 64% of the variability in weight.

In the second block, the predictor variable fat grams is added to the regression equation which is reassessed for significance. This second regression model with both height and fat

TABLE 11.1

MULTIPLE REGRESSION

Listwise Deletion of Missing Data

	Mean	Std Dev
WEIGHT	136.400	23.810
HEIGHT	65.500	2.273
FATGRAMS	57.000	9.487

N of Cases = 10

Correlation, 1-tailed Sig:

	WEIGHT	HEIGHT	FATGRAMS
WEIGHT	1.000	.799	-.287
	.	.003	.211
HEIGHT	.799	1.000	-.026
	.003	.	.472
FATGRAMS	-.287	-.026	1.000
	.211	.472	.

Equation Number 1   Dependent Variable.. WEIGHT

Block Number 1.   Method: Enter HEIGHT

Variable(s) Entered on Step Number
 1.. HEIGHT

Multiple R	.79861			
R Square	.63778	R Square Change	.63778	
Adjusted R Square	.59250	F Change	14.08610	
Standard Error	15.19944	Signif F Change	.00560	

Analysis of Variance

	DF	Sum of Squares	Mean Square
Regression	1	3254.21505	3254.21505
Residual	8	1848.18495	231.02312

F = 14.08610   Signif F = .0056

TABLE 11.1 (continued)

MULTIPLE REGRESSION

Variables in the Equation

Variable	B	SE B	Beta	T	Sig T
HEIGHT	8.365591	2.228955	.798612	3.753	.0056
(Constant)	-411.546237	146.075632		-2.817	.0226

Variables Not in the Equation

Variable	Beta In	Partial	Min Toler	T	Sig T
FATGRAMS	-.266375	-.442450	.999336	-1.305	.2330

End Block Number 1   All requested variables entered.

Equation Number 1   Dependent Variable.. WEIGHT

Block Number 2.   Method: Enter FATGRAMS

Variable(s) Entered on Step Number
 2.. FATGRAMS

Multiple R	.84184		
R Square	.70869	R Square Change	.07091
Adjusted R Square	.62546	F Change	1.70389
Standard Error	14.57189	Signif F Change	.2330

Analysis of Variance

	DF	Sum of Squares	Mean Square
Regression	2	3616.01962	1808.00981
Residual	7	1486.38038	212.34005

F = 8.51469   Signif F = .0133

Variables in the Equation

Variable	B	SE B	Beta	T	Sig T
HEIGHT	8.293704	2.137636	.791749	3.880	.0061
FATGRAMS	-.668557	.512174	-.266375	-1.305	.2330
(Constant)	-368.729809	143.834540		-2.564	.0374

grams included yields a calculated F = 8.51469, which is significant at p = .0133 (df$_{Reg}$ = k = 2, df$_{Res}$ = N - k - 1 = 10 - 2 - 1 = 7). However, to determine if the addition of fat grams to the model adds significantly to predictability compared to the model with height alone, the partial F-test results must be examined. The F change score is calculated as:

$$F_{Change} = \frac{\left(\dfrac{R_2^2 - R_1^2}{k_2 - k_1}\right)}{\left(\dfrac{1 - R_2^2}{N - k_2 - 1}\right)} = \frac{\left(\dfrac{.70869 - .63778}{2 - 1}\right)}{\left(\dfrac{1 - .70869}{10 - 2 - 1}\right)} = \frac{.07091}{.04162} = 1.70389$$

The F-change value tested with 1 and 7 degrees of freedom is not significant (p = .2330). Thus, adding fat grams to the regression model does not result in a significant increase in prediction over the model with height alone. These results are confirmed by the findings from the t-test of the partial regression coefficient for fat grams. The t-value for fat grams is calculated as follows:

$$t = \frac{b}{s_b} = \frac{-.668557}{.512174} = -1.305$$

This calculated t-value is nonsignificant, p = .2330 (equivalent to the significance level for the partial F-test results). Examination of the standardized regression coefficients (Beta values) also supports the idea that height is a much stronger predictor of weight (β = .791749) than is fat grams (β = -.266374).

The final result is to retain the first regression model with only height included as a predictor variable since the addition of fat grams does not add significantly to predicting weight, after variability in height is taken into account. The final regression model, including only height as a predictor variable, accounts for almost 64% of the variability in weight. (Note: As an interesting homework exercise,

use the same data given for this problem and conduct a hierarchical multiple regression analysis entering fat grams in the first block and height in the second block. The final results will differ from those obtained here, illustrating the importance of order of entry of predictor variables).

Computer Problems

Conduct a standard multiple regression to examine each of the following hypotheses. Indicate whether each regression model is significant. If significant, identify the percentage of variance in the criterion variable that is accounted for by the predictor variables and which specific predictor variables are significant.

1. Students' perceptions of the instructor's enthusiasm (**ENTHUS**), knowledge of the subject matter (**KNOW**), and interest in the students (**CARE**) will be significant predictors of their overall rating of the instructor (**INSTRUCT**).
2. Students' perceptions of the instructor's expertise (**EXPERT**), friendliness (**FRIEND**), experience (**EXPER**), and confidence (**CONFID**) will be significant predictors of their overall rating of the course (**COURSE**).
3. Students' perceptions of having learned something valuable from the course (**VALUE**), being able to apply the material in other contexts (**APPLY**), and having an increased interest in the subject matter (**LIKECLAS**) will be significant predictors of their overall rating of the course (**COURSE**).

Conduct a hierarchical multiple regression analysis to examine each of the following research questions, entering the predictor variables in the order specified. Indicate whether each regression model is significant and whether the addition of predictor variables improves prediction. After each analysis, indicate which regression model, if any, offers the best prediction of the criterion variable.

4. Is the amount of effort (**EFFORT**) students put into the course a significant predictor of their perceived outcome (**OUTCOME**), after the extent to which they find the course challenging (**CHALL**) is taken into account in the model? The hierarchical multiple regression should be conducted in two steps, with CHALL entered in the first block and EFFORT entered in the second block.

5. Is the extent to which students find e-mail use efficient (**EFFIC**) a significant predictor of their use of e-mail to contact their professor (**TEACH1**), after the extent to which e-mail is perceived to be fun (**FUN**) and easy (**EASY**) are taken into account in the model? The hierarchical multiple regression should be conducted in two steps, with FUN and EASY entered together in the first block and EFFIC entered in the second block.

6. Is students' overall rating of the instructor (**INSTRUCT**) a significant predictor of their overall rating of the course (**COURSE**), after their estimated grade in the course (**GRADE**) is taken into account in the model? Is the extent to which students perceive themselves as someone who likes to learn (**LEARN**) a significant predictor of their overall rating of the course, after students' estimated grade in the course and their overall rating of the instructor are taken into account? The hierarchical multiple regression should be conducted in three steps, with GRADE entered in the first block, INSTRUCT entered in the second block, and LEARN entered in the third block.

Chapter 12 ❖ Chi-Square Analysis

Parametric vs. Nonparametric Tests

Throughout this book we have been focusing on statistical tests used to analyze interval- or ratio-level data because this type of data is the most frequently collected in the social sciences. The z-test, t-test, F-test, Pearson r, and linear regression are all statistical techniques for analyzing interval- and ratio-level data. As a group, these procedures are called *parametric tests* because they deal with estimating characteristics of populations, which are referred to as parameters. For instance, the t-test uses sample data to estimate how likely it is that two groups represent the same population. In contrast, when data is measured at the nominal- or ordinal-level, population parameters cannot be estimated. Thus, statistical techniques involving nominal- or ordinal-level data which do not deal with estimates of population parameters are referred to as *nonparametric tests*. In this chapter we describe the most common nonparametric test for nominal-level data: the chi-square test.

The Chi-Square (χ^2) Test

The chi-square test is used to determine if there is a significant difference in the number or frequency of observations across categories of a nominal-level variable. This concept is similar to the t- and F-tests, which involve comparing mean differences, except that frequencies or counts are used to examine group differences rather than means. Consider a professor who is interested in whether college students prefer lecture-oriented classes or dis-cussion-oriented classes. She hypothesizes that university students will prefer classes with an interactive discussion focus more than classes with a noninteractive lecture approach. The professor interviews 50 students on campus one day and asks them which of the two class styles they prefer. Subsequently, she counts the number of students who prefer each class style and obtains the following data:

Observed Values (O)	
Lecture	Discussion
35	15

The first step in solving this statistical problem is to state clearly the research hypothesis:

H: Students will prefer lecture-oriented classes more than discussion-oriented classes.

Stated statistically, the null and research hypotheses involve assessing whether the frequency observed for each category, called the *observed value (O)*, differs from the frequency one would theoretically expect to observe if there was no difference in preference for the two class styles, called the *expected* or *theoretical value (T)*. In this example, the theoretical value equals 25 per group, since if there was no difference in preference for the two class styles half of the students would prefer lecture and half would prefer discussion. Thus, the null hypothesis states that all observed frequencies equal all theoretical frequencies and the alternative hypothesis says that there is at least one difference between an observed and a theoretical frequency:

$$H_0: \quad O = T$$
$$H_a: \quad O \neq T$$

Clearly the observed frequencies of 35 and 15 are not equal to the theoretical frequency of 25. However, some difference between observed and theoretical values may occur simply due to random factors in the same way that two group means can differ somewhat even though both groups still represent the same population. Recall that a t-test, for instance, involves assessing whether an observed difference in sample means is indicative of a true difference in the two groups (i.e., they represent two different populations) or is simply due to random factors (i.e., the two groups are part of the same population). Similarly, conducting a chi-square test involves determining whether any difference between observed and theoretical frequencies is indicative of a true difference in observations across categories or is simply due to random factors.

The class style problem described above is an example of a *chi-square goodness-of-fit test*. This type of chi-square also is called a *one-sample* or *one-way chi-square* because subjects from a single sample are distributed across categories. The chi-square goodness-of-fit test involves determining whether there is a difference in the number of observations in each category compared with the theoretical values. In other words, this test assesses how well the observed data "fits" a theoretical set of data. The better the observed values fit the expected values, the less likely the chi-square test is to be significant. The more the observed values differ from the expected values (i.e., the less well they fit), the more likely it is that there is a significant difference in observations across

categories.

A second type of chi-square test is the *chi-square test of association*. This chi-square test also is referred to as a *multiple-sample* or *two-way chi-square* because this procedure examines whether the distribution of observations across categories differs between two or more samples. With this test, two dimensions or variables are of interest, categories and samples, whereas with the one-way chi-square only one variable, categories, was of interest since there was only one sample. Suppose the researcher above wishes to determine if there is a difference in males' and females' preference for lecture- vs. discussion-oriented classes. With two samples, 25 males and 25 females, the researcher obtains the following data:

	Observed Values (O)	
	Lecture	Discussion
Males	20	5
Females	15	10

A table with samples on one side and categories on the other side is called a *two-way frequency* or *contingency table*. Contingency tables are commonly identified by the number of levels for each of the dimension, similar to the method for referring to factorial designs. This problem is an example of a 2 x 2 contingency table: there are two variables so there are two numbers. The first number, representing gender, has 2 levels (male, female) and the second number, representing class style, has 2 levels (lecture, discussion). Similarly, a problem examining whether there is a difference in preference for lecture vs. discussion among freshmen, sophomores, juniors, and seniors involves a 4 x 2 contingency table.

Chi-Square Goodness-of-Fit Test (One Sample)

The chi-square test is conducted by comparing the observed frequencies with the theoretical or expected frequencies. Typically, theoretical frequencies are those frequencies that would be expected if there was no difference in the distribution across categories for the sample.[1] For example, the observed frequencies for the one-sample chi-square problem regarding preference for lecture- vs. discussion-oriented classes were:

Observed Values (O)	
Lecture	Discussion
35	15

Of the single sample of 50 students, 35 indicated that they prefer lecture style classes and 15 students indicated that they prefer a discussion format. If there was no difference in students' preference for these two class styles, the number of students one would expect to indicate preferring each class style is 25:

Theoretical Values (T)	
Lecture	Discussion
25	25

For the one-sample chi-square, the theoretical or expected frequencies are computed as the total sample size (N) divided by the number of categories (K):

$$T = \frac{N}{K}$$

Each category has the same number of expected values, indicating no difference in the distribution of observations across categories. For the current problem, the theoretical values for each of the two categories are:

$$T = \frac{N}{K} = \frac{50}{2} = 25$$

Notice that the sum of the theoretical frequencies (25 + 25) still equals the total sample size (50) for this study. Only the way in which these 50 individuals are distributed across categories is altered.

The chi-square statistic is a measure of how far the observed frequencies deviate from the theoretical frequencies. The more the observed values differ from the theoretical values, the higher the chi-square statistic is and the more likely it is that there is a significant difference among categories. The chi-square statistic is calculated as the squared difference between the observed (O) and theoretical value (T) for each category divided by the theoretical value for that category. This value is then summed across all categories to yield the chi-square statistic:

$$\chi^2 = \sum \frac{(O - T)^2}{T}$$

For the present problem, the chi-square value is computed as follows:

$$\chi^2 = \sum \frac{(O-T)^2}{T} = \frac{(35-25)^2}{25} + \frac{(15-25)^2}{25} = \frac{10^2}{25} + \frac{(-10)^2}{25} = \frac{100}{25} + \frac{100}{25} = 4 + 4 = 8$$

To determine whether the calculated chi-square value is large enough to conclude with a Type I error of .05 or less that the distribution of observations across categories is not equal (i.e., that at least one O differs from one T), the calculated chi-square is compared with a critical value obtained from the chi-square distribution. The sampling distribution of the chi-square statistic is a theoretical distribution similar to the sampling distribution of differences or the sampling distribution of correlation coefficients (r). If there truly was no difference in the distribution of observations across categories in a population, the chi-square statistic should be zero. However, when a sample of data from the population is drawn and a chi-square statistic is computed, this chi-square value may differ from zero due to sampling error. That is, the chi-square statistic obtained from sample data from a population with no difference among categories may differ somewhat from zero due purely to chance or random factors. The chi-square test is conducted by comparing a calculated chi-square value with a critical chi-square value to determine if the calculated chi-square falls within the outermost 5% or 1% of the sampling distribution of the chi-square statistic. If the calculated chi-square value does fall in the outermost part of the chi-square distribution, there is a very small chance that there truly is no difference among categories (5% or less, 1% or less) and instead there really is a difference in the frequency of observations across categories. Because calculation of the chi-square statistic involves a squared difference, only positive chi-square values will ever be computed. Thus, only the upper tail of the chi-square distribution is used for hypothesis testing, so there is no one- vs. two-tailed test. Both directional and nondirectional hypotheses are tested with the same critical values, as was true with the F-test.

As with other sampling distributions we have described, there actually is not one chi-square distribution but many such distributions depending upon the number of degrees of freedom in the problem. With a one-sample chi-square, degrees of freedom equal the number of categories (K) minus one:

$$df = K - 1$$

The critical values for the set of chi-square distributions are located in Appendix A. For the present example, df = K - 1 = 2 - 1 = 1. The critical values for a chi-square distribution with 1 degree of freedom are $\chi^2_{(1).05} = 3.84$ and $\chi^2_{(1).01} = 6.63$. To conduct the chi-square test, the calculated value of chi-square is compared with the critical values to determine whether to reject the null hypothesis and, if so, at what probability level. In this problem, the calculated chi-square of 8 is larger than the critical value of 6.63 at the .01 level; thus, the null hypothesis is rejected at $p < .01$. The distribution of observations across categories is significantly different from what would be expected by chance if there truly was no difference, with less than a .01 chance of being wrong in this decision. Students prefer lecture-oriented classes significantly more than discussion-oriented classes, contrary to what the researcher predicted.

Chi-Square Test of Association (Multiple Samples)

Conducting the chi-square test of association is very similar to the chi-square goodness-of-fit test. The major differences between the two tests are in the computation of the theoretical values and the degrees of freedom. Recall the data obtained for the two-sample problem where the researcher was interested in whether men and women have a difference in preference for lecture- vs. discussion-oriented classes:

	Observed Values (O)	
	Lecture	Discussion
Males	20	5
Females	15	10

The first step in solving this problem is to calculate the theoretical values for each cell of the contingency table, retaining the same total sample sizes and category totals as was actually observed. For the present problem, there were 25 males and 25 females, and 35 subjects indicated preferring lecture-oriented classes and 15 indicated preferring discussions. Thus, the following row and column totals reflect the total number of subjects in each sample and each category:

Observed Values (O)			
	Lecture	Discussion	Row Total
Males	20	5	25
Females	15	10	25
Column total	35	15	50

The theoretical values are calculated based on these same row and column totals. That is, the four cells of the theoretical table may differ from the cells in the observed table, but the row and column totals will be identical in both contingency tables. The theoretical values are computed by redistributing observations to cells in the contingency table based on the number one would expect to observe if there was no difference in preference between the samples.

For instance, of a sample in which half of the people are men and half are women, if 35 people indicate preferring lecture-style classes and there is no difference in men's and women's preference for lectures vs. discussions, then we would expect $35 \div 2 = 17.5$ men and 17.5 women to prefer lectures. Similarly, if 15 students prefer discussions and there is no difference in men's and women's preferences, half of these 15 students ($15 \div 2 = 7.5$) should be men and half should be women. In sum, if

there truly is no difference in males' and females' preference for lecture- vs. discussion-oriented classes, the distribution of observations is expected to be the following:

Theoretical Values (T)			
	Lecture	Discussion	Row Total
Males	17.5	7.5	25.0
Females	17.5	7.5	25.0
Column total	35.0	15.0	50.0

Notice that the sum of the theoretical values across samples and across categories is exactly equal to the totals actually observed. That is, the row and column totals are identical in both contingency tables. With an equal number of subjects in each sample, as with this example, the total number of observations in a category can simply be divided equally among all samples.

However, the calculation is slightly more complex if there is an unequal number of subjects in each sample. The following formula allows calculation of the theoretical values for each cell of a theoretical contingency table for both equal and unequal sample sizes:

$$T = \frac{R \times C}{G}$$

"T" is the theoretical frequency for a particular cell of the theoretical contingency table, "R" is the marginal frequency for the row of the cell (i.e., the total observed frequency for the row), "C" is the marginal frequency for the column of the cell (i.e., the total observed frequency for the column), and "G" is the grand total number of observations in the entire study. Thus, for instance, the expected or theoretical number of males who prefer lectures is calculated as:

$$T = \frac{R \times C}{G} = \frac{25 \times 35}{50} = \frac{875}{50} = 17.5$$

Once both observed and theoretical frequencies are obtained, calculation of the chi-square statistic is identical to the formula presented for the one-sample chi-square test. Observed and theoretical values for each cell of the contingency table are compared and summed to yield the calculated chi-square value:

$$\chi^2 = \sum \frac{(O - T)^2}{T}$$

The more the observed and theoretical values differ, the larger the chi-square statistic will be. For the present problem, the chi-square value is computed as follows:

$$\chi^2 = \sum \frac{(O-T)^2}{T} = \frac{(20-17.5)^2}{17.5} + \frac{(15-17.5)^2}{17.5} + \frac{(5-7.5)^2}{7.5} + \frac{(10-7.5)^2}{7.5} =$$

$$= \frac{2.5^2}{17.5} + \frac{(-2.5)^2}{17.5} + \frac{(-2.5)^2}{7.5} + \frac{2.5^2}{7.5} = \frac{6.25}{17.5} + \frac{6.25}{17.5} + \frac{6.25}{7.5} + \frac{6.25}{7.5} =$$

$$= .357 + .357 + .833 + .833$$

$$= 2.38$$

With a calculated chi-square value, the researcher must then ascertain if this value falls in the outermost 5% or 1% of the sampling distribution of the chi-square statistic in order to determine whether to reject the null hypothesis. Because there are many chi-square distributions, depending on the number of samples and categories involved, the set of sampling distributions is distinguished by degrees of freedom. Recall that with the one-sample chi-square, which involved multiple categories only, the degrees of freedom was equal to the number of categories minus one: df = K - 1. With the multiple-sample chi-square, there are two variables to consider: the number of categories and the number of sam-

ples. Thus, the degrees of freedom are computed using both of these components:

$$df = (I - 1) \times (K - 1)$$

Degrees of freedom for the chi-square test of association is calculated as the product of the number of samples (I) minus one and the number of categories (K) minus one. In the present problem, there are two samples and two categories, so the degrees of freedom are calculated as:

$$df = (I - 1) \times (K - 1) = (2 - 1) \times (2 - 1) = 1$$

The critical values from the chi-square table for a chi-square with one degree of freedom are $\chi^2_{(1).05} = 3.84$ and $\chi^2_{(1).01} = 6.63$.

Since the calculated chi-square of 2.38 is not greater than or equal to the critical chi-square value of 3.84 at the .05 level, the null hypothesis is not rejected. The researcher must conclude that there is no difference in males' and females' preference for the two classroom teaching styles. That is, there is no association between gender and class style preference.

Beyond the Chi-Square Test

When only two categories are involved in a one-sample chi-square problem, as with our example, the nature of a significant chi-square is clear (e.g., students preferred lecture-oriented classes more than discussion-oriented classes). Similarly, in a multiple-sample chi-square problem with two samples and two categories, the nature of a significant difference also is clear (e.g., if the chi-square had been significant in our example, the results would indicate that men preferred lectures over discussions whereas women had no preference).

However, the interpretation of significant chi-square results is not so obvious when the problem involves more than two categories and/or more than two samples. For instance, suppose for the one-sample problem that there actually were three class styles: lectures, discussions, and computer-based instruction. The following data was obtained from a sample of 50 students:

Observed Values (O)		
Lecture	Discussion	Computer
18	10	22

In this case, if the calculated chi-square is significant, the nature of the differences is not immediately apparent. Are computer-based classes preferred more than lectures and discussions? Are lectures preferred more than discussions? Are computer-based classes preferred more than discussions but not more than lectures? These questions may sound familiar to those posed when significant ANOVA results were obtained. Recall that a significant F-test indicated only that there was some significant difference in group means, not exactly which groups differed from which other groups. Similarly, a significant chi-square involving more than two categories or more than two samples indicates only that there is some difference in the distribution of observations across categories, not which categories differ more or less than expected. To determine exactly which groups differ, a *post-hoc test* is necessary. One of the most common post-hoc tests for the chi-square is an analog to the Scheffé procedure for the F-test, which is described in more advanced statistical texts.

The chi-square goodness-of-fit test and the chi-square test of association are conducted in virtually identical ways, with the only differences involving whether there is more than one sample involved. Although a popular and versatile test, the chi-square procedure is limited to only two categorical (nominal-level) variables with any number of levels (e.g., I samples and K categories). In the same way that a researcher is often interested in looking at differences in means for a dependent variable as a function of two or more independent variables, a multiple-factor ANOVA problem, so, too, are researchers sometimes interested in looking at an association among more than two variables. For instance, the professor studying the question of preference for different class styles might be interested in whether

	Lecture	
	Male	Female
Freshman		
Sophomore		
Junior		
Senior		

	Discussion	
	Male	Female
Freshman		
Sophomore		
Junior		
Senior		

FIGURE 12.1: A log-linear problem with three categorical variables – preferred class style, student gender, and student class level

there is an association among gender, class level, and preference for class style. Graphically, this three-variable problem can be depicted as shown in Figure 12.1. With this problem, there are three categorical or nominal-level variables: preferred class style (lecture, discussion), student gender (male, female), and student class level (freshman, sophomore, junior, senior).

Recall that with the t-test only levels or groups of one independent variable could be compared. If the problem involved more than two groups and one independent variable or more than one independent variable, an F-test was required instead of a t-test for statistical analysis. To control the Type I error, the F-test allows comparisons among multiple groups versus conducting multiple t-tests. Similarly, when more than two categorical variables are involved, conducting multiple chi-square tests to examine all relationships among the variables would inflate the Type I error beyond an acceptable level. Additionally, such an approach would not allow an examination of interactions among variables. Thus, an extension of the chi-square test called *log-linear analysis* is used to analyze such data. Typically, one variable is designated the dependent variable and the other variables are considered independent variables, just like analysis of variance. Then, associations between the independent variables and the dependent variable are examined. As with ANOVA, main and interaction effects can be identified with log-linear analysis.

For instance, in the above problem, class style would be designated the dependent variable with student gender and class level as independent variables. Only associations involving the dependent variable are of interest. A significant association or relationship obtained between gender and class style is analogous to a main effect for gender, meaning there is a difference in preference for class style between males and females. This is equivalent to the chi-square test of association problem examined above. A significant association between class level and class style is analogous to a main effect for class level, indicating students from different class levels have a different preference for lectures and discussions. Finally, a significant association among all three categorical variables, class style, gender, and class level, is analogous to an interaction effect for gender and class level, indicating a difference in preference for class styles as a function of both gender and class level.

An Example of Chi-Square Analysis

A researcher is interested in whether there is a difference in the primary source of political information among students who attend private colleges versus public universities. The researcher devises a list of five possible primary sources of political information: friends, family, political organizations, television, and newspapers. He then solicits 100 students from Stanford, a private college, and 100 students from the University of Michigan, a public university, to participate in his study. He asks each of the 200 students which of the five sources is their major or primary source of political information. He obtains the following data, with the row and column totals indicated:

	Observed Values (O)		
	Stanford	U. of Michigan	Row Total
Friends	25	35	60
Family	20	20	40
Political orgs.	30	15	45
Television	10	20	30
Newspapers	15	10	25
Column total	100	100	200

QUESTION: Is there a difference in private vs. public university students' primary source of political information?

ANSWER:

Step 1: State the hypotheses.

This problem involves a chi-square test of association, since the question of interest concerns whether there is an association or relationship between type of college attended and primary source of political information. The null hypothesis is that each theoretical frequency is equal to each observed frequency and the alternative hypothesis is that some theoretical frequency differs from some observed frequency:

$$H_0: \quad O = T$$
$$H_a: \quad O \neq T$$

Step 2: Calculate the theoretical or expected frequencies.

Since this problem involves more than one sample, it is a multiple-sample chi-square problem or a chi-square test of association. Because there are two nominal-level variables, categories and samples, the theoretical frequencies are computed based on the observed row and column totals, that is, the marginal frequencies. The general formula for computing the theoretical frequencies for the chi-square test of association is used:

$$T = \frac{RxC}{G}$$

Based on this formula, the following theoretical values are obtained:

	Theoretical Values (T)		
	Stanford	U. of Michigan	Row Total
Friends	$\frac{60(100)}{200} = 30$	$\frac{60(100)}{200} = 30$	60
Family	$\frac{40(100)}{200} = 20$	$\frac{40(100)}{200} = 20$	40
Political orgs.	$\frac{45(100)}{200} = 22.5$	$\frac{45(100)}{200} = 22.5$	45
Television	$\frac{30(100)}{200} = 15$	$\frac{30(100)}{200} = 15$	30
Newspapers	$\frac{25(100)}{200} = 12.5$	$\frac{25(100)}{200} = 12.5$	25
Column total	100	100	200

Step 3: Calculate the value for χ^2.

Using the chi-square formula to compare each observed frequency with its corresponding theoretical frequency yields the following calculated chi-square value:

$$\chi^2 = \sum \frac{(O-T)^2}{T} = \frac{(25-30)^2}{30} + \frac{(35-30)^2}{30} + \frac{(20-20)^2}{20} + \frac{(20-20)^2}{20} + \frac{(30-22.5)^2}{22.5}$$
$$+ \frac{(15-22.5)^2}{22.5} + \frac{(10-15)^2}{15} + \frac{(20-15)^2}{15} + \frac{(15-12.5)^2}{12.5} + \frac{(10-12.5)^2}{12.5}$$
$$= \frac{(-5)^2}{30} + \frac{5^2}{30} + \frac{0^2}{20} + \frac{0^2}{20} + \frac{7.5^2}{22.5} + \frac{(-7.5)^2}{22.5} + \frac{(-5)^2}{15} + \frac{5^2}{15} + \frac{2.5^2}{12.5} + \frac{(-2.5)^2}{12.5}$$
$$= .833 + .833 + 0 + 0 + 2.5 + 2.5 + 1.667 + 1.667 + .5 + .5$$
$$= 11$$

Step 4: Calculate the degrees of freedom.

Because this is a chi-square test of association, one degree of freedom is lost from the total number of samples (I) and one degree of freedom is lost from the total number of categories (K). Degrees of freedom are calculated as:

$$df = (I - 1)x(K - 1) = (2 - 1)x(5 - 1) = (1)x(4) = 4$$

Step 5: Look up the critical value at the .05 level.

Using the chi-square table, the critical value for a χ^2 with 4 degrees of freedom at the .05 significance level is $\chi^2_{(4).05} = 9.49$.

Step 6: Compare the calculated χ^2-value to the critical χ^2-value at the .05 level.

Since the calculated value $\chi^2 = 11$ is larger than the critical value $\chi^2_{(4).05} = 9.49$, the null hypothesis is rejected at the $p < .05$ level. There is a significant difference between Stanford and University of Michigan students' major sources of political information, with a Type I error (or chance of being wrong) of less than .05.

Step 7: Look up the critical value at the .01 level.

Using the chi-square table, the critical value for a χ^2 with 4 degrees of freedom at the .01 significance level is $\chi^2_{(4).01} = 13.28$.

Step 8: Compare the calculated χ^2-value to the critical χ^2-value at the .01 level.

Since the calculated value $\chi^2 = 11$ is not larger than the critical value $\chi^2_{(4).01} = 13.28$, the null hypothesis cannot be rejected at the $p < .01$ level.

Step 9: State the final conclusion both statistically and in words.

The final conclusion statistically is to reject H_0 at the $p < .05$ significance level. Private and public university students differ significantly in their primary sources of political information, with less than a 5% chance that there really is no difference. Notice that this conclusion does not indicate anything about the nature of the differences between private and public university students. A post-hoc test is needed to determine exactly where the differences lie. For instance, a post-hoc test might indicate that University of Michigan students are more likely to use friends as their primary source of political information whereas Stanford students are more likely to use political organizations.

Summary

The chi-square test examines differences across categories for nominal-level data. There are two versions of the chi-square procedure. The chi-square goodness-of-fit test involves one sample and multiple categories and is used to determine if there is a difference between the expected and observed frequencies across categories. The chi-square test of association involves multiple samples and multiple categories and is used to assess whether there is a difference in the distribution of theoretical and observed values across categories among the different samples. When a chi-square test involves more than two samples or more than two categories, a significant result is followed by a post-hoc test to determine exactly where the differences are. An extension of the chi-square test when more than two variables are involved is log-linear analysis.

Key Terms

- chi-square goodness-of-fit test (one-sample or one-way chi-square)
- chi-square test of association (multiple-sample or two-way chi-square)
- contingency table
- log-linear analysis
- nonparametric tests
- observed values (O)
- parametric tests
- post-hoc test
- theoretical (expected) values (T)

Problems

1. (*Parametric* or *nonparametric*) tests are based on interval- or ratio-level measurements and estimate population characteristics, whereas (*parametric* or *nonparametric*) tests are based on nominal- or ordinal-level data and do not estimate population characteristics.

2. Indicate the appropriate level(s) of measurement (*nominal, ordinal, interval/ratio*) for each of the following:
    a. t-test
    b. mode
    c. standard deviation
    d. chi-square test
    e. correlation (Pearson r)
    f. median
    g. mean
    h. F-test
    i. linear regression
    j. log-linear analysis

3. A legal researcher wishes to determine if people are more likely to become repeat offenders if they commit their first crime before the age of 18, between 18 and 30 years of age, or over age 30. She uses arrest records to obtain a random sample of 50 people who committed their first crime before age 18, 50 people who committed their first crime between 18 and 30, and 50 people who committed their first crime over age 30. She then identifies how many of these people committed any subsequent crimes (committed additional crimes vs. did not commit additional crimes). What type of statistical test should the researcher use to analyze her data?

4. What are the two types of chi-square tests and what is the difference between them?

5. In a one-sample or one-way chi-square design:
    a. What is the formula for calculating the chi-square?

    b. How is the theoretical value for a cell calculated?
    c. What is the formula to compute degrees of freedom?
    d. How many variables are involved in the analysis?
    e. Which is analyzed: a difference among categories or a difference among samples?

6. In a multiple-sample or two-way chi-square design:
    a. What is the formula for calculating the chi-square?
    b. How is the theoretical value for a cell calculated?
    c. What is the formula to compute degrees of freedom?
    d. How many variables are involved in the analysis?
    e. Which is analyzed: a difference among categories or a difference among samples?

7. For each of the following problems, indicate whether a *chi-square goodness-of-fit test*, a *chi-square test of association*, or a *log-linear analysis* should be conducted. If the test is a chi-square, also provide the degrees of freedom for the statistical test.
    a. Freshmen, sophomores, juniors, and seniors are classified according to their college major: economics, mathematics, communication, physics, psychology, sociology, English, French, German, art, music, law and society, chemistry, or biology.
    b. Male and female chief executive officers are categorized according to how much time they spend at work (< 40 hours per week, 40-50 hours per week, > 50 hours per week) and by their yearly income (< $50,000 per year, $50,000-$100,000 per year, > $100,000 per year).
    c. Students are classified according to their letter grade (A, B, C, D, F) in a

class.

d. Amusement parks in California (Disneyland, Magic Mountain, Knotts Berry Farm, Sea World) are categorized according to their primary ride (roller coasters, water rides, children's rides) and their gross annual profit (< $100 million, $100-$500 million, > $500 million).

e. Eighty subjects are observed initiating a conversation with an elderly person and classified according to their method of beginning the conversation: question about other person, statement about other person, statement about self, statement about environment, question about environment, statement about external event/person, or question about external event/person.

f. Fifty men and 50 women are asked to indicate whether they favor the death penalty unconditionally, favor the death penalty only in certain circumstances, or whether they do not favor the death penalty under any conditions.

8. For each of the following chi-square problems, indicate if the chi-square value is significant and at what level.

   a. 4 x 4 contingency table $\chi^2 = 17$
   b. one-sample χ^2 with 6 categories $\chi^2 = 9.86$
   c. 3 x 8 contingency table $\chi^2 = 30.33$
   d. 2 x 2 contingency table $\chi^2 = 5.69$
   e. one-sample χ^2 with 3 categories $\chi^2 = 10.87$
   f. 6 x 6 contingency table $\chi^2 = 36.93$
   g. one-sample χ^2 with 10 categories $\chi^2 = 22.32$

9. A ticket agency wants to give away tickets to a Broadway show for promotional purposes. They ask their employees to pick a show currently playing on Broadway that they think will generate the most public interest. The number of employees who selected each Broadway show is as follows:

		Observed Values (O)		
Phantom of the Opera	Cats	Oklahoma	My Fair Lady	Miss Saigon
19	15	10	9	9

Is there a significant difference in employees' selection for the Broadway show they think will generate the most public interest? Conduct a χ^2 analysis and state the results both statistically and in words.

10. A travel agency surveys college seniors to determine the locations to which students would most like to travel after obtaining their degrees. The following data are obtained:

	Observed Values (O)		
Europe	Australia	Africa	China/ Far East
40	24	18	32

Is there a significant difference in students' selection of a geographical location? Conduct a χ^2 analysis and state the results both statistically and in words.

11. A psychologist and educational researcher is interested in how many unique pieces of information children can remember as a function of the number of distractions in the environment when the information is being committed to memory. He divides 90 children into three equal groups (samples) and exposes those in each group to varying levels of environmental distractions: no distractions, television only, or television and two people talking. While in their designated environment, children are given a piece of paper containing 30 words and asked to remember these words. The children are allowed 10 minutes to learn the words. Later, the researcher asks the

children to recall as many words from the list as possible and subsequently classifies them into one of three categories: those who remembered 0-10 words, those who remembered 11-20 words, and those who remembered 21-30 words. For the 90 children he obtains the following data:

	Observed Values (O)		
	0-10 wds	11-20 wds	21-30 wds
No distractions	0	5	25
Television	5	5	20
Television + talking	10	10	10

Is there a significant difference in recall of words among children who learn the words with different levels of environmental distraction? Conduct a χ^2 analysis and state the results both statistically and in words.

12. A university administration is interested in whether students from different class levels (freshmen, sophomores, juniors, seniors) support stricter eligibility requirements to remain enrolled at the university. They ask 100 randomly selected students from each class whether they support stricter standards. The following data is obtained:

	Observed Values (O)	
	Support	Do Not Support
Freshmen	25	75
Sophomores	25	75
Juniors	35	65
Seniors	40	60

Is there a significant difference in support of stricter eligibility requirements for the different class levels? Conduct a χ^2 analysis and state the results both statistically and in words.

13. Review Chapters 6-12. For each of the following situations, indicate the type of statistical test that should be conducted: (*t-test, single-factor ANOVA, multiple-factor ANOVA, linear regression, multiple regression, chi-square goodness-of-fit, chi-square test of association, log-linear analysis*).

   a. A researcher is interested in determining whether number of cups of coffee drunk per day predicts number of hours of sleep.

   b. A researcher wishes to determine whether men or women are more likely to use avoidance or confrontation strategies when conflict arises.

   c. A researcher wants to assess if students who watch TV five hours per day score differently on college exams (measured in terms of exam score from 0 to 100) than do students who watch either no TV per day or two hours of TV per day.

   d. A researcher is interested in knowing if men or women disclose more intimate information (measured in terms of number of statements) in conversations with same-sex partners or opposite-sex partners.

   e. A researcher would like to see if men or women who attend small (< 500 students) or large (≥ 500 students) high schools are more likely to attend small (< 5,000 students) or large (≥ 5,000 students) colleges.

   f. A researcher is interested in whether the number of hours of TV a person watches per day, the number of hours a person exercises per day, and the number of friends a person has predict gross income.

   g. A researcher wishes to determine if people are more satisfied (measured on a 1-7 point Likert-scale) with purchases they make from a catalogue or from a store.

Note

1 Theoretical frequencies also can be frequencies expected due to some a priori hypothesis. For instance, if it is known that discussion classes are preferred 2 to 1 over lecture classes, the observed distribution for a sample of students could be compared with a theoretical distribution with twice as many observations expected in discussion classes vs. lecture classes.

Divining the Social Order: Class, Gender, and Magazine Astrology Columns

Adapted from article by same title, Evans, W. (1996). *Journalism and Mass Communication Quarterly, 73*, 389-400.

IN AN attempt to understand the social function of astrology, this study compared astrological advice in women's magazines that varied by readers' socioeconomic status. Women's magazines were selected because they were more likely to feature an astrology column than were men's magazines. Three magazines in mass circulation were selected per SES category: *Soap Opera Magazine, Soap Opera Weekly,* and *True Story* were identified as working-class magazines; *Elle, Mademoiselle* and *Vogue* were identified as middle-class magazines. All 12 horoscopes from each selected magazine issue were analyzed, resulting in a total of 864 observations – 144 from each magazine. One of the many questions coded was whether horoscopes addressed financial matters, and if so, whether good or bad fortune was predicted. The results for this research question indicated:

> … a statistically significant relationship between zodiac sign and predictions of bad financial fortune ($\chi^2 = 23.73$, d.f. = 11, $p < .05$). Gemini and Sagittarius were slightly more likely than other signs to be warned about financial troubles in 1992. However, except for bad financial fortune, no variable was significantly associated with zodiac sign, that is, no particular zodiac sign fared significantly better or worse than any other zodiac sign on any of the variables measured in this study.

> Middle-class readers were slightly but significantly more likely than working-class readers to receive astrological encouragement to spend money ($\chi^2 = 6.43$, d.f. = 1, $p < .05$). In contrast, working-class readers were more likely than middle-class readers to be advised not to spend money ($\chi^2 = 3.93$, d.f. = 1, $p < .05$). Working-class horoscopes sometimes offered rather severe financial advice such as, "Pay your bills immediately, save the money that is left, and do not live beyond your means." No middle-class horoscope offered similarly harsh advice.

(continued on page 250)

Divining the Social Order: Class, Gender, and Magazine Astrology Columns (continued)

Middle-class readers were more likely than working-class readers to be told that travel was likely or recommended (χ^2 = 18.09, d.f. = 1, $p < .001$). Warnings against travel were uncommon in both working- and middle-class horoscopes.

Messages about the limitations of money (e.g., "money can't buy happiness") were significantly more likely to appear in working-class than in middle-class horoscopes (χ^2 = 4.60, d.f. = 1, $p < .05$), although such messages were fairly uncommon even in working-class horoscopes.

Percentage of Horoscopes Addressing Financial Issues by Magazine Group

	Magazine Group	
	Working Class %	Middle Class %
Financial issues addressed	23.2	20.9
Good fortune predicted	13.7	12.0
Bad fortune predicted	10.8	10.8
Spending encouraged*	1.2	4.2
Spending discouraged*	5.1	2.3
Travel encouraged**	2.6	9.7
Travel discouraged	1.6	.7
Limitations of money noted*	3.2	.9
	n = 432	n = 432

* $p < .05$
** $p < .001$

Based on the results pertaining to this research question and others, the author concluded that readers' social class was a far better predictor than readers' zodiac sign of the nature of astrological advice and predictions offered: "This study suggests only that the range of symbolic resources that a consumer will find in horoscopes is in large part a function of the consumer's gender and social class. In this sense, this study represents a first step toward understanding the social function of mass-mediated astrology" (p. 398).

Gender Stereotypes in MTV Commercials: The Beat Goes on

Adapted from article by same title, Signorielli, N., McLeod, D., & Healy, E. (1994). *Journal of Broadcasting & Electronic Media, 38,* 91-101.

THE RESEARCHERS examined whether commercials aired on MTV were gender-stereotyped. Given that the MTV cable channel has a larger adolescent audience than other television networks, one goal of the study was to explore what messages are being sent about gender roles on this station. Specifically, the researchers hypothesized that men and women would be portrayed in stereotypical ways. Five hypotheses were proposed along these lines and we highlight two:

> H_1: Female characters will be rated as more attractive than male characters.
> H_2: Female characters will be more likely than male characters to wear skimpy or sexy clothing.

A total of 119 MTV commercials sampled in the after-school and late evening hours were used as the data for this study. Physical attractiveness was measured on a 5-point attractiveness scale (1 = ugly and 5 = very attractive) and type of clothing was measured on a 4-point scale (1 = nonsexy and 4 = outright nudity). The coding results are discussed below:

> Females were rated as more attractive than males, $\chi^2(3, N = 517) = 206.60, p < .001$. More than half of male characters were placed in the middle category of the attractiveness scale, with slightly more than one third rated as attractive. Hardly any male characters (2.2%) were rated as extremely attractive or beautiful. Conversely, more than half of female characters were rated as extremely attractive or beautiful, and almost one quarter were rated as attractive. Few female characters were rated as neutral in attractiveness (15.1%) or unattractive (8.0%).

> Female characters were more likely than male characters to be portrayed wearing skimpy or sexy clothing, $\chi^2(2, N = 513) = 148.0, p < .001$. The clothing worn by almost all (93.5%) male characters was rated as neutral. A small percentage of male characters (6.5%) were coded as wearing clothing that was somewhat sexy. While slightly less than half the women in the sample (46.2%) were coded as wearing neutral clothing, comparatively large percentages of women were coded as wearing somewhat sexy (24.4%) or very sexy (29.4%) clothing.

The researchers concluded that commercials on MTV are presenting stereotypical information about gender roles. The researchers argue that this is another outlet that is most likely preserving and perpetuating gender stereotypes to youth.

🖥 Computer Section

Overview of Chi-Square Analysis

Chi-square analysis is used to determine if there is a difference in the distribution of observations across categories for one or more samples. Conducting a chi-square analysis on the computer involves using a chi-square command and specifying the variable(s) to be used for the analysis. The chi-square goodness-of-fit test (one-sample) requires specification of the categorical variable of interest. The chi-square test of association (multiple samples) requires indication of both the categorical variable and the sample variable. Levels or possible values of each variable also may need to be specified (e.g., 1-2 for two categories/samples).

Example Output for Chi-Square Goodness-of-Fit Test (One Sample)

A drug company conducted a survey to investigate which brand of aspirin doctors recommended most. The company surveyed 495 doctors and asked them which of five major brands of aspirin they recommend most frequently to their patients. The data shown in Table 12.1 below were obtained.

Interpretation of One-Sample Chi-Square Output

Since this problem involved only a single sample of 495 doctors, a chi-square goodness-of-fit test was conducted. The categorical variable examined was BRAND, the type of

---

TABLE 12.1

CHI-SQUARE TEST

BRAND   TYPE OF ASPIRIN

Category		Cases Observed	Expected	Residual
IBUPROFEN	0	107	99.00	8.00
ADVIL	1	262	99.00	163.00
BAYER	2	30	99.00	-69.00
TYLENOL	3	72	99.00	-27.00
BUFFERIN	4	24	99.00	-75.00
Total		495		

Chi-Square	D.F.	Significance
381.2929	4	.0000

aspirin that doctors recommend. The range of possible values of the variable was 0 to 4, where the value 0 corresponds with the brand Ibuprofen and the value 4 corresponds with the brand Bufferin. Examination of the observed frequencies revealed a total of 107 of the 495 doctors recommended Ibuprofen, 262 of the 495 doctors recommended Advil, and so forth.

For the one-sample chi-square situation, the theoretical or expected frequency in each category is simply the total number of respondents divided by the total number of conditions:

$$T = \frac{N}{K} = \frac{495}{5} = 99$$

This theoretical value means that if there was no difference in doctors' recommendations of the different types of aspirin, 99 doctors would recommend each brand of aspirin. The residual is the difference between the observed number of doctors recommending each type of aspirin and the theoretical number of doctors who would recommend each type of aspirin if there were no differences (e.g., 107 - 99 = 8 for Ibuprofen). This difference, O - T, is part of the numerator of the formula used to compute the chi-square value:

$$\chi^2 = \sum \frac{(O-T)^2}{T}$$

The results of this analysis yielded a calculated chi-square value of 381.2929:

$$\chi^2 = \sum \frac{(O-T)^2}{T} = \frac{(107-99)^2}{99} + \frac{(262-99)^2}{99} +$$
$$\frac{(30-99)^2}{99} + \frac{(72-99)^2}{99} + \frac{(24-99)^2}{99} = 381.2929$$

This one-sample chi-square problem has df =

K - 1 = 5 - 1 = 4 degrees of freedom. Since the calculated chi-square of 381.2929 is larger than the critical chi-square value $\chi^2_{(4).01} = 13.28$, the null hypothesis is rejected at $p < .01$. In fact, with such a large calculated chi-square value, the results actually are significant at $p = .0000$. The results indicate a highly significant difference in the brand of aspirin doctors most recommend. Although at this point a post-hoc test is needed to ascertain exactly which types of aspirin are recommended more or less frequently, by looking at the data we can guess that Advil is recommended more than the other brands, whereas Bayer and Bufferin are recommended less than the other brands (though they may not differ significantly from recommendation of Tylenol, for example).

Example Output for Chi-Square Test of Association (Multiple Samples)

A researcher is interested in examining whether men or women are more likely to seek a second opinion after being diagnosed with a serious illness. As part of a larger questionnaire dealing with hospital satisfaction, the researcher asks patients if they were diagnosed with a serious illness by the hospital. If patients answer positively, that they were diagnosed with a serious illness, a follow-up question was asked regarding whether patients sought a second opinion following the initial diagnosis. A total of 500 patients participated in the larger hospital satisfaction survey. Of those 500 patients who completed the survey, 337 indicated that they were diagnosed with a serious illness and thus had usable responses. The chi-square analysis shown in Table 12.2 was conducted on men's and women's responses to the question concerning whether they sought a second opinion after being diagnosed with a serious illness.

Interpretation of Multiple-Sample Chi-Square Output

This analysis involved examining whether there was a difference in the number of men vs. women (the sample variable GENDER) who sought a second opinion on their medical diagnosis (the categorical variable 2ND). Results show that a total of 157 men and 180 women answered this part of the questionnaire. A total of 174 respondents (65 men and 109 women) sought a second opinion on their diagnosis and 163 respondents (92 men and 71 women) did not seek a second opinion on their diagnosis.

With a multiple-sample chi-square problem, the theoretical values are calculated as the total responses in the row of the cell multiplied by the total responses in the column of the cell divided by the total number of responses in the study:

$$T = \frac{R \times C}{G}$$

For example, if there was no difference in men's and women's seeking of a second opinion, a total of 75.938 men would be expected to not seek a second opinion, calculated as follows:

TABLE 12.2

2ND Seek second opinion by GENDER Respondent's Gender

		GENDER Male 1	Female 2	Row Total
2ND				
Yes	1	65	109	174 51.6
No	2	92	71	163 48.4
Column Total		157 46.6	180 53.4	337 100.0

Chi-Square	Value	DF	Significance
Pearson	12.31961	1	.00045
Continuity Correction	11.56456	1	.00067
Likelihood Ratio	12.39026	1	.00043

Minimum Expected Frequency: 75.938

Number of Missing Observations: 163

$$T = \frac{R \times C}{G} = \frac{163 \times 157}{337} = 75.938$$

The computer output notes that this is the minimum expected frequency for any cell in the contingency table.

This problem has df = (I - 1)x(K - 1) = (2 - 1)x(2 - 1) = (1)x(1) = 1 degree of freedom. The chi-square analysis yields a calculated chi-square value of 12.31961 which is significant at p = .00045 (critical $\chi^2_{(1),.01} = 6.64$). This is the Pearson chi-square and is equivalent to the calculation described in the text. The computer output also provides several alternative chi-square values which are calculated slightly differently, and researchers may have a preference for one of these methods depending on the nature of the problem. However, these analyses should yield similar results, and the Pearson chi-square is suitable in most circumstances. In sum, the results reveal that there is a significant difference in men's vs. women's seeking of a second opinion following a serious medical diagnosis. Women are more likely to seek a second opinion than are men.

Computer Problems

Conduct a chi-square goodness-of-fit test to examine the following hypotheses regarding differences among each categorical variable.

1. Students will be more likely to indicate that the subject matter is a strength of the course than is the pace of lectures (**STRENGTH**).

2. Students will be more likely to indicate that the main reason they checked the announcement board was for surveillance than for any other reason (**BOARD2**).
3. Students will be more likely to indicate that they contacted their classmates via e-mail for diversion and as a social function than for any other reasons (**STUDENT2**).
4. Students will be more likely to indicate that they contacted their instructors via e-mail for expression than for any other reason (**TEACH2**).

Conduct a chi-square test of association to examine the following hypotheses regarding the relationship between each sample variable and each categorical variable.

5. Students in the cooperative classroom (**CLASS**) will be more likely to indicate course structure was the major strength of the course (**STRENGTH**) than will students in the competitive or individualistic classrooms.
6. Male and female students (**STDTSEX**) will differ significantly in their reasons for using e-mail to contact their classmates (**STUDENT2**).
7. Students' reasons for using e-mail to contact their instructor (**TEACH2**) will differ significantly as a function of the instructor's gender (**GENDER**).
8. Juniors and seniors (**CLSLVL**) will be more likely to indicate they will receive an "A" in the class (**GRADE**) than will freshmen and sophomores.

Appendix A ❖ Tables

Critical Values of *T*

For any given df, the table shows the values of *t* corresponding to various levels of probability. The obtained *t* is significant at a given level if it is equal to or *greater than* the value shown in the table.

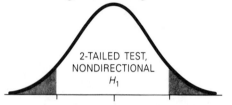

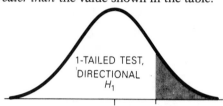

	Level of significance					Level of significance		
df	.05	.01	.001		df	.05	.01	.005
1	12.706	63.657	636.619		1	6.314	31.821	63.657
2	4.303	9.925	31.598		2	2.920	6.965	9.925
3	3.182	5.841	12.941		3	2.353	4.541	5.841
4	2.776	4.604	8.610		4	2.132	3.747	4.604
5	2.571	4.032	6.859		5	2.015	3.365	4.032
6	2.447	3.707	5.959		6	1.943	3.143	3.707
7	2.365	3.499	5.405		7	1.895	2.998	3.499
8	2.306	3.355	5.041		8	1.860	2.896	3.355
9	2.262	3.250	4.781		9	1.833	2.821	3.250
10	2.228	3.169	4.587		10	1.812	2.764	3.169
11	2.201	3.106	4.437		11	1.796	2.718	3.106
12	2.179	3.055	4.318		12	1.782	2.681	3.055
13	2.160	3.012	4.221		13	1.771	2.650	3.012
14	2.145	2.977	4.140		14	1.761	2.624	2.977
15	2.131	2.947	4.073		15	1.753	2.602	2.947
16	2.120	2.921	4.015		16	1.746	2.583	2.921
17	2.110	2.898	3.965		17	1.740	2.567	2.898
18	2.101	2.878	3.922		18	1.734	2.552	2.878
19	2.093	2.861	3.883		19	1.729	2.539	2.861
20	2.086	2.845	3.850		20	1.725	2.528	2.845
21	2.080	2.831	3.819		21	1.721	2.518	2.831
22	2.074	2.819	3.792		22	1.717	2.508	2.819
23	2.069	2.807	3.767		23	1.714	2.500	2.807
24	2.064	2.797	3.745		24	1.711	2.492	2.797
25	2.060	2.787	3.725		25	1.708	2.485	2.787
26	2.056	2.779	3.707		26	1.706	2.479	2.779
27	2.052	2.771	3.690		27	1.703	2.473	2.771
28	2.048	2.763	3.674		28	1.701	2.467	2.763
29	2.045	2.756	3.659		29	1.699	2.462	2.756
30	2.042	2.750	3.646		30	1.697	2.457	2.750
40	2.021	2.704	3.551		40	1.684	2.423	2.704
60	2.000	2.660	3.460		60	1.671	2.390	2.660
120	1.980	2.617	3.373		120	1.658	2.358	2.617
∞	1.960	2.576	3.291		∞	1.645	2.326	2.576

Source: Table C is taken from Table III (page 46) of Fisher and Yates, *Statistical Tables for Biological, Agricultural, and Medical Research,* 6th ed., published by Longman Group Ltd., 1974. London (previously published by Oliver and Boyd, Edinburgh), and by permission of the authors and publishers.

Critical Values of F

The obtained F is significant at a given level if it is equal to or *greater than* the value shown in the table. 0.05 (top row in each pair) and 0.01 (bottom row in each pair) points for the distribution of F.

The values shown are the right tail of the distribution obtained by dividing the larger variance estimate by the smaller variance estimate. To find the complementary left or lower tail for a given df and α-level, reverse the degrees of freedom and find the reciprocal of that value in the F-table. For example, the value cutting off the top 5% of the area for 7 and 12 df is 2.85. To find the cutoff point of the bottom 5% of the area, find the tabled value of the $\alpha = 0.05$ level for 12 and 7 df. This is found to be 3.57. The reciprocal is $1/3.57 = 0.28$. Thus 5% of the area falls *at or below an* $F = 0.28$.

Source: G. W. Snedecor and W. G. Cochran, *Statistical Methods*, 8th ed. © 1989 by Iowa State University Press, Ames, Iowa. Reprinted by permission.

Degrees of freedom for numerator

df (denom.)	1	2	3	4	5	6	7	8	9	10	11	12	14	16	20	24	30	40	50	75	100	200	500	∞
1	161 / 4052	200 / 4999	216 / 5403	225 / 5625	230 / 5764	234 / 5859	237 / 5928	239 / 5981	241 / 6022	242 / 6056	243 / 6082	244 / 6106	245 / 6142	246 / 6169	248 / 6208	249 / 6234	250 / 6258	251 / 6286	252 / 6302	253 / 6323	253 / 6334	254 / 6352	254 / 6361	254 / 6366
2	18.51 / 98.49	19.00 / 99.01	19.16 / 99.17	19.25 / 99.25	19.30 / 99.30	19.33 / 99.33	19.36 / 99.34	19.37 / 99.36	19.38 / 99.38	19.39 / 99.40	19.40 / 99.41	19.41 / 99.42	19.42 / 99.43	19.43 / 99.44	19.44 / 99.45	19.45 / 99.46	19.46 / 99.47	19.47 / 99.48	19.47 / 99.48	19.48 / 99.49	19.49 / 99.49	19.49 / 99.49	19.50 / 99.50	19.50 / 99.50
3	10.13 / 34.12	9.55 / 30.81	9.28 / 29.46	9.12 / 28.71	9.01 / 28.24	8.94 / 27.91	8.88 / 27.67	8.84 / 27.49	8.81 / 27.34	8.78 / 27.23	8.76 / 27.13	8.74 / 27.05	8.71 / 26.92	8.69 / 26.83	8.66 / 26.69	8.64 / 26.60	8.62 / 26.50	8.60 / 26.41	8.58 / 26.30	8.57 / 26.27	8.56 / 26.23	8.54 / 26.18	8.54 / 26.14	8.53 / 26.12
4	7.71 / 21.20	6.94 / 18.00	6.59 / 16.69	6.39 / 15.98	6.26 / 15.52	6.16 / 15.21	6.09 / 14.98	6.04 / 14.80	6.00 / 14.66	5.96 / 14.54	5.93 / 14.45	5.91 / 14.37	5.87 / 14.24	5.84 / 14.15	5.80 / 14.02	5.77 / 13.93	5.74 / 13.83	5.71 / 13.74	5.70 / 13.69	5.68 / 13.61	5.66 / 13.57	5.65 / 13.52	5.64 / 13.48	5.63 / 13.46
5	6.61 / 16.26	5.79 / 13.27	5.41 / 12.06	5.19 / 11.39	5.05 / 10.97	4.95 / 10.67	4.88 / 10.45	4.82 / 10.27	4.78 / 10.15	4.74 / 10.05	4.70 / 9.96	4.68 / 9.89	4.64 / 9.77	4.60 / 9.68	4.56 / 9.55	4.53 / 9.47	4.50 / 9.38	4.46 / 9.29	4.44 / 9.24	4.42 / 9.17	4.40 / 9.13	4.38 / 9.07	4.37 / 9.04	4.36 / 9.02
6	5.99 / 13.74	5.14 / 10.92	4.76 / 9.78	4.53 / 9.15	4.39 / 8.75	4.28 / 8.47	4.21 / 8.26	4.15 / 8.10	4.10 / 7.98	4.06 / 7.87	4.03 / 7.79	4.00 / 7.72	3.96 / 7.60	3.92 / 7.52	3.87 / 7.39	3.84 / 7.31	3.81 / 7.23	3.77 / 7.14	3.75 / 7.09	3.72 / 7.02	3.71 / 6.99	3.69 / 6.94	3.68 / 6.90	3.67 / 6.88
7	5.59 / 12.25	4.74 / 9.55	4.35 / 8.45	4.12 / 7.85	3.97 / 7.46	3.87 / 7.19	3.79 / 7.00	3.73 / 6.84	3.68 / 6.71	3.63 / 6.62	3.60 / 6.54	3.57 / 6.47	3.52 / 6.35	3.49 / 6.27	3.44 / 6.15	3.41 / 6.07	3.38 / 5.98	3.34 / 5.90	3.32 / 5.85	3.29 / 5.78	3.28 / 5.75	3.25 / 5.70	3.24 / 5.67	3.23 / 5.65
8	5.32 / 11.26	4.46 / 8.65	4.07 / 7.59	3.84 / 7.01	3.69 / 6.63	3.58 / 6.37	3.50 / 6.19	3.44 / 6.03	3.39 / 5.91	3.34 / 5.82	3.31 / 5.74	3.28 / 5.67	3.23 / 5.56	3.20 / 5.48	3.15 / 5.36	3.12 / 5.28	3.08 / 5.20	3.05 / 5.11	3.03 / 5.06	3.00 / 5.00	2.98 / 4.96	2.96 / 4.91	2.94 / 4.88	2.93 / 4.86
9	5.12 / 10.56	4.26 / 8.02	3.86 / 6.99	3.63 / 6.42	3.48 / 6.06	3.37 / 5.80	3.29 / 5.62	3.23 / 5.47	3.18 / 5.35	3.13 / 5.26	3.10 / 5.18	3.07 / 5.11	3.02 / 5.00	2.98 / 4.92	2.93 / 4.80	2.90 / 4.73	2.86 / 4.64	2.82 / 4.56	2.80 / 4.51	2.77 / 4.45	2.76 / 4.41	2.73 / 4.36	2.72 / 4.33	2.71 / 4.31
10	4.96 / 10.04	4.10 / 7.56	3.71 / 6.55	3.48 / 5.99	3.33 / 5.64	3.22 / 5.39	3.14 / 5.21	3.07 / 5.06	3.02 / 4.95	2.97 / 4.85	2.94 / 4.78	2.91 / 4.71	2.86 / 4.60	2.82 / 4.52	2.77 / 4.41	2.74 / 4.33	2.70 / 4.25	2.67 / 4.17	2.64 / 4.12	2.61 / 4.05	2.59 / 4.01	2.56 / 3.96	2.55 / 3.93	2.54 / 3.91
11	4.84 / 9.65	3.98 / 7.20	3.59 / 6.22	3.36 / 5.67	3.20 / 5.32	3.09 / 5.07	3.01 / 4.88	2.95 / 4.74	2.90 / 4.63	2.86 / 4.54	2.82 / 4.46	2.79 / 4.40	2.74 / 4.29	2.70 / 4.21	2.65 / 4.10	2.61 / 4.02	2.57 / 3.94	2.53 / 3.86	2.50 / 3.80	2.47 / 3.74	2.45 / 3.70	2.42 / 3.66	2.41 / 3.62	2.40 / 3.60
12	4.75 / 9.33	3.88 / 6.93	3.49 / 5.95	3.26 / 5.41	3.11 / 5.06	3.00 / 4.82	2.92 / 4.65	2.85 / 4.50	2.80 / 4.39	2.76 / 4.30	2.72 / 4.22	2.69 / 4.16	2.64 / 4.05	2.60 / 3.98	2.54 / 3.86	2.50 / 3.78	2.46 / 3.70	2.42 / 3.61	2.40 / 3.56	2.36 / 3.49	2.35 / 3.46	2.32 / 3.41	2.31 / 3.38	2.30 / 3.36
13	4.67 / 9.07	3.80 / 6.70	3.41 / 5.74	3.18 / 5.20	3.02 / 4.86	2.92 / 4.62	2.84 / 4.44	2.77 / 4.30	2.72 / 4.19	2.67 / 4.10	2.63 / 4.02	2.60 / 3.96	2.55 / 3.85	2.51 / 3.78	2.46 / 3.67	2.42 / 3.59	2.38 / 3.51	2.34 / 3.42	2.32 / 3.37	2.28 / 3.30	2.26 / 3.27	2.24 / 3.21	2.22 / 3.18	2.21 / 3.16
14	4.60 / 8.86	3.74 / 6.51	3.34 / 5.56	3.11 / 5.03	2.96 / 4.69	2.85 / 4.46	2.77 / 4.28	2.70 / 4.14	2.65 / 4.03	2.60 / 3.94	2.56 / 3.86	2.53 / 3.80	2.48 / 3.70	2.44 / 3.62	2.39 / 3.51	2.35 / 3.43	2.31 / 3.34	2.27 / 3.26	2.24 / 3.21	2.21 / 3.14	2.19 / 3.11	2.16 / 3.06	2.14 / 3.02	2.13 / 3.00
15	4.54 / 8.68	3.68 / 6.36	3.29 / 5.42	3.06 / 4.89	2.90 / 4.56	2.79 / 4.32	2.70 / 4.14	2.64 / 4.00	2.59 / 3.89	2.55 / 3.80	2.51 / 3.73	2.48 / 3.67	2.43 / 3.56	2.39 / 3.48	2.33 / 3.36	2.29 / 3.29	2.25 / 3.20	2.21 / 3.12	2.18 / 3.07	2.15 / 3.00	2.12 / 2.97	2.10 / 2.92	2.08 / 2.89	2.07 / 2.87

Degrees of freedom for denominator

(Continued)

Each cell gives the 5% point (upper value) and the 1% point (lower value). The left-hand column is degrees of freedom for denominator.

df																								
16	2.01 / 2.75	2.02 / 2.77	2.04 / 2.80	2.07 / 2.86	2.09 / 2.89	2.13 / 2.96	2.16 / 3.01	2.20 / 3.10	2.24 / 3.18	2.28 / 3.25	2.33 / 3.37	2.37 / 3.45	2.42 / 3.55	2.45 / 3.61	2.49 / 3.69	2.54 / 3.78	2.59 / 3.89	2.66 / 4.03	2.74 / 4.20	2.85 / 4.44	3.01 / 4.77	3.24 / 5.29	3.63 / 6.23	4.49 / 8.53
17	1.96 / 2.65	1.97 / 2.67	1.99 / 2.70	2.02 / 2.76	2.04 / 2.79	2.08 / 2.86	2.11 / 2.92	2.15 / 3.00	2.19 / 3.08	2.23 / 3.16	2.29 / 3.27	2.33 / 3.35	2.38 / 3.45	2.41 / 3.52	2.45 / 3.59	2.50 / 3.68	2.55 / 3.79	2.62 / 3.93	2.70 / 4.10	2.81 / 4.34	2.96 / 4.67	3.20 / 5.18	3.59 / 6.11	4.45 / 8.40
18	1.92 / 2.57	1.93 / 2.59	1.95 / 2.62	1.98 / 2.68	2.00 / 2.71	2.04 / 2.78	2.07 / 2.83	2.11 / 2.91	2.15 / 3.00	2.19 / 3.07	2.25 / 3.19	2.29 / 3.27	2.34 / 3.37	2.37 / 3.44	2.41 / 3.51	2.46 / 3.60	2.51 / 3.71	2.58 / 3.85	2.66 / 4.01	2.77 / 4.25	2.93 / 4.58	3.16 / 5.09	3.55 / 6.01	4.41 / 8.28
19	1.88 / 2.49	1.90 / 2.51	1.91 / 2.54	1.94 / 2.60	1.96 / 2.63	2.00 / 2.70	2.02 / 2.76	2.07 / 2.84	2.11 / 2.92	2.15 / 3.00	2.21 / 3.12	2.26 / 3.19	2.31 / 3.30	2.34 / 3.36	2.38 / 3.43	2.43 / 3.52	2.48 / 3.63	2.55 / 3.77	2.63 / 3.94	2.74 / 4.17	2.90 / 4.50	3.13 / 5.01	3.52 / 5.93	4.38 / 8.18
20	1.84 / 2.42	1.85 / 2.44	1.87 / 2.47	1.90 / 2.53	1.92 / 2.56	1.96 / 2.63	1.99 / 2.69	2.04 / 2.77	2.08 / 2.86	2.12 / 2.94	2.18 / 3.05	2.23 / 3.13	2.28 / 3.23	2.31 / 3.30	2.35 / 3.35	2.40 / 3.45	2.45 / 3.56	2.52 / 3.71	2.60 / 3.87	2.71 / 4.10	2.87 / 4.43	3.10 / 4.94	3.49 / 5.85	4.35 / 8.10
21	1.81 / 2.36	1.82 / 2.38	1.84 / 2.42	1.87 / 2.47	1.90 / 2.51	1.93 / 2.58	1.96 / 2.63	2.00 / 2.72	2.05 / 2.80	2.09 / 2.88	2.15 / 2.99	2.20 / 3.07	2.25 / 3.17	2.28 / 3.24	2.32 / 3.31	2.37 / 3.40	2.42 / 3.51	2.49 / 3.65	2.57 / 3.81	2.68 / 4.04	2.84 / 4.37	3.07 / 4.87	3.47 / 5.78	4.32 / 8.02
22	1.78 / 2.31	1.80 / 2.33	1.81 / 2.37	1.84 / 2.42	1.87 / 2.46	1.91 / 2.53	1.93 / 2.58	1.98 / 2.67	2.03 / 2.75	2.07 / 2.83	2.13 / 2.94	2.18 / 3.02	2.23 / 3.12	2.26 / 3.18	2.30 / 3.26	2.35 / 3.35	2.40 / 3.45	2.47 / 3.59	2.55 / 3.76	2.66 / 3.99	2.82 / 4.31	3.05 / 4.82	3.44 / 5.72	4.30 / 7.94
23	1.76 / 2.26	1.77 / 2.28	1.79 / 2.32	1.82 / 2.37	1.84 / 2.41	1.88 / 2.48	1.91 / 2.53	1.96 / 2.62	2.00 / 2.70	2.04 / 2.78	2.10 / 2.89	2.14 / 2.97	2.20 / 3.07	2.24 / 3.14	2.28 / 3.21	2.32 / 3.30	2.38 / 3.41	2.45 / 3.54	2.53 / 3.71	2.64 / 3.94	2.80 / 4.26	3.03 / 4.76	3.42 / 5.66	4.28 / 7.88
24	1.73 / 2.21	1.74 / 2.23	1.76 / 2.27	1.80 / 2.33	1.82 / 2.36	1.86 / 2.44	1.89 / 2.49	1.94 / 2.58	1.98 / 2.66	2.02 / 2.74	2.09 / 2.85	2.13 / 2.93	2.18 / 3.03	2.22 / 3.09	2.26 / 3.17	2.30 / 3.25	2.36 / 3.36	2.43 / 3.50	2.51 / 3.67	2.62 / 3.90	2.78 / 4.22	3.01 / 4.72	3.40 / 5.61	4.26 / 7.82
25	1.71 / 2.17	1.72 / 2.19	1.74 / 2.23	1.77 / 2.29	1.80 / 2.32	1.84 / 2.40	1.87 / 2.45	1.92 / 2.54	1.96 / 2.62	2.00 / 2.70	2.06 / 2.81	2.11 / 2.89	2.16 / 2.99	2.20 / 3.05	2.24 / 3.13	2.28 / 3.21	2.34 / 3.32	2.41 / 3.46	2.49 / 3.63	2.60 / 3.86	2.76 / 4.18	2.99 / 4.68	3.38 / 5.57	4.24 / 7.77
26	1.69 / 2.13	1.70 / 2.15	1.72 / 2.19	1.76 / 2.25	1.78 / 2.28	1.82 / 2.36	1.85 / 2.41	1.90 / 2.50	1.95 / 2.58	1.99 / 2.66	2.05 / 2.77	2.10 / 2.86	2.15 / 2.96	2.18 / 3.02	2.22 / 3.09	2.27 / 3.17	2.32 / 3.29	2.39 / 3.42	2.47 / 3.59	2.59 / 3.82	2.74 / 4.14	2.96 / 4.64	3.37 / 5.53	4.22 / 7.72
27	1.67 / 2.10	1.68 / 2.12	1.71 / 2.16	1.74 / 2.21	1.76 / 2.25	1.80 / 2.33	1.84 / 2.38	1.88 / 2.47	1.93 / 2.55	1.97 / 2.63	2.03 / 2.74	2.08 / 2.83	2.13 / 2.93	2.16 / 2.98	2.20 / 3.06	2.25 / 3.14	2.30 / 3.26	2.37 / 3.39	2.46 / 3.56	2.57 / 3.79	2.73 / 4.11	2.96 / 4.60	3.35 / 5.49	4.21 / 7.68
28	1.65 / 2.06	1.67 / 2.09	1.69 / 2.13	1.72 / 2.18	1.75 / 2.22	1.78 / 2.30	1.81 / 2.35	1.87 / 2.44	1.91 / 2.52	1.96 / 2.60	2.02 / 2.71	2.06 / 2.80	2.12 / 2.90	2.15 / 2.95	2.19 / 3.03	2.24 / 3.11	2.29 / 3.23	2.36 / 3.36	2.44 / 3.53	2.56 / 3.76	2.71 / 4.07	2.95 / 4.57	3.34 / 5.45	4.20 / 7.64
29	1.64 / 2.03	1.65 / 2.06	1.68 / 2.10	1.71 / 2.15	1.73 / 2.19	1.77 / 2.27	1.80 / 2.32	1.85 / 2.41	1.90 / 2.49	1.94 / 2.57	2.00 / 2.68	2.05 / 2.77	2.10 / 2.87	2.14 / 2.92	2.18 / 3.00	2.22 / 3.08	2.28 / 3.20	2.35 / 3.32	2.43 / 3.50	2.54 / 3.73	2.70 / 4.04	2.93 / 4.54	3.33 / 5.42	4.18 / 7.60
30	1.62 / 2.01	1.64 / 2.03	1.66 / 2.07	1.69 / 2.13	1.72 / 2.16	1.76 / 2.24	1.79 / 2.29	1.84 / 2.38	1.89 / 2.47	1.93 / 2.55	1.99 / 2.66	2.04 / 2.74	2.09 / 2.84	2.12 / 2.90	2.16 / 2.98	2.21 / 3.06	2.27 / 3.17	2.34 / 3.30	2.42 / 3.47	2.53 / 3.70	2.69 / 4.02	2.92 / 4.51	3.32 / 5.39	4.17 / 7.56
32	1.59 / 1.96	1.61 / 1.98	1.64 / 2.02	1.67 / 2.08	1.69 / 2.12	1.74 / 2.20	1.76 / 2.25	1.82 / 2.34	1.86 / 2.42	1.91 / 2.51	1.97 / 2.62	2.02 / 2.70	2.07 / 2.80	2.10 / 2.86	2.14 / 2.94	2.19 / 3.01	2.25 / 3.12	2.32 / 3.25	2.40 / 3.42	2.51 / 3.66	2.67 / 3.97	2.90 / 4.46	3.30 / 5.34	4.15 / 7.50
34	1.57 / 1.91	1.59 / 1.94	1.61 / 1.98	1.64 / 2.04	1.67 / 2.08	1.71 / 2.15	1.74 / 2.21	1.80 / 2.30	1.84 / 2.38	1.89 / 2.47	1.95 / 2.58	2.00 / 2.66	2.05 / 2.76	2.08 / 2.82	2.12 / 2.89	2.17 / 2.97	2.23 / 3.08	2.30 / 3.21	2.38 / 3.38	2.49 / 3.61	2.65 / 3.93	2.88 / 4.42	3.28 / 5.29	4.13 / 7.44

Degrees of freedom for denominator

(Continued)

Degrees of freedom for numerator

The following table gives, for each pair of degrees of freedom, the upper value = $F_{0.05}$ and the lower value = $F_{0.01}$ (top / bottom). Column headers are degrees of freedom for numerator; row labels are degrees of freedom for denominator.

denom \ numer	1	2	3	4	5	6	7	8	9	10	11	12	14	16	20	24	30	40	50	75	100	200	500	∞
36	4.11 / 7.39	3.26 / 5.25	2.86 / 4.38	2.63 / 3.89	2.48 / 3.58	2.36 / 3.35	2.28 / 3.18	2.21 / 3.04	2.15 / 2.94	2.10 / 2.86	2.06 / 2.78	2.03 / 2.72	1.98 / 2.62	1.93 / 2.54	1.87 / 2.43	1.82 / 2.35	1.78 / 2.26	1.72 / 2.17	1.69 / 2.12	1.65 / 2.04	1.62 / 2.00	1.59 / 1.94	1.56 / 1.90	1.55 / 1.87
38	4.10 / 7.35	3.25 / 5.21	2.85 / 4.34	2.62 / 3.86	2.46 / 3.54	2.35 / 3.32	2.26 / 3.15	2.19 / 3.02	2.14 / 2.91	2.09 / 2.82	2.05 / 2.75	2.02 / 2.69	1.96 / 2.59	1.92 / 2.51	1.85 / 2.40	1.80 / 2.32	1.76 / 2.22	1.71 / 2.14	1.67 / 2.08	1.63 / 2.00	1.60 / 1.97	1.57 / 1.90	1.54 / 1.86	1.53 / 1.84
40	4.08 / 7.31	3.23 / 5.18	2.84 / 4.31	2.61 / 3.83	2.45 / 3.51	2.34 / 3.29	2.25 / 3.12	2.18 / 2.99	2.12 / 2.88	2.07 / 2.80	2.04 / 2.73	2.00 / 2.66	1.95 / 2.56	1.90 / 2.49	1.84 / 2.37	1.79 / 2.29	1.74 / 2.20	1.69 / 2.11	1.66 / 2.05	1.61 / 1.97	1.59 / 1.94	1.55 / 1.88	1.53 / 1.84	1.51 / 1.81
42	4.07 / 7.27	3.22 / 5.15	2.83 / 4.29	2.59 / 3.80	2.44 / 3.49	2.32 / 3.26	2.24 / 3.10	2.17 / 2.96	2.11 / 2.86	2.06 / 2.77	2.02 / 2.70	1.99 / 2.64	1.94 / 2.54	1.89 / 2.46	1.82 / 2.35	1.78 / 2.26	1.73 / 2.17	1.68 / 2.08	1.64 / 2.02	1.60 / 1.94	1.57 / 1.91	1.54 / 1.85	1.51 / 1.80	1.49 / 1.78
44	4.06 / 7.24	3.21 / 5.12	2.82 / 4.26	2.58 / 3.78	2.43 / 3.46	2.31 / 3.24	2.23 / 3.07	2.16 / 2.94	2.10 / 2.84	2.05 / 2.75	2.01 / 2.68	1.98 / 2.62	1.92 / 2.52	1.88 / 2.44	1.81 / 2.32	1.76 / 2.24	1.72 / 2.15	1.66 / 2.06	1.63 / 2.00	1.58 / 1.92	1.56 / 1.88	1.52 / 1.82	1.50 / 1.78	1.48 / 1.75
46	4.05 / 7.21	3.20 / 5.10	2.81 / 4.24	2.57 / 3.76	2.42 / 3.44	2.30 / 3.22	2.22 / 3.05	2.14 / 2.92	2.09 / 2.82	2.04 / 2.73	2.00 / 2.66	1.97 / 2.60	1.91 / 2.50	1.87 / 2.42	1.80 / 2.30	1.75 / 2.22	1.71 / 2.13	1.65 / 2.04	1.62 / 1.98	1.57 / 1.90	1.54 / 1.86	1.51 / 1.80	1.48 / 1.76	1.46 / 1.72
48	4.04 / 7.19	3.19 / 5.08	2.80 / 4.22	2.56 / 3.74	2.41 / 3.42	2.30 / 3.20	2.21 / 3.04	2.14 / 2.90	2.08 / 2.80	2.03 / 2.71	1.99 / 2.64	1.96 / 2.58	1.90 / 2.48	1.86 / 2.40	1.79 / 2.28	1.74 / 2.20	1.70 / 2.11	1.64 / 2.02	1.61 / 1.96	1.56 / 1.88	1.53 / 1.84	1.50 / 1.78	1.47 / 1.73	1.45 / 1.70
50	4.03 / 7.17	3.18 / 5.06	2.79 / 4.20	2.56 / 3.72	2.40 / 3.41	2.29 / 3.18	2.20 / 3.02	2.13 / 2.88	2.07 / 2.78	2.02 / 2.70	1.98 / 2.62	1.95 / 2.56	1.90 / 2.46	1.85 / 2.39	1.78 / 2.26	1.74 / 2.18	1.69 / 2.10	1.63 / 2.00	1.60 / 1.94	1.55 / 1.86	1.52 / 1.82	1.48 / 1.76	1.46 / 1.71	1.44 / 1.68
55	4.02 / 7.12	3.17 / 5.01	2.78 / 4.16	2.54 / 3.68	2.38 / 3.37	2.27 / 3.15	2.18 / 2.98	2.11 / 2.85	2.05 / 2.75	2.00 / 2.66	1.97 / 2.59	1.93 / 2.53	1.88 / 2.43	1.83 / 2.35	1.76 / 2.23	1.72 / 2.15	1.67 / 2.06	1.61 / 1.96	1.58 / 1.90	1.52 / 1.82	1.50 / 1.78	1.46 / 1.71	1.43 / 1.66	1.41 / 1.64
60	4.00 / 7.08	3.15 / 4.98	2.76 / 4.13	2.52 / 3.65	2.37 / 3.34	2.25 / 3.12	2.17 / 2.95	2.10 / 2.82	2.04 / 2.72	1.99 / 2.63	1.95 / 2.56	1.92 / 2.50	1.86 / 2.40	1.81 / 2.32	1.75 / 2.20	1.70 / 2.12	1.65 / 2.03	1.59 / 1.93	1.56 / 1.87	1.50 / 1.79	1.48 / 1.74	1.44 / 1.68	1.41 / 1.63	1.39 / 1.60
65	3.99 / 7.04	3.14 / 4.95	2.75 / 4.10	2.51 / 3.62	2.36 / 3.31	2.24 / 3.09	2.15 / 2.93	2.08 / 2.79	2.02 / 2.70	1.98 / 2.61	1.94 / 2.54	1.90 / 2.47	1.85 / 2.37	1.80 / 2.30	1.73 / 2.18	1.68 / 2.09	1.63 / 2.00	1.57 / 1.90	1.54 / 1.84	1.49 / 1.76	1.46 / 1.71	1.42 / 1.64	1.39 / 1.60	1.37 / 1.56
70	3.98 / 7.01	3.13 / 4.92	2.74 / 4.08	2.50 / 3.60	2.35 / 3.29	2.23 / 3.07	2.14 / 2.91	2.07 / 2.77	2.01 / 2.67	1.97 / 2.59	1.93 / 2.51	1.89 / 2.45	1.84 / 2.35	1.79 / 2.28	1.72 / 2.15	1.67 / 2.07	1.62 / 1.98	1.56 / 1.88	1.53 / 1.82	1.47 / 1.74	1.45 / 1.69	1.40 / 1.62	1.37 / 1.56	1.35 / 1.53
80	3.96 / 6.96	3.11 / 4.88	2.72 / 4.04	2.48 / 3.56	2.33 / 3.25	2.21 / 3.04	2.12 / 2.87	2.05 / 2.74	1.99 / 2.64	1.95 / 2.55	1.91 / 2.48	1.88 / 2.41	1.82 / 2.32	1.77 / 2.24	1.70 / 2.11	1.65 / 2.03	1.60 / 1.94	1.54 / 1.84	1.51 / 1.78	1.45 / 1.70	1.42 / 1.65	1.38 / 1.57	1.35 / 1.52	1.32 / 1.49
100	3.94 / 6.90	3.09 / 4.82	2.70 / 3.98	2.46 / 3.51	2.30 / 3.20	2.19 / 2.99	2.10 / 2.82	2.03 / 2.69	1.97 / 2.59	1.92 / 2.51	1.88 / 2.43	1.85 / 2.36	1.79 / 2.26	1.75 / 2.19	1.68 / 2.06	1.63 / 1.98	1.57 / 1.89	1.51 / 1.79	1.48 / 1.73	1.42 / 1.64	1.39 / 1.59	1.34 / 1.51	1.30 / 1.46	1.28 / 1.43
125	3.92 / 6.84	3.07 / 4.78	2.68 / 3.94	2.44 / 3.47	2.29 / 3.17	2.17 / 2.95	2.08 / 2.79	2.01 / 2.65	1.95 / 2.56	1.90 / 2.47	1.86 / 2.40	1.83 / 2.33	1.77 / 2.23	1.72 / 2.15	1.65 / 2.03	1.60 / 1.94	1.55 / 1.85	1.49 / 1.75	1.45 / 1.68	1.39 / 1.59	1.36 / 1.54	1.31 / 1.46	1.27 / 1.40	1.25 / 1.37
150	3.91 / 6.81	3.06 / 4.75	2.67 / 3.91	2.43 / 3.44	2.27 / 3.13	2.16 / 2.92	2.07 / 2.76	2.00 / 2.62	1.94 / 2.53	1.89 / 2.44	1.85 / 2.37	1.82 / 2.30	1.76 / 2.20	1.71 / 2.12	1.64 / 2.00	1.59 / 1.91	1.54 / 1.83	1.47 / 1.72	1.44 / 1.66	1.37 / 1.56	1.34 / 1.51	1.29 / 1.43	1.25 / 1.37	1.22 / 1.33
200	3.89 / 6.76	3.04 / 4.71	2.65 / 3.88	2.41 / 3.41	2.26 / 3.11	2.14 / 2.90	2.05 / 2.73	1.98 / 2.60	1.92 / 2.50	1.87 / 2.41	1.83 / 2.34	1.80 / 2.28	1.74 / 2.17	1.69 / 2.09	1.62 / 1.97	1.57 / 1.88	1.52 / 1.79	1.45 / 1.69	1.42 / 1.62	1.35 / 1.53	1.32 / 1.48	1.26 / 1.39	1.22 / 1.33	1.19 / 1.28
400	3.86 / 6.70	3.02 / 4.66	2.62 / 3.83	2.39 / 3.36	2.23 / 3.06	2.12 / 2.85	2.03 / 2.69	1.96 / 2.55	1.90 / 2.46	1.85 / 2.37	1.81 / 2.29	1.78 / 2.23	1.72 / 2.12	1.67 / 2.04	1.60 / 1.92	1.54 / 1.84	1.49 / 1.74	1.42 / 1.64	1.38 / 1.57	1.32 / 1.47	1.28 / 1.42	1.22 / 1.32	1.16 / 1.24	1.13 / 1.19
1000	3.85 / 6.66	3.00 / 4.62	2.61 / 3.80	2.38 / 3.34	2.22 / 3.04	2.10 / 2.82	2.02 / 2.66	1.95 / 2.53	1.89 / 2.43	1.84 / 2.34	1.80 / 2.26	1.76 / 2.20	1.70 / 2.09	1.65 / 2.01	1.58 / 1.89	1.53 / 1.81	1.47 / 1.71	1.41 / 1.61	1.36 / 1.54	1.30 / 1.44	1.26 / 1.38	1.19 / 1.28	1.13 / 1.19	1.08 / 1.11
∞	3.84 / 6.64	2.99 / 4.60	2.60 / 3.78	2.37 / 3.32	2.21 / 3.02	2.09 / 2.80	2.01 / 2.64	1.94 / 2.51	1.88 / 2.41	1.83 / 2.32	1.79 / 2.24	1.75 / 2.18	1.69 / 2.07	1.64 / 1.99	1.57 / 1.87	1.52 / 1.79	1.46 / 1.69	1.40 / 1.59	1.35 / 1.52	1.28 / 1.41	1.24 / 1.36	1.17 / 1.25	1.11 / 1.15	1.00 / 1.00

Degrees of freedom for denominator

Critical values of the Pearson product-moment correlation

If the observed value of r is *greater than or equal to* the tabulated value for the appropriate level of significance (columns) and degrees of freedom (rows), then reject H_0. The degrees of freedom are the number of pairs of scores minus two, or $N-2$. The critical values in the table are both + and − for nondirectional (two-tail) tests.

	Level of significance for a directional (one-tailed) test				
	.05	.025	.01	.005	.0005
	Level of significance for a non-directional (two-tailed) test				
$df = N-2$	.10	.05	.02	.01	.001
1	.9877	.9969	.9995	.9999	1.0000
2	.9000	.9500	.9800	.9900	.9990
3	.8054	.8783	.9343	.9587	.9912
4	.7293	.8114	.8822	.9172	.9741
5	.6694	.7545	.8329	.8745	.9507
6	.6215	.7067	.7887	.8343	.9249
7	.5822	.6664	.7498	.7977	.8982
8	.5494	.6319	.7155	.7646	.8721
9	.5214	.6021	.6851	.7348	.8471
10	.4973	.5760	.6581	.7079	.8233
11	.4762	.5529	.6339	.6835	.8010
12	.4575	.5324	.6120	.6614	.7800
13	.4409	.5139	.5923	.6411	.7603
14	.4259	.4973	.5742	.6226	.7420
15	.4124	.4821	.5577	.6055	.7246
16	.4000	.4683	.5425	.5897	.7084
17	.3887	.4555	.5285	.5751	.6932
18	.3783	.4438	.5155	.5614	.6787
19	.3687	.4329	.5034	.5487	.6652
20	.3598	.4227	.4921	.5368	.6524
25	.3233	.3809	.4451	.4869	.5974
30	.2960	.3494	.4093	.4487	.5541
35	.2746	.3246	.3810	.4182	.5189
40	.2573	.3044	.3578	.3932	.4896
45	.2428	.2875	.3384	.3721	.4648
50	.2306	.2732	.3218	.3541	.4433
60	.2108	.2500	.2948	.3248	.4078
70	.1954	.2319	.2737	.3017	.3799
80	.1829	.2172	.2565	.2830	.3568
90	.1726	.2050	.2422	.2673	.3375
100	.1638	.1946	.2301	.2540	.3211

SOURCE: Table G is taken from Table VII of Fisher & Yates, *Statistical tables for biological, agricultural and medical research*, published by Longman Group UK Ltd., London (previously published by Oliver and Boyd Ltd., Edinburgh), with permission of the authors and the publishers.

Critical Values of χ^2

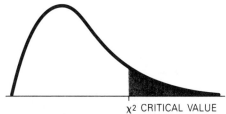

χ^2 CRITICAL VALUE

Degrees of freedom df	.10	.05	.02	.01
1	2.706	3.841	5.412	6.635
2	4.605	5.991	7.824	9.210
3	6.251	7.815	9.837	11.341
4	7.779	9.488	11.668	13.277
5	9.236	11.070	13.388	15.086
6	10.645	12.592	15.033	16.812
7	12.017	14.067	16.622	18.475
8	13.362	15.507	18.168	20.090
9	14.684	16.919	19.679	21.666
10	15.987	18.307	21.161	23.209
11	17.275	19.675	22.618	24.725
12	18.549	21.026	24.054	26.217
13	19.812	22.362	25.472	27.688
14	21.064	23.685	26.873	29.141
15	22.307	24.996	28.259	30.578
16	23.542	26.296	29.633	32.000
17	24.769	27.587	30.995	33.409
18	25.989	28.869	32.346	34.805
19	27.204	30.144	33.687	36.191
20	28.412	31.410	35.020	37.566
21	29.615	32.671	36.343	38.932
22	30.813	33.924	37.659	40.289
23	32.007	35.172	38.968	41.638
24	33.196	36.415	40.270	42.980
25	34.382	37.652	41.566	44.314
26	35.563	38.885	42.856	45.642
27	36.741	40.113	44.140	46.963
28	37.916	41.337	45.419	48.278
29	39.087	42.557	46.693	49.588
30	40.256	43.773	47.962	50.892

Source: Ronald A. Fisher, *Statistical Methods for Research Workers*, 14th ed., Table III, p. 113. Copyright © 1970 by University of Adelaide. Reprinted by permission of Luminis Pty., Ltd., Adelaide, South Australia.

Appendix B ❖ Chapter Problem Answers

Chapter 1

2. a. Part one – survey; part two – interview.
    b. The survey in part one is a quantitative method and the interview in part two is a qualitative method.
    c. Some advantages to the quantitative approach include its objectivity, replicability, time, and cost efficiency. Some advantages to the qualitative approach include in-depth understanding of the phenomenon under study and the generation of theories and hypotheses based on real-life observations rather than arm-chair speculations.
    d. The comparisons between the quantitative and qualitative methods is not one of superiority but of appropriateness. The best method to use depends on the question being asked and the stage of the research. If the researcher is in an exploratory stage, most likely qualitative techniques are more useful in gathering in-depth insight. In contrast, if the researcher is in a confirmatory stage, quantitative approaches provide a better route to gather objective evidence. Often researchers combine both methods in a way that makes the best sense for the study.

4. Inferential; descriptive.

6. a. No. Not all women in the United States are represented in the *Cosmopolitan* survey. In other words, a nonrandom sample was used to generalize to all women in the United States. Only those women who read that issue of Cosmo politan *and* chose to complete and return the survey are represented. In order to substantiate that all women in the United States felt happy or unhappy in their relationships every woman in the United States would have had to have been given an equal opportunity to participate in the survey, which they were not.
    b. The lawyers need to be cautious with how they apply the results from the experiment. The results most likely can only be generalized (applied) to university students (the target population of the experiment). In addition, the students evaluated "scenarios," not real-life cases. The results may vary across ethnic groups as well as according to the strength of ethnic identification of individuals within the groups. The investigation gives something for lawyers to think about but more evidence is needed before the lawyers should radically change their procedure.
    c. Again, the numbers are not representative of everyone in the United States. It is biased to those who have televisions, watch CNN, and are willing to call in and pay a minimal fee to cast their vote. In addition, the same person may have called in several times. In order to represent all people in the United States, CNN would need to gather a random sample (all people have an equal chance of being selected) of U.S. citizens.

Chapter 2

2. Population; sample.
4. Random or representative.
6. Random sampling refers to a way of selecting people (units) for a sample from a population such that each member of the population has an equal chance of being included in the population. In contrast, random assignment is a process of randomly putting people into conditions or groups in an experiment.
8. The independent variable is the type of store (department, specialty) and the dependent variable is the amount of profit.
10. a. interval
    b. nominal
    c. ordinal
    d. ratio
12. The researcher can give you an exam on the material covered in this course. If grades are assigned, the measurement is ordinal and if scores are assigned, the measurement is interval.

Chapter 3

2. Score; frequency.
4. A normal distribution is perfectly symmetrical around the middle whereas a skewed distribution has an elongated tail.
6. c. Scores on a very easy test.
8. a. Median.
    b. Mean.
    c. Mode.
    d. Mode.
    e. Mean.
    f. Lower.
    g. Higher.
    h. Mean.
    i. None. They all fall at exactly the same point – the center.
    j. Mode.

10. a. Platykurtic curve.
    b. Leptokurtic curve.
    c. Leptokurtic curve.
    d. Platykurtic curve.
12. a. Variance.
    b. Median.
    c. Range.
    d. Standard deviation.
    e. Mean.
    f. Mode.
14. Height: $\bar{X} = \dfrac{\sum X}{N} = \dfrac{69 + 67 + 64 + 66 + 62 + 65}{6} = 65.5$

    Order numbers to form a distribution: 62, 64, 65, 66, 67, 69. The middlemost score is between 65 and 66; Mdn = 65.5. Mo = none (no score occurs more frequently than any other score). R = 69 - 62 = 7. Weight: $\bar{X}$ = 128.2; Mdn = 130; Mo none; R = 42.

Chapter 4

2. Population distribution.
    a. μ
    b. σ
    c. $z = \dfrac{X - \mu}{\sigma}$
4. Distribution of differences.
    a. μ
    b. σ_{diff}
    c. $z = \dfrac{(\bar{X}_1 - \bar{X}_2) - 0}{\sigma_{diff}}$
6. Statistics – sample distribution. Parameters – population distribution, sampling distribution, distribution of differences. The distributions that use statistics are based on observations from a sample, whereas distributions that use parameters are based on all observations from a population.
8. Standard deviation.
10. The standard error of the difference (or the standard error of the mean difference).
12. Standard deviation.

14.

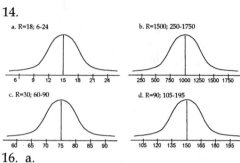

a. R=18; 6-24   b. R=1500; 250-1750

c. R=30; 60-90   d. R=90; 105-195

16. a.

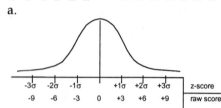

b. 3

c. -6

Chapter 5

2. The alternative hypothesis.
4. a. Alternative hypothesis; one-tailed.
   b. Alternative hypothesis; two-tailed.
   c. Null hypothesis; one-tailed.
   d. Alternative hypothesis; one-tailed.
   e. Null hypothesis; two-tailed.
   f. Null hypothesis; one-tailed.
6. a. $H_a\ \mu_{stu} \neq \mu_{prof}; H_0: \mu_{stu} = \mu_{prof}$
   b. $H_a\ \mu_{pov} > \mu_{nonp}; H_0: \mu_{pov} \leq \mu_{nonp}$
   c. $H_a\ \mu_{men} \neq \mu_{wom}; H_0: \mu_{men} = \mu_{wom}$
   d. $H_a\ \mu_{pri} \neq \mu_{pub}; H_0: \mu_{pri} = \mu_{pub}$
8. a. Snow, $p = .01$
   b. Overcast, $p = .25$
   c. Foggy, $p = .50$
10. $p < .05; p < .01$; The probability levels refer to the researcher's willingness to accept that 1 or 5 times out of 100 their conclusion regarding the null hypothesis could be wrong or that there is a 95% or 99% chance that the alternative hypothesis is correct. At these established levels the researcher is able to reject the null hypothesis.

12. One-tailed test.
14. a. ± 1.96
    b. ± 2.58
    c. +1.65 or -1.65
    d. +2.33 or -2.33
16. a. Do not reject (accept) H_0
    b. Reject H_0
    c. Do not reject (accept) H_0
    d. Reject H_0
    e. Do not reject (accept) H_0
    f. Do not reject (accept) H_0
    g. Reject H_0
18. Type I error.
20. .05; .01.
22. $H_a\ \mu_{stu} > \mu_{pop}; H_0: \mu_{stu} \leq \mu_{pop}$

$$z = \frac{\overline{X} - \mu}{\sigma_{\overline{x}}} = \frac{108 - 100}{3} = 2.67$$

Reject H_0 at $p < .01$. Since the observed value z=2.67 is greater than the critical value 2.33, the principal can conclude that students at his school are indeed more intelligent, on average, than the general population.

Chapter 6

2. $t = \dfrac{\overline{X}_1 - \overline{X}_2}{\sigma_{diff}}$

4. Distribution of differences.
6. Rejects.
8. Increase sample size or use a one-tailed test.
10. The larger the sample size (N) the greater your ability to reject H_0. A statistical test is more powerful with larger sample sizes.
12. a. Two-tailed hypothesis; the direction of the means is not specified.
    b. $H_a: \mu_1 \neq \mu_2; H_0: \mu_1 = \mu_2$
    c. $t = \dfrac{\overline{X}_1 - \overline{X}_2}{\sigma_{diff}} = \dfrac{4 - 6.5}{1.20} = \dfrac{-2.5}{1.20} = -2.08$
       df = $(N_1 - 1) + (N_2 - 1) = (10 - 1) + (10 - 1) = 9 + 9 = 18$

d. $t_{(18).05} = 2.101$; $t_{(18).01} = 2.878$

e. Since the calculated value t = -2.08 is not larger (in absolute terms) than the critical value at the $p < .05$ level (2.101), do not reject H_0. People do not react differently to a negative political ad than to a neutral political ad.

f. You would recommend either type of ad based on this data; it makes no difference.

g. H_a: $\mu_1 < \mu_2$; H_0: $\mu_1 \geq \mu_2$

h. Since the calculated value t = -2.08 is larger (in the predicted direction) than the critical value for the one-tail test $t_{(18).05} = 1.734$, reject H_0 at the $p < .05$ level. Note: you cannot reject at the preferred $p < .01$ level with a critical value $t_{(18).01} = 2.552$.

14. a. Two-tailed hypothesis; the direction of the means is not specified.

b. H_a: $\mu_1 \neq \mu_2$; H_0: $\mu_1 = \mu_2$

c. $t = \dfrac{\overline{X_1} - \overline{X_2}}{\sigma_{diff}} = \dfrac{98.06 - 102.35}{2.45} = \dfrac{-4.29}{2.45} = -1.75$

df = $(N_1 - 1) + (N_2 - 1) = (61 - 1) +$

$(61 - 1) = 60 + 60 = 120$.

Critical values: $t_{(120).05} = 1.98$; $t_{(120).01} = 2.61$. Since the calculated value of t = -1.75 is not larger (in absolute terms; ignore the sign) than the critical value $t_{(120).05} = 1.98$, do not reject H_0.

d. Do not reject H_0; the individual therapy program did not significantly affect delinquent boys' levels of measured anxiety.

16. a. One-tailed hypothesis; the direction of the means is predicted (that the mean number of seconds before initiating a conversation will be lower with the female than with the male).

b. H_a: $\mu_F < \mu_M$; H_0: $\mu_F \geq \mu_M$

c. No. The standard error of the difference is negative (which can never happen). Also, if you use our preferred second method for conducting a t-test you should notice that the means are not in the predicted direction; therefore, you stop before ever calculating a value for t.

d. The means are in the predicted direction (the female has a lower mean than the male).

$t = \dfrac{\overline{X_1} - \overline{X_2}}{\sigma_{diff}} = \dfrac{5 - 9}{2.30} = \dfrac{-4}{2.30} = -1.74$

df = $(N_1 - 1) + (N_2 - 1) = (13 - 1) +$

$(13 - 1) = 12 + 12 = 24$

Critical values: $t_{(24).05} = 1.711$; $t_{(24).01} = 2.492$. Since the calculated value t = -1.74 is larger (in the predicted direction) than the critical value $t_{(24).05} = 1.711$, reject H_0 at $p < .05$. Can we do any better? No. Since the calculated value t = -1.74 is not larger than the critical value at the .01 level $t_{(24).01} = 2.492$.

e. Reject H_0 at $p < .05$; men initiate a conversation with a female significantly faster than with a male.

Chapter 7

2. A factor.

4. F; post-hoc

6. A post-hoc test should be conducted once a significant overall difference is found with the F-test.

8. a. With 4 groups, $df_B = K - 1 = 4 - 1 = 3$. With 10 subjects per groups there are a total of $N = 10 \times 4 = 40$ subjects in the study. With 40 subjects (N) and 4 groups (K), $df_W = N - K = 40 - 4 = 36$.

Critical values: $F_{(3,36).05} = 2.86$; $F_{(3,36).01} = 4.38$. Reject H_0 at $p < .05$.

b. Critical values: $F_{(9,80).05} = 1.99$; $F_{(9,80).01} = 2.64$. Reject H_0 at $p < .01$.

c. $df_B = K - 1 = 5 - 1 = 4$.

   $df_W = N - K$. Do not have sufficient information on the total number of subjects in the study (N) to compute df_W. The statistical decision cannot be determined from the information given.

d. $df_B = K - 1 = 3 - 1 = 2$. $df_W = N - K = 17 - 3 = 14$. Critical values: $F_{(2,14).05} = 3.74$; $F_{(2,14).01} = 6.51$. Do not reject H_0.

e. $df_B = K - 1 = 13 - 1 = 12$. $N = 32 \times 13 = 416$. $df_W = N - K = 416 - 12 = 404$. Critical values: $F_{(12,404).05} \approx 1.78$; $F_{(12,404).01} \approx 2.23$. Reject H_0 at $p < .01$. Note: $\approx$ means "approximately equals" since these critical values are extrapolated from the two critical values with degrees of freedom closest to those in this problem.

10. a. With $df_B = 5$, there must be 6 groups (K) since $df_B = K - 1 = 6 - 1 = 5$.

   b. With $df_T = 10$ there must be 11 total subjects (N) since $df_T = N - 1 = 11 - 1 = 10$.

   c. $F = \dfrac{MS_B}{MS_W} = \dfrac{10}{5} = 2$

   Critical values: $F_{(5,5).05} = 5.05$; $F_{(5,5).01} = 10.97$. Since the calculated value F = 2.00 is not larger than the critical value $F_{(5,5).05} = 5.05$, do reject H_0.

   d. Do not reject H_0. There is not a difference among the six groups.

12. a. H_a: $\mu_5 \neq \mu_{10} \neq \mu_{15}$
      H_0: $\mu_5 = \mu_{10} = \mu_{15}$

   b. $N = 30$ since there were 10 employees per group.

c.

Source	SS	df	MS	F
Between	180	2	90	3.04
Within	800	27	29.63	
Total	980	29		

$df_B = K - 1 = 3 - 1 = 2$
$df_W = N - K = 30 - 3 = 27$
$df_T = N - 1 = 30 - 1 = 29$ (or $df_T = df_B + df_W = 2 + 27 = 29$)

$$MS_B = \frac{SS_B}{df_B} = \frac{180}{2} = 90$$

$$MS_W = \frac{SS_W}{df_W} = \frac{800}{27} = 29.63$$

$$F = \frac{MS_B}{MS_W} = \frac{90}{29.63} = 3.04$$

Critical values: $F_{(2,27).05} = 3.35$; $F_{(2,27).01} = 5.49$. Since the calculated value F = 3.04 is not larger than the critical value $F_{(2,27).05} = 3.35$, do not reject H_0.

d. Do not reject H_0. There is no difference in productivity rates as a function of positive reinforcement from supervisors.

e. It doesn't matter since there was no difference among the three groups.

f.

Source	SS	df	MS	F
Between	180	2	90	6.41
Within	800	57	14.04	
Total	980	59		

$df_B = K - 1 = 3 - 1 = 2$
$N = 20 \times 3 = 60$ employees in the study
$df_W = N - K = 60 - 3 = 57$
$df_T = N - 1 = 60 - 1 = 59$ (or $df_T = df_B + df_W = 2 + 57 = 59$)

$$MS_B = \frac{SS_B}{df_B} = \frac{180}{2} = 90$$

$$MS_W = \frac{SS_W}{df_W} = \frac{800}{57} = 14.04$$

$$F = \frac{MS_B}{MS_W} = \frac{90}{14.04} = 6.41$$

Critical values: $F_{(2,57).05} \approx 3.16$; $F_{(2,57).01} \approx 5.00$. Since the calculated value F = 6.41 is larger than the critical value $F_{(2,57).05} = 3.16$, reject H_0 at $p <$ .05. Can we do any better? Yes. Since the calculated value F = 6.41 is larger than the critical value at the .01 level $F_{(2,57).01} \approx 5.00$, reject H_0 at $p < .01$.

g. Reject H_0 at $p < .01$. There is some difference in workers' productivity rates as a function of time receiving positive praise from supervisors.

h. Cannot be determined without conducting a post-hoc test.

Chapter 8

2. a. 2
    b. 5
    c. 2
    d. 3
    e. 3
    f. 4
4. a. $4 \times 3 = 12$
    b. $2 \times 2 \times 2 = 8$
    c. $2 \times 3 \times 4 = 24$
6. Main effect.
8. a. There are three independent variables each with two levels: type of conference (face-to-face, televised), type of firm (national, international), and type of employee (management, regular). So, this is a 2 x 2 x 2 factorial design.
    b. Since there are three independent variable, there are three possible main effects.
    c. There are a total of four possible interaction effects: three two-way interactions (conference x firm, conference x employee, firm x employee) and one three-way interaction (conference x firm x employee).

10. a. Main effects for caffeine and sleep. No interaction effect.

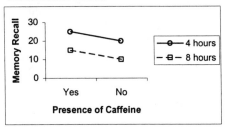

    b. An interaction effect and no main effects.

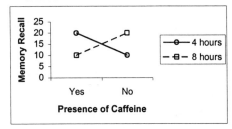

    c. Main effects for caffeine and sleep and an interaction effect.

	Yes	No	
4 hrs	$\bar{X} = 25$	$\bar{X} = 25$	$\bar{X} = 25$
8 hrs	$\bar{X} = 10$	$\bar{X} = 25$	$\bar{X} = 17.5$
	$\bar{X} = 17.5$	$\bar{X} = 25$	

12. a. There are three independent variables: gender (male, female), exposure (5 minutes, 10 minutes, 15 minutes), and presence of extra warning (present, absent), so this is a 2 x 3 x 2 factorial design.
    b. Three possible main effects since there are three independent variables.
    c. There are four possible interaction effects: three two-way interactions (gender x exposure, gender x warning, exposure x warning) and one three-way interaction: (gender x exposure x warning).

d.

Source	SS	df	MS	F
Gender	40	1	40	6.67
Exposure	30	2	15	2.50
Warning	20	1	20	3.33
Ge. x Exp.	60	2	30	5.00
Gen. x Wa.	20	1	20	3.33
Exp. x Wa.	20	2	10	1.67
Ge. x Ex. x Wa.	80	2	40	6.67
Error	648	108	6	
Total	918	119		

Critical values for assessing effects with 1 and 108 degrees of freedom:
$F_{(1,108).05} \approx 3.94$; $F_{(1,108).01} \approx 6.90$
Critical values for assessing effects with 2 and 108 degrees of freedom:
$F_{(2,108).05} \approx 3.09$; $F_{(2,108).01} \approx 4.82$.

Effect	F	p < .05	p < .01	Decision
Gen.	6.67	3.94	6.90	reject H$_0$, p < .05
Exp.	2.50	3.09	4.82	accept H$_0$
Wa.	3.33	3.94	6.90	accept H$_0$
Gen. x Exp.	5.00	3.09	4.82	reject H$_0$, p < .01
Gen x Wa.	3.33	3.94	6.90	accept H$_0$
Exp. x Wa.	1.67	3.09	4.82	accept H$_0$
Ge. x Ex. x Wa.	6.67	3.09	4.82	reject H$_0$, p < .01

e. Yes. Main effect for gender; interaction effect between gender and exposure; interaction effect between gender, exposure, and warning.
f. See chart above, part d.
Main effect for gender: males and females exert significantly different levels of self control.
Interaction of gender x exposure: ability to exert self control is based on a combined effect between gender and exposure.
Interaction of gender x exposure x

warning: ability to exert self control is based on a combined effect among all three variables: gender, exposure, warning.

Chapter 9

2. a. -1.00 to +1.00.
b. The direction of the relationship (positive or negative).
c. Increases.
d. Decreases.
e. The strength of the association.
4. Pearson product-moment correlation coefficient; r.
6. a. r = .82
b. H$_0$: ρ = 0; H$_a$: ρ ≠ 0
c. df = N - 2 = 5 - 2 = 3
Critical values: $r_{(3).05}$ = .805; $r_{(3).01}$ = .934. Since the calculated value r = .82 is larger than the critical value at the .05 level $r_{(3).05}$ = .805, reject H$_0$ at p < .05.
d. Reject H$_0$ at p < .05. There is positive correlation between perceptions of a person's attractiveness and intelligence.
8. a. A low, negative correlation.
b. H$_0$: ρ = 0; H$_a$: ρ ≠ 0
c. df = N - 2 = 52 - 2 = 50
Critical values: $r_{(50).05}$ = .273; $r_{(50).01}$ = .354. Since the calculated value r = -.24 is not larger (in absolute terms) than the critical value $r_{(50).05}$ = .273, do not reject (accept) H$_0$.
d. Do not reject (accept) H$_0$. There is no significant relationship between amount of eye contact and talkativeness.
10. The coefficient of determination; r^2.
12. The shaded area represents the shared variance.
a. r^2 = .16; 16% of the variance is explained.

b. No correlation; 0% of the variance is explained.

c. Perfect correlation; 100% of the variance is explained.

d. $r^2 = .81$; 81% of the variance is explained.

Chapter 10

2. The regression line or the line of best fit.

4. $Y = bX + a$; Y= predicted score, b = slope of regression line, X = specific score, a = y-intercept.

6. The a (y-intercept) refers to where the line crosses the y-axis.

8. The accuracy of the predicted value.

10. Small.

12. a. df = N - 2 = 30 - 2 = 28

Critical values: $r_{(28).05}$ = .361; $r_{(28).01}$ = .463. Since the calculated value r = -0.28 is not larger (in absolute terms) than the critical value $r_{(28).05}$ = .361, do not reject H_0. The correlation is not significant so the researcher cannot predict sleep based on number of cigarettes smoked better than chance.

b. df = N - 2 = 22 - 2 = 20

Critical values: $r_{(20).05}$ = .423; $r_{(20).01}$ = .537. Since the calculated value r = 0.47 is larger than the critical value $r_{(20).05}$ = .423, reject H_0 at $p < .05$ (but cannot reject at .01). The correlation is significant, so the manager can predict employees' gossiping based on number of cups of coffee drank better than chance.

Chapter 11

2. Partial correlation.

4. $R_{Y•ABC}$, $R^2_{Y•ABC}$. The coefficient of determination refers to the amount of variability in one variable that is accounted for

by the variability in two or more other variables. Specifically, the percentage of variance accounted for in Y by A, B and C.

6. $r_{M(N•OP)}$, $r^2_{M(N•OP)}$. The coefficient of determination refers to the amount of variability in M explained by N alone and not by any other predictor variables.

8. a. $R^2_{GPA•(SAT)(HSSize)} = \dfrac{N+P+Q}{M+N+P+Q}$

b. $r^2_{(SAT)(HSSize)•GPA} = \dfrac{R}{O+R}$

c. $r^2_{HSSize(GPA•SAT)} = \dfrac{P}{P+Q+R+S}$

d. $r^2_{(SAT)(GPA)} = \dfrac{N+Q}{N+O+Q+R}$

e. $R^2_{SAT•(HSSize)(GPA)} = \dfrac{N+Q+R}{N+O+Q+R}$

f. $r^2_{(GPA)(SAT)HSSize} = \dfrac{N}{M+N}$

g. $r^2_{GPA(SAT•HSSize)} = \dfrac{N}{M+N+P+Q}$

10. Partial regression coefficient; standardized regression coefficient.

a. b

b. Beta

12. a. Standard multiple regression.

b. Statistical multiple regression.

c. Hierarchical multiple regression.

14. a. GRADE = .79(STUDY) + .58(OFFICE) - .68(MISS) + 73.

b. GRADE = .79(15) + .58(3) - .28(0) + 73 = 86.59.

c. GRADE = .79(4) + .58(0) - .28(16) + 73 = 71.68.

d. Student b is predicted to have the highest exam grade.

e. Calculated F = 4.1; critical $F_{(3,40).05}$ = 2.84; critical $F_{(3,40).01}$ = 4.31. Yes. The regression equation is significant at $p < .05$.

f. STUDY: calculated t = .79/.34 = 2.32; critical $t_{(42).05}$ = 1.68; critical $t_{(42).01}$ = 2.42. Number of hours studying is a

significant predictor at $p < .05$.
OFFICE: calculated $t = .58/.42 = 1.38$;
critical $t_{(42).05} = 1.68$; critical $t_{(42).01} = 2.42$. Number of hours of office hours attended is not a significant predictor.
MISS: calculated $t = -.28/.09 = 3.11$;
critical $t_{(42).05} = 1.68$; critical $t_{(42).01} = 2.42$. Number of classes missed is a significant predictor at $p < .01$.
Number of classes missed is a better predictor ($p < .01$) than is number of hours studying ($p < .05$). Number of office hours attended is a nonsignificant predictor.

Chapter 12

2. a. Interval, ratio.
   b. Nominal, ordinal, interval, ratio.
   c. Interval, ratio.
   d. Nominal.
   e. Interval, ratio.
   f. Ordinal, interval, ratio.
   g. Interval, ratio.
   h. Interval, ratio.
   i. Interval, ratio.
   j. Nominal.
4. One-sample (one-way design) assesses differences among categories. Multiple-sample (two-way design) assesses differences among samples.
6. a. $\chi^2 = \Sigma \dfrac{(O-T)^2}{T}$
   b. $T = \dfrac{RxC}{G}$
   c. $df = (R-1) \times (C-1)$
   d. Two.
   e. Difference among samples.
8. a. $df = (R-1) \times (C-1) = (4-1) \times (4-1) = 3 \times 3 = 9$. Critical values: $\chi^2_{(9).05} = 16.92$;
   $\chi^2_{(9).01} = 21.67$. Since the calculated value $\chi^2 = 17$ is larger than the critical value $\chi^2_{(9).05} = 16.92$ reject H_0 at $p <$

$.05$. Can we do any better? No, since the calculate value $\chi^2 = 17$ is not larger than the critical value at the $.01$ level $\chi^2_{(9).01} = 21.67$. Final conclusion: reject H_0 at $p < .05$.

b. $df = (C-1) = (6-1) = 5$. Critical values: $\chi^2_{(5).05} = 11.07$; $\chi^2_{(5).01} = 15.09$. Do not reject H_0.

c. $df = (3-1) \times (8-1) = 2 \times 7 = 14$. Critical values: $\chi^2_{(14).05} = 23.68$; $\chi^2_{(14).01} = 29.14$. Reject H_0 at $p < .01$.

d. $df = (2-1) \times (2-1) = 1 \times 1 = 1$. Critical values: $\chi^2_{(1).05} = 3.84$; $\chi^2_{(1).01} = 6.63$. Reject H_0 at $p < .05$.

e. $df = (3-1) = 2$. Critical values: $\chi^2_{(2).05} = 5.99$; $\chi^2_{(2).01} = 9.21$. Reject H_0 at $p < .01$.

f. $df = (6-1) \times (6-1) = 5 \times 5 = 25$. Critical values: $\chi^2_{(25).05} = 37.65$; $\chi^2_{(25).01} = 44.31$. Do not reject H_0.

g. $df = (10-1) = 9$. Critical values: $\chi^2_{(9).05} = 16.92$; $\chi^2_{(9).01} = 21.67$. Reject H_0 at $p < .01$.

10. One-sample χ^2. A total of $N = 40 + 32 + 18 + 23 = 113$ students were surveyed. Theoretical (expected) value =

$$T = \frac{N}{K} = \frac{113}{4} = 28.25$$

$$\chi^2 = \Sigma \frac{(O-T)^2}{T}$$

$$= \frac{(40-28.25)^2}{28.25} + \frac{(32-28.25)^2}{28.25} + \frac{(18-28.25)^2}{28.25} + \frac{(23-28.25)^2}{28.25}$$

$$= 4.89 + 0.50 + 3.72 + 0.98$$

$$= 10.09$$

$df = (C-1) = (4-1) = 3$. Critical values: $\chi^2_{(3).05} = 7.81$; $\chi^2_{(3).01} = 11.34$. Since the calculated value $\chi^2 = 10.09$ is larger than the critical value $\chi^2_{(4).05} = 9.49$, reject H_0 at

$p < .05$. There is a significant difference in students' selection of a geographical location.

12. Using the formula for computing the theoretical values, $T = \frac{R x C}{G}$, and maintaining the same marginal frequencies as were observed, we obtain the following table of theoretical values:

	Support	Do Not Support	
Freshmen	31.25	68.75	100
Sophomores	31.25	68.75	100
Juniors	31.25	68.75	100
Seniors	31.25	68.75	100
	125	275	400

$$\chi^2 = \Sigma \frac{(O-T)^2}{T}$$

$$= \frac{(25-31.25)^2}{31.25} + \frac{(75-68.75)^2}{68.75} + \frac{(25-31.25)^2}{31.25} + \frac{(75-68.75)^2}{68.75}$$

$$+ \frac{(35-31.25)^2}{31.25} + \frac{(65-68.75)^2}{68.75} + \frac{(40-31.25)^2}{31.25} + \frac{(60-68.75)^2}{68.75}$$

$$= 1.25 + 0.57 + 1.25 + 0.57 + 0.45 + 0.20 + 2.45 + 1.11$$

$$= 7.85$$

$df = (R - 1) \times (C - 1) = (4 - 1) \times (2 - 1) = 3 \times 1 = 3$. Critical values: $\chi^2_{(3)}.05 = 7.81$; $\chi^2_{(3)}.01 = 11.34$. Since the calculated value $\chi^2 = 7.85$ is than the critical value $\chi^2_{(4)}.05 = 7.81$, reject H_0 at $p < .05$. Students from different class levels differentially support stricter eligibility requirements to remain enrolled at the university.

Appendix C ❖ Computer Problem Answers

Chapter 2

2. Examples of descriptive labels for variables:

gender	'instructors gender'
condit	'learning location'
class	'class structure'
clslvl	'grade level'
stdtsex	'students gender'
grade	'estimated grade'

Chapter 3

2. a. 60 women
    b. 60 men
4. a. 34 believed they earned A's.
    b. 43 believed they earned B's.
    c. 26 believed they earned C's.
    d. 17 believed they didn't pass.
6. a. $\overline{X}$ =5.03
    b. SD=1.09
    c. Students in the live condition felt somewhat positive about the course.
8. a. $\overline{X}$ =4.77
    b. SD=1.17
    c. Students felt somewhat positive about the instructor.
10. a. $\overline{X}$ =4.88
    b. SD=1.25
    c. Students felt somewhat positive towards the male instructor, but with slightly more variation than for the female instructor.
12. The students definitely perceived the male instructor to be quite composed (calm, poised, confident) and dynamic (energetic, outgoing, active). He was perceived as adequate in terms of his intelligence (qualification, experience, expertise) and friendliness (nice, good-natured, approachable).
14. a. Contacting classmates through e-mail.
    b. Providing feedback to the instructor.
    c. The means aren't very high for any of the four uses of e-mail in the course. Perhaps, the best option is to leave it open as an alternative rather than a requirement in future classes.

Chapter 4

2.

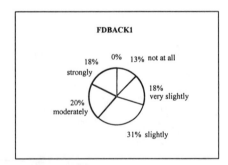

4. The distribution is moderately skewed.

6. a. Seek (mediated)

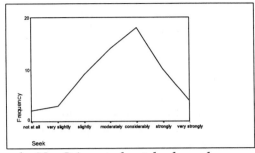

b. No. It is a moderately skewed distribution.

c. Seek (live)

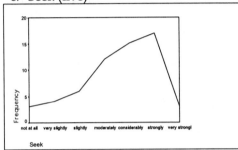

8. a. Yes
    b. Range: -1.49 to +1.70

Chapter 6

2. a. Reject the null hypothesis; $t[118]= 5.44$, $p = .000$, one-tailed. Those in the live condition felt the instructor presented the material in a more interesting way ($\overline{X} = 5.33$) than did those in the mediated condition ($\overline{X} = 4.18$).
    b. Do not reject (accept) the null hypothesis; $t[118]= 1.14$, $p = .225$, two-tailed. There were no differences in perceptions of how qualified the instructor was between the live ($\overline{X} = 3.86$) and mediated ($\overline{X} = 3.58$) conditions.
    c. Reject the null hypothesis; $t[118]= -2.73$, $p = .007$, one-tailed. Those in the mediated condition ($\overline{X} = 4.55$) were significantly more interested in the material than were those in the live

condition ($\overline{X} = 3.70$).

4. a. Reject the null hypothesis; $t[118]= -1.99$, $p = .049$, two-tailed. Males and females differed in their perceptions of e-mail as threatening. Specifically, male students felt more comfortable with the e-mail system ($\overline{X} = 4.55$) than did female students ($\overline{X} = 4.03$).
    b. Reject the null hypothesis; $t[118]= -3.80$, $p = .000$, two-tailed. Males and females differed in their frequency of e-mail use to contact their professor. Specifically, male students used e-mail to contact the professor more frequently ($\overline{X} = 3.62$) than did female students ($\overline{X} = 2.82$).
    c. Do not reject (accept) the null hypothesis; $t[118] = -.30$, $p = .768$, two-tailed. There were no differences in how frequently male ($\overline{X} = 3.75$) and female ($\overline{X} = 3.67$) students used e-mail to contact their classmates.

Chapter 7

2. a. Do not reject (accept) the null hypothesis; $F[3, 116] = .40$, $p = .756$. No post-hoc tests were conducted. There were no differences among the four groups in terms of how knowledgeable they perceived their instructor.
    b. Reject the null hypothesis; $F[3, 116] = 4.30$, $p = .007$. Scheffé tests revealed that juniors ($\overline{X} = 5.20$) rated the instructor as more outgoing than sophomores ($\overline{X} = 4.21$).
    c. Do not reject (accept) the null hypothesis; $F[3, 116] = .59$, $p = .626$. No post-hoc tests were conducted. There were no differences among the four groups in terms of whether they learned something valuable from the course.
    d. Reject the null hypothesis; $F[3, 116] =$

13.59, p = .000. Scheffé tests revealed that juniors ($\overline{X}$ = 4.69) and seniors ($\overline{X}$ = 5.59) are more comfortable seeking help from the instructor than are freshmen ($\overline{X}$ = 3.60) and sophomores ($\overline{X}$ = 3.91).

Chapter 8

2. a. There is a main effect for learning location: $F[1, 116]$ = 38.44, p = .000. Students in the live condition ($\overline{X}$ = 5.18) rated the instructor as more aware when students didn't understand material than did those in the mediated condition ($\overline{X}$ = 3.88). There is no significant main effect for instructor's gender nor a significant interaction effect for learning location by gender.
    b. There is a main effect for instructor's gender: $F[1, 116]$ = 7.47, p = .007. Students with a female instructor ($\overline{X}$ = 4.08) were more likely to indicate using e-mail to contact their classmates than those with a male instructor ($\overline{X}$ = 3.33). There is no significant main effect for learning location nor a significant interaction effect for learning location by gender.
    c. There is a main effect for learning location: $F[1, 116]$ = 11.73, p = .001. Students in the mediated condition ($\overline{X}$ = 4.78) indicated a greater interest in the subject matter as a result of taking the course than those in the live classroom ($\overline{X}$ = 3.70). There is no significant main effect for instructor's gender nor a significant interaction effect for learning location by gender.

Chapter 9

2. a. r = -.19, p = .038. Reject the null hypothesis; How students evaluated the course was related to how intellectually challenging they rated the class.
    b. r = -.03, p = .709. Do not reject (accept) the null hypothesis; There was no relationship between how the students rated the course and the instructor's demonstrated enthusiasm for the subject.
    c. r = -.11, p = .117. Do not reject (accept) the null hypothesis; There was no relationship between how the students rated the course and the perceived expertise of the instructor.
    d. r = .26, p = .002. Reject the null hypothesis; The higher the students evaluated the course, the more they expressed an interest in the course subject matter.
    e. r = -.25, p = .003. Reject the null hypothesis; The higher the students evaluated the course, the less helpful they found e-mail.

Chapter 10

2. The regression equation, $F[1, 118]$ = 1.43, p = .235, as well as the bivariate regression coefficient, b = -.09, p = .235, are non-significant.
4. The regression equation is significant; $F[1, 118]$ = 7.68, p = .006. The bivariate regression coefficient is significant b = .22, p = .006. The application of course material accounted for 6% of the variance (R^2 = .06).
6. The regression equation is significant; $F[1, 118]$ = 43.5, p = .000. The bivariate regression coefficient is significant b = .46, p = .000. How fun students perceived e-mail accounted for 27% of the variance (R^2 = .27).

Chapter 11

2. The regression model is non-significant ($F[4, 115] = .830, p = .509$). Students' perceptions of the instructor's expertise, friendliness, experience and confidence were not significant predictors of their overall rating of the course.

4. The regression model is significant ($F[1, 118] = 20.33, p = .000$) in the first block of the hierarchical analysis. How intellectually challenging students find a course is a significant predictor ($b = -.41, p = .000$) of perceived outcome and accounts for 15% of the variance ($R^2 = .15$). The second regression model, which adds the amount of effort students put into the course is also significant ($F[2, 117] = 11.41, p = .000$). However, the F change score ($F[2, 117] = 2.28, p = .134$) and the partial regression coefficient ($b = .10, p = .134$) show that the amount of effort students put into the course does not significantly add to the predictive ability above and beyond what is gained from how intellectually challenging they find the course. Thus, retain the first regression model with intellectual challenge as the only predictor variable as effort does not add significantly to predicting students' perceived outcome in the course.

6. The regression model in all three blocks is non-significant. Students' overall rating of the instructor ($F[2, 117] = .434, p = .649$), their estimated grade in the course ($F[1, 118] = .079, p = .779$), and the perceptions of themselves as people who like to learn ($F[3, 116] = .693, p = .558$) do not add significantly to predicting the overall rating of the course. None of these regression models should be retained.

Chapter 12

2. $\chi^2[5] = 37.60, p = .000$. Students were more likely to use the announcement board for surveillance and convenience reasons than for other reasons.

4. $\chi^2[5] = 35.30, p = .000$. Students were more likely to contact their instructor for convenience and expression reasons, and somewhat for surveillance reasons, than for either diversion of social function reasons.

6. $\chi^2[5] = 2.59, p = .763$. There was no difference in male vs. female students' reasons for contacting their classmates through e-mail.

8. $\chi^2[9] = 16.81, p = .052$. Freshman were more likely to perceive they earned C's than other grades; Sophomores were more likely to perceive they earned B's than other grades; Juniors and seniors were more likely to perceive they earned A's or B's than other grades.